Casebook of Clinical Hypnosis

Casebook of Clinical Hypnosis

EDITED BY

Steven Jay Lynn
Irving Kirsch
Judith W. Rhue

AMERICAN PSYCHOLOGICAL ASSOCIATION • WASHINGTON, DC

Published by
American Psychological Association
750 First Street, NE
Washington, DC 20002

Copies may be ordered from
APA Order Department
P. O. Box 2710
Hyattsville, MD 20784

In the UK and Europe, copies may be ordered from
American Psychological Association
3 Henrietta Street
Covent Garden, London
WC2E 8LU England

Typeset in Goudy by PRO-IMAGE Corporation, Techna-Type Div., York, PA

Printer: Braun-Brumfield, Inc., Ann Arbor, MI
Cover and Jacket Designer: Berg Design, Albany, NY
Technical/Production Editor: Edward B. Meidenbauer

Library of Congress Cataloging-in-Publication Data
Casebook of clinical hypnosis / edited by Steven Jay Lynn, Irving
  Kirsch, and Judith W. Rhue.
      p.   cm.
  Includes bibliographical references and index.
  ISBN 1-55798-365-8 (alk. paper)
  1. Hypnotism—Therapeutic use—Case studies. I. Lynn, Steven
Jay. II. Kirsch, Irving, 1943–   . III. Rhue, Judith W.
RC495.C39   1996
616.89'162—dc20   96-11150
                                                                           CIP

British Library Cataloguing-in-Publication Data
A CIP record is available from the British Library.

Printed in the United States of America
First edition

To my beloved sister, Leslie Ehrlich.
Steven Jay Lynn

To Christine with love.
Irving Kirsch

To the lights of my life, my children, Martha Kate, Grant, Steven, and
Alexandra.
Judith W. Rhue

CONTENTS

PART III: HYPNOTHERAPY WITH CHILDREN AND ADOLESCENTS

PART IV: A CLINICAL CASE CONFERENCE: ELLEN

CONTRIBUTORS

Salvador Amigó, PhD, is Associate Professor of psychology at the University of Valencia and director of the Clinic for the Investigation and Treatment of Psychological Stress. He developed self-regulation therapy in 1990, and since then has conducted clinical applications and scientific investigations of that treatment. The results of his studies have been presented in numerous congresses and have been published in internationally recognized books and scientific journals.

Arreed Barabasz, EdD, PhD, ABPP, is director of the Attentional Processes Lab at Washington State University and Professor of Counseling Psychology. He previously was Associate Professor of Psychology (Clinical) at Harvard Medical School. He is chair of the State Board of Psychology Examiners and diplomate of the American Board of Professional Psychology (Clinical). He is a fellow of the American Psychological Association, the American Psychological Society, and the Society for Clinical and Experimental Hypnosis. He has received awards for both clinical and research excellence.

Marianne Barabasz, EdD, is Associate Professor of Counseling Psychology at Washington State University and a licensed clinical psychologist. She is a fellow of the Society for Clinical and Experimental Hypnosis and the American Association for Applied and Preventive Psychology. She has published 50 research papers and recently coauthored the book *Clinical and Experimental Restricted Environmental Stimulation* with Arreed Barabasz.

Antonio Capafons, PhD, is Professor of Psychology at the University of Valencia (Spain). He has written extensively on cognitive–behavioral self-control, hypnosis, and emotional self-regulation therapy. His research topics are related to sport psychology, biofeedback, and the prevention of heart disorders (smoking and obesity reduction). Dr. Capafons is the originator of the "rapid self-hypnosis" method, and he is currently researching the experimental and clinical application of waking suggestions, from an active–alert, non-trance perspective.

John F. Chaves, PhD, is Professor and Head, Division of Behavioral Medicine and Bioethics, Indiana University School of Dentistry, Indianapolis. He is past president of the Division of Psychological Hypnosis of the American Psychological Association and is a fellow of the Society for Clinical and Experimental Hypnosis. He is coeditor, with N. P. Spanos, of *Hypnosis: The Cognitive–Behavioral Perspective*, and has published widely on hypnosis and pain management.

William C. Coe, PhD, is a Professor of psychology at California State University, Fresno, where he was voted "Outstanding Professor of the Year," 1988. He has served as president and secretary of the American Psychological Association's Division of Psychological Hypnosis. He has written four books, including *Hypnosis: A Social Psychological Analysis* (with T. R. Sarbin). His awards include Outstanding Contributions to Psychotherapy from the California School of Professional Psychology, Fresno, and Best Theoretical Paper in Hypnosis from the Society for Clinical and Experimental Hypnosis.

Edmund Thomas Dowd, PhD, ABPP, is Professor of Psychology at Kent State University. He received his PhD from the University of Minnesota and previously taught at Florida State University and the University of Nebraska. He is editor of the *Journal of Cognitive Psychotherapy* and president-elect of the International Association for Cognitive Psychotherapy. His scholarly interests are in cognitive therapy, psychological reactance, and hypnotherapy.

Albert Ellis, PhD, President of the Institute for Rational-Emotive Therapy in New York City, is the founder of rational-emotive therapy, and is the grandfather of cognitive–behavior therapy. He has been president of the Division of Consulting Psychology of the American Psychological Association and president of the Society for the Scientific Study of Sex. He has won many awards, including Distinguished Professional Contributions to Knowledge from the American Psychological Association and the Professional

Development Award of the American Counseling Association. He has published more than 600 articles and over 50 books.

Joseph P. Green, PhD, is Assistant Professor of Psychology at Ohio University (Lima) and has a private practice. He has won awards for research excellence from the American Psychological Association Division of Psychological Hypnosis, and he has published numerous articles and book chapters on hypnosis, dissociation, and smoking cessation.

Richard Horevitz, PhD, ABPH, is in private practice at the Phoenix Institute in Chicago, specializing in the treatment of complex PTSD and forensic psychology. He is Adjunct Assistant Professor of Psychology in the Departments of Psychology and Psychiatry, University of Illinois Chicago. He is past president of Division 30 of APA, as well as fellow of APA, the Society for Clinical and Experimental Hypnosis, and the International Society for the Study of Dissociation, among other professional organizations. He has published many articles and chapters on hypnosis and dissociation.

Lynne M. Hornyak, PhD, is a clinical psychologist in private practice in Washington, DC. She is a fellow of the Society for Clinical and Experimental Hypnosis, a certified American Society of Clinical Hypnosis consultant, and past president of the Washington Society of Clinical Hypnosis. Dr. Hornyak specializes in the treatment of eating disorders and other women's health issues and is coeditor of *Experiential Therapies for Eating Disorders*.

Irving Kirsch, PhD, is a Professor of Psychology at the University of Connecticut. He is a former president of the American Psychological Association's Division of Psychological Hypnosis and the current North American Editor of the international journal, *Contemporary Hypnosis*. Dr. Kirsch is an author or editor of 5 books and more than 100 journal articles and book chapters on placebo effects, hypnosis, psychotherapy, the history of psychology, and the philosophy of science.

Carol Lankton, MA, is in private practice in Gulf Breeze, Florida. She is an Approved Consultant in Clinical Hypnosis with the American Society for Clinical Hypnosis, and a Clinical Member of the American Association of Marriage and Family Therapy. She has written several books, including *The Answer Within, Enchantment and Intervention,* and *Tales of Enchantment*.

Stephen Lankton, MSW, is in private practice in Gulf Breeze, Florida. He is a diplomate of the American Hypnosis Board for Clinical Social Work, an Approved Consultant in Clinical Hypnosis with the American Society for Clinical Hypnosis, an Approved

Supervisor and fellow of the American Association of Marriage and Family Therapy, a Diplomate in Social Work (NASW & ABECSW), and a fellow of the American Academy of Pain Management. He has written several books, including *The Answer Within* and *Tales of Enchantment*. He has edited the *Ericksonian Monographs* for 10 years.

Steven Jay Lynn, PhD, is a Professor of Psychology at Binghamton University and an Adjunct Professor of Psychology at Ohio University. He is a former president of the American Psychological Association's Division of Psychological Hypnosis, a consulting editor of the *Journal of Abnormal Psychology*, and a Clinical Section Associate Editor of the *American Journal of Clinical Hypnosis*. The fellow of numerous professional organizations, Dr. Lynn is an author or editor of 11 books and more than 125 journal articles and book chapters on hypnosis, memory, psychotherapy, dissociation, fantasy, and victimization.

William J. Matthews, PhD, is a professor and director of the School Psychology and Counselor Education Program in the School of Education at the University of Massachusetts in Amherst. Dr. Matthews has written numerous research and clinically oriented articles and book chapters on Ericksonian approaches to hypnosis and psychotherapy. He has lectured both nationally and internationally on the work of Milton H. Erickson and is currently the editor of the *Annual of Brief Therapy: Dialogue in Evolution*, a publication of the Milton H. Erickson Foundation.

Joan Murray-Jobsis, PhD, is a clinician in private practice in Chapel Hill, North Carolina, and is also a Clinical Associate Professor at the University of North Carolina at Chapel Hill. Dr. Murray-Jobsis is a past president and fellow of the American Society of Clinical Hypnosis. She is a diplomate of both the American Board of Professional Psychology and the American Board of Psychological Hypnosis, and she has published extensively in the area of hypnotherapy with borderline and psychotic patients.

Michael R. Nash, PhD, is an associate professor at the University of Tennessee and is actively engaged in clinical training, research, and teaching. A past president of the American Psychological Association's Division of Psychological Hypnosis, he is a fellow of both the Society for Clinical and Experimental Hypnosis and the American Psychological Association. Dr. Nash is coeditor, with Erika Fromm, of *Contemporary Hypnosis Research*.

Jonathan Neufeld, MS, is a doctoral candidate in clinical psychology at Ohio University. He has presented many papers on the topics of simulation and assessment of hypnosis, and he has published in the area of clinical hypnosis.

Judith Pintar, MA (Anthropology), is working on her PhD in sociology at the University of Illinois at Urbana-Champaign, where her dissertation research involves the social and cultural aspects of shared social trauma. She is also a professional recording artist, storyteller, and director of children's theater. She is the author of *The Halved Soul: Retelling the Myths of Romantic Love.*

Judith W. Rhue, PhD, is a professor of family medicine at the Ohio University College of Osteopathic Medicine, and has a private practice. She is a fellow of the American Psychological Association's Division of Psychological Hypnosis and of the Society for Clinical and Experimental Hypnosis (SCEH). She has received several awards from SCEH for the best hypnosis books published during 1991 (*Theories of Hypnosis: Current Models and Perspectives*), 1992 (*Handbook of Clinical Hypnosis*), and 1993 (*Dissociation: Theoretical and Research Perspectives*). Dr. Rhue serves on the editorial boards of the *International Journal of Clinical and Experimental Hypnosis,* the *American Journal of Clinical Hypnosis,* and *Contemporary Hypnosis.*

Nancy E. Schoenberger earned her PhD in clinical psychology from the University of Connecticut in 1993. She is an Assistant Professor of Psychiatry at the University of Medicine and Dentistry of New Jersey. She is currently working on a project funded by the Office of Alternative Medicine of the NIH to study alternative therapies in the treatment of stroke, spinal cord injury, and traumatic brain injury.

William H. Smith, PhD, is dean of the Karl Menninger School of Psychiatry and Mental Health Sciences, responsible for all professional education at the Menninger Clinic in Topeka, Kansas. The Director of Postdoctoral Training in clinical psychology at Menninger since 1978 and the Chief Clinical Psychologist for eight of those years, Dr. Smith is a diplomate of both the American Board of Professional Psychology and the American Board of Psychological Hypnosis. He is a member of the Society for Clinical and Experimental Hypnosis and an Approved Consultant for the American Society of Clinical Hypnosis.

David Spiegel, MD, is Professor of Psychiatry and Behavioral Sciences at Stanford University School of Medicine, where he has been a member of the faculty for 20 years, and is currently Director of the Psychosocial Treatment Laboratory. He is a fellow of the American Psychiatric Association and the American College of Psychiatrists, and is President of the Society for Clinical and Experimental Hypnosis. He has published three books and more than 200 journal articles and chapters on hypnosis, psychosocial oncology, and psychotherapy.

Michael D. Yapko, PhD, is a clinical psychologist in private practice in Solana Beach, California. He teaches nationally and internationally, and is the author of *Essentials of Hypnosis, Hypnosis and the Treatment of Depression, Trancework,* and *Breaking the Patterns of Depression.* He is a fellow of the American Society of Clinical Hypnosis, and is a recipient of the Milton H. Erickson award for scientific excellence in hypnosis.

PREFACE

This book is the sequel to our *Handbook of Clinical Hypnosis*, in which we attempted to provide practitioners, researchers, and students with a survey of modern clinical hypnosis. Our goal was to present a diversity of viewpoints relevant to the science and practice of clinical hypnosis. We felt that such a book was necessary, given the explosion of interest in the scientific and clinical foundations of hypnosis that has occurred over the past decade or so—a trend legitimized by evidence that hypnosis can increase the effectiveness of cognitive–behavioral treatments of a variety of disorders (Kirsch, Montgomery, & Sapirstein, 1995).

Although hypnosis has indeed come of age, it was our perception that myths and misconceptions about hypnosis nevertheless persisted even among seasoned clinicians, which deterred some from their using hypnotic techniques. Our *Handbook*, we hope, served the dual purpose of demystifying and legitimizing hypnotic techniques for curious therapists unfamiliar with hypnosis and of advancing a scientifically rigorous yet compassionate approach for therapists already acquainted with the virtues of hypnotherapy.

Although the *Handbook* contained many suggestions for applying hypnotic techniques and strategies, it was necessarily limited in the depth of coverage of any given topic. What was missing was a closer look at what a hypnotherapist does on a case-by-case and session-by-session basis. What specific strategies can be implemented? When is it appropriate to introduce hypnosis? What challenges do therapists encounter, and how do they deal with them? What interpersonal issues emerge in treatment? We invited a panel of eminent hypnotherapists, many of whom contributed to the *Handbook*, to select interesting and memorable cases to address these and other questions to illustrate what they actually do in hypnotherapy. Hence, much of each chapter is devoted to the explication of clinical techniques and strategies; many chapters contain transcripts of actual sessions and suggestions administered, providing a window into the world of clinicians' best work with their clients.

Most of the chapters follow a consistent organizational scheme, presenting background and assessment information, the treatment rationale, the role of hypnosis in treatment, outcome and follow-up data, and concluding comments. This uniform organization facilitates comparisons across therapists' approaches to treatment, the theoretical underpinnings of therapy, and the psychological problems treated. These problems encompass eating disorders, posttraumatic stress disorder, depression, anxiety, personality disorders, enuresis, somatoform disorder, dissociative identity disorder, aftereffects of sexual abuse and rape, dysmenorrhea, nicotine dependence, and attention-deficit disorder. In short, the reader will learn how hypnosis can be integrated into a wide range of psychotherapies for an equally diverse set of clinical problems with children, adolescents, and adults.

Although the *Handbook* provided equally broad coverage of hypnotherapeutic approaches, it lacked incisive comparison of the ways different clinicians would approach the same client. To highlight the ways in which hypnosis theory can be translated into clinical practice, in the *Casebook* experts who are exponents of very different theoretical perspectives (i.e., psychoanalytic, multimodal, rational-emotive, and Ericksonian) discuss their hypnotic treatment of a client with a phobia of using the bathroom in public places.

Because readers vary in terms of their expertise and background in clinical hypnosis, the introductory chapter frames the cases with a general introduction to hypnotherapy. This chapter includes information for practicing clinicians that is firmly grounded in the scientific literature. Here we discuss the definition of hypnosis, myths and misconceptions of hypnosis, indications and contraindications for hypnosis, the assessment of hypnotic responsiveness, and strategies for minimizing occasional negative responses that occur during hypnosis and other psychotherapies.

Like the *Handbook*, this book is intended for anyone who wishes to learn about clinical hypnosis. As such, it is ideally suited for use as a textbook for graduate and postgraduate courses and workshops. We believe that novice hypnotherapists as well as more seasoned clinicians have much to gain from the renowned contributors to this volume who generously share their challenging, enlightening, and, at times, entertaining therapeutic moments with the reader.

In closing, we would like to thank Ted Baroody for his many contributions as our developmental editor, James Council for his helpful review of the manuscript, and Brad Smith for his valuable assistance with the review process.

STEVEN JAY LYNN
IRVING KIRSCH
JUDITH W. RHUE

REFERENCE

Kirsch, I., Montgomery, G., & Sapirstein, G. (1995). Hypnosis as an adjunct to cognitive behavioral psychotherapy: A meta-analysis. *Journal of Consulting and Clinical Psychology, 63*, 214–220.

I

INTRODUCTION

1

CLINICAL HYPNOSIS: ASSESSMENT, APPLICATIONS, AND TREATMENT CONSIDERATIONS

STEVEN JAY LYNN, IRVING KIRSCH, JONATHAN NEUFELD, and
JUDITH W. RHUE

Since the beginning of recorded history, procedures that today are labeled *suggestive* have been used to treat a wide range of psychological disturbances and physical conditions (Gravitz, 1991; Spanos & Chaves, 1991). The seemingly magical and dramatic changes in hypnotized subjects' appearance, experiences, and behaviors have largely been responsible for the widespread interest in hypnosis both as a catalyst for psychological and physical treatments and as a fascinating phenomenon in its own right.

Hypnosis is enjoying a wave of popularity (see Lynn & Rhue, 1991a). Not only do substantial numbers of mental health professionals use hypnosis regularly to treat a wide range of problems (Kraft & Rudolfa, 1982; Rhue, Lynn, & Kirsch, 1993), but also hypnosis has moved into the orbit of mainstream psychology. This latter observation is evidenced by the sharp increase in the number of hypnosis articles, spanning a wide range of disciplines, that has been published in recent years (Nash, Minton, & Baldridge, 1988). The cross-fertilization of the clinical and research domains can be seen in recent compendiums of hypnosis research (Fromm & Nash, 1992), hypnotherapeutic approaches (Rhue et al., 1993), and theories of hypnosis (Lynn & Rhue, 1991a), which all contain discussions of clinical work (see Lynn, 1994).

Clinicians have responded to the lure of seemingly powerful experiential techniques with a boom of interest in incorporating hypnosis into

3

the treatment of an array of clinical problems, ranging from anxiety disorders to personality and schizophrenic disorders (Kraft & Rudolfa, 1982). Fortunately, clinical research indicates that hypnosis is more than a faddish addition to the clinician's grab bag of psychotherapeutic tools. Meta-analyses (Kirsch, Montgomery, & Sapirstein, 1995; Smith, Glass, & Miller, 1980) have demonstrated that the addition of hypnosis to cognitive–behavioral and psychodynamic treatments substantially enhances their efficacy, and researchers have made important contributions to understanding hypnosis, assuring that clinical hypnosis can be more firmly grounded in scientific findings (see Lynn, 1994; Nash et al., 1988).

As the field of clinical hypnosis has matured, evidence exists that there is increasing agreement about what hypnosis is, what hypnosis is not, and how hypnosis can be used to modify experience and behavior (see Kirsch & Lynn, 1995). Perhaps the fundamental point on which there is virtual consensus is that hypnosis is not a treatment in itself. As Dowd (chapter 14, this volume) observes, hypnosis is a specialized technique that can be used as an adjunctive intervention integrated into a more encompassing psychological and perhaps medical treatment package.

Clinical hypnosis refers to a very wide variety of nonstandardized and changeable methods that can serve as a catalyst to an equally wide variety of psychotherapies (Barber, 1985). Thus, one can speak of psychoanalytic hypnotherapy, rational–emotive hypnotherapy, Ericksonian hypnotherapy, or multimodal hypnotherapy, as evidenced by the section of this book that discusses a single case from multiple therapeutic orientations. However, in many instances, the therapeutic use of hypnosis involves a blending of ideas and techniques from different theoretical perspectives, reflecting the tendency toward technical eclecticism that characterizes much of the field of contemporary psychotherapy (see Lynn & Garske, 1985). As it is practiced today, clinical hypnosis can be defined as the addition of hypnosis to accepted psychological or medical treatment. As such, it should be practiced only by professionals who have the appropriate training and credentials to provide the treatment that is being augmented by hypnosis.

WHAT IS HYPNOSIS?

There has long (Hilgard, 1973a) been agreement about the "domain of hypnosis," that is, the sorts of phenomena that are included (e.g., muscular movements, sensory distortions, hallucinations, posthypnotic amnesia, and hypnotic dreams) and lie outside it (e.g., faked or shammed responses to suggestions). Recently, however, a consensus has begun to emerge about how to define hypnosis, across theorists and practitioners with widely divergent views about hypnosis: The American Psychological Association Division of Psychological Hypnosis (1993) has adopted a definition of hypnosis as a procedure during which <u>changes</u> in sensations, perceptions, thoughts, feelings, or behavior <u>are suggested</u> (Kirsch, 1994; Chaves, 1994; Fromm, Hilgard, & Kihlstrom, 1994).

definition

The hypnosis community was once divided into two "warring camps" (i.e., state vs. nonstate), one consisting of those who viewed hypnosis as a special process (e.g., an altered state of consciousness) and another of those who viewed hypnosis in mundane, social–psychological terms. This, however, is no longer the case. There is general agreement among most researchers that the effects of hypnosis are not due to the induction of a special state. On other important issues, notable theoretical tensions and differences persist, but these substantive theoretical differences cannot be categorized into two groups of theories, and the ideological antagonisms that once plagued the field seem to have abated (see Kirsch & Lynn, 1995).

Most hypnosis researchers agree that the impressive effects of hypnosis stem from social influence and personal abilities, not from a trancelike state of consciousness (see Kirsch & Lynn, 1995). Relatedly, many practitioners have come to appreciate the social, interpersonal, and psychodynamic determinants of hypnotic responses, while they utilize sophisticated methods of exploiting clients' fantasy, imaginative, and dissociative abilities in psychotherapy. Many of these methods are detailed in this casebook.

Many clinicians now recognize that how clients respond to suggestions depends less on the nature and success of a particular induction than on the following variables: (a) clients' prehypnotic attitudes, beliefs, intentions, and expectations about hypnosis; (b) their ability to think, fantasize, and absorb themselves in suggestions; (c) their ability to form a trusting relationship with the hypnotist; (d) their ability to interpret suggestions appropriately and view their responses as successful; (e) their ability to discern task demands and cues; (f) their ongoing interaction with the hypnotist; and (g) the appropriateness of the therapeutic methods and suggestions to treating the presenting problem (see also Barber, 1985).

In the past 25 years or so, great strides have been made in learning about the basic phenomena and parameters of hypnosis. With increasing confidence, clinicians can practice with the assurance that many of their clinical intuitions and the information they share with clients have an empirical basis. Research has perhaps played its most influential role in demystifying hypnosis. Research-based information can be incorporated into clinical hypnosis with many clients who, before hypnotic work can begin in earnest, require education that disabuses them of misconceptions about hypnosis that can interfere with a complete response to hypnotic suggestions.

For example, many people believe that hypnosis is something that is done to them, rather than something that they do. They think that hypnotized people lose control of themselves and can be made to do or say whatever the hypnotist wants. They think that they will feel drastically altered, as if they had taken a powerful drug, and they may fear that they will not be able to come out of this altered state. Some believe that subjects who have been hypnotized are unable to remember what occurred during hypnosis. Less common misconceptions include the idea that only weak-willed people are capable of being hypnotized or that hypnosis might weaken one's will-power (Kirsch et al., 1993).

Clinicians can now rely on the following empirically derived information to educate their clients and inform their practice:

- The ability to experience hypnotic phenomena does not indicate gullibility or weakness (Barber, 1969).
- Hypnosis is not a sleeplike state (Banyai, 1991).
- Hypnosis depends more on the efforts and abilities of the subject than on the skill of the hypnotist (Hilgard, 1965).
- Subjects retain the ability to control their behavior during hypnosis, to refuse to respond to suggestions, and to even oppose suggestions (see Lynn, Rhue, & Weekes, 1990).
- Spontaneous amnesia is relatively rare (Simon & Salzberg, 1985), and its unwanted occurrence can be prevented by informing clients that they will be able to remember everything that they are comfortable remembering about the session.
- Suggestions can be responded to with or without hypnosis, and the function of a formal induction is primarily to increase suggestibility to a minor degree (see Barber, 1969; Hilgard, 1965).
- Hypnosis is not a dangerous procedure when practiced by qualified clinicians and researchers (see Lynn, Martin, & Frauman, 1996).
- Most hypnotized subjects are neither faking nor merely complying with suggestions (Kirsch, Silva, Carone, Johnston, & Simon, 1989).
- Hypnosis does not increase the accuracy of memory (Sheehan & McConkey, 1993) or foster a literal reexperiencing of childhood events (Nash, 1987).
- Direct, traditionally worded hypnotic techniques appear to be just as effective as permissive, open-ended, indirect suggestions (Lynn, Neufeld, & Mare, 1993).
- A wide variety of hypnotic inductions can be effective (e.g., inductions that emphasize alertness can be just as effective as inductions that promote physical relaxation; Banyai, 1991).
- Most hypnotized subjects do not describe their experience as "trance" but as focused attention on suggested events (McConkey, 1986).

- Hypnosis is not a reliable means of recovering repressed memories but might increase the danger of creating false memories (Lynn & Nash, 1994).
- Hypnotizability can be substantially modified (Gorassini & Spanos, 1986: Spanos, 1991). Many initially low-hypnotizable participants can respond like high-hypnotizable participants after positive attitudes about hypnosis are instantiated and training in imagining, interpreting, and responding to suggestions is undertaken. Research in at least five laboratories (see Spanos, 1991) has shown that more than half of participants who test as low hypnotizable can, after assessment and training in a variety of cognitive–behavioral skills, test in the high-hypnotizable range on a variety of assessment instruments and suggestions, some of which were not specifically targeted in the training. Gfeller (1993) has written perceptively about how hypnotizability can be modified, enhanced, and exploited in clinical situations.

WHY USE HYPNOSIS?

We now know more about hypnosis than we ever did in the past. But why introduce hypnotic techniques into psychotherapy? Among the reasons for employing hypnotic procedures are the following.

Hypnosis as a Means of Providing Structure and Increasing Salience

Hypnosis provides an excellent context for techniques that are deeply experiential. In this context, clients can detach from the external world and devote their full attention to therapeutic ideas and suggestions. The ideas presented to the client are less likely to be the trivial or negative type of ideation that is typical of many people's routine thought processes (see Barber, 1985). Hypnosis can thus provide a structure for therapeutic suggestions and activities, facilitating a focus on selected thoughts, feelings, and images. Not surprisingly, under these circumstances, hypnotizable clients often report profound perceptual and affective changes.

Disinhibition of the Client and Therapist

One of the advantages of defining therapeutic methods as "hypnotic" is that it affords the therapist and the client with a remarkable degree of flexibility. This is true, in part, because clients tend to imbue the hypnotic situation with virtually magical properties that they believe will set in motion important changes in consciousness, feelings, and behavior. Therapists, in turn, "have a chance to talk to their patients in a very personal and meaningful way that is difficult to do in a two-way conversation. They can now say virtually anything they believe will be beneficial to the patients" (Barber, 1985, p. 349).

Hypnotherapists can suggest therapeutic images and experiences that could never occur in reality. For example, Murray-Jobsis (chapter 9, this volume) writes about how she was able to foster a borderline client's sense of self by creating images of a positive alternative scenario to the client's real-life history of abuse and neglect, even though the client clearly understood that the "healing script" was imaginary. Hypnotherapists can also talk with clients in metaphoric, rather than strictly literal, terms. Rhue, Lynn, and Pintar (chapter 12, this volume) illustrate many ways in which imaginative and metaphoric stories can be finely tuned to traumatized children's changing attentional, emotional, and behavioral reactions to traumatic events. The use of such stories can permit traumatized children to connect what happens to invented story characters with events in their own lives.

The nature and scope of hypnotic suggestions is limited only by the therapist's and the client's imagination and creativity. Therapists need not be constrained by a set or formulaic way of delivering hypnotic suggestions. Some therapists deliver suggestions in traditional, direct, and authoritative terms (see Ellis, chapter 16, this volume); other therapists use more permissive, open-ended, and metaphoric language (see Matthews, Lankton, and Lankton, chapter 18, this volume, and Dowd, chapter 14, this volume); and still other therapists combine direct and more open-ended suggestions (see Rhue, Lynn, and Pintar). As alluded to above, there is no evidence that indicates that one type of suggestion (i.e., direct vs. indirect) is generally more effective than another.

Whereas many therapists use suggestions intended to promote a relaxed physical state, other practitioners attempt to establish an alert state of focused awareness or concentration (see Barabasz and Barabasz, chapter 13, this volume). Regardless of the specific suggestions delivered, most therapists represented in this book strongly advocate individually tailoring suggestions to the client's needs and dynamics. There is also consensus that hypnotic procedures be integrated into a well thought out treatment plan, with a viable theoretical rationale.

Hypnosis as a Nondeceptive Placebo

Many clients have positive attitudes about hypnosis and sincerely wish to experience hypnotic effects. For such clients, the hypnotic context may enhance their confidence in the effectiveness of therapy and thereby produce a placebo effect without the deception that is generally associated with placebos (see Kirsch, 1993).

Facilitating the Therapeutic Relationship

Hypnosis can foster a positive collaborative working alliance with the client. As Smith comments (chapter 6, this volume) in his chapter on the treatment of an adult survivor of sexual abuse, during hypnosis a positive relationship with the therapist can be rapidly established in which the therapist is experienced as attentive, benign, and respectful of the client's need for control. Murray-Jobsis (chapter 9, this volume), in turn, argues that hypnosis is the treatment of choice for people with borderline personality disorder because hypnotic imagery is an ideal vehicle for presenting and rehearsing a corrective process of separation and individuation against a background of bonding and connectedness with the therapist.

Hypnotic Stabilization and Soothing

Hypnosis can be a powerful stabilizing and self-control technique that can interrupt negative patterns of thoughts, feelings, and behaviors. Specific and individualized suggestions can be devised to promote self-soothing, mental and physical relaxation, ego strengthening, creativity, a sense of well-being, and feelings of mastery and self-control. For example, one widely used suggestion, described in many of the cases that follow, is for clients to experience the self in a "safe place" of comfort and security, where it is possible to relax completely.

Suggestions for relaxation, well-being, and control have a wide range of applicability and often constitute the building blocks on which interventions for various disorders are based. Yapko's chapter on depression illustrates how hypnotic procedures can be used to increase frustration tolerance, help a person to separate past and present events, recognize ongoing experience as changeable and malleable, and shift from a reactive to a proactive position in life. Several of the chapters provide excellent illustrations of how hypnosis and relaxation techniques can be used in cognitive–behavioral treatments to treat somatoform disorder (Chaves, chapter 7, this volume), public speaking anxiety (Schoenberger, chapter 2, this volume), and destructive habits such as cigarette smoking (Green, chapter 11, this volume).

Spiegel (chapter 5, this volume) maintains that hypnosis can be especially useful in accessing and altering trauma-related states. Hypnosis can be used to work through traumatic memories, while controlling affect and regressive experiences during abreactions. It can also be used to analyze traumatic memories and experiences in terms of sequence and causality so that a coherent narrative can be formed and to focus on the damaging impact of sexual abuse and other traumatic events, while integrating past traumatic experiences into a more encompassing and positive sense of the self in the present.

Therapeutic Imagery

Hypnosis is conducive to the use of imaginative techniques in which specific actions or tasks are mentally rehearsed while the client is relaxed, feeling confident, and engaged in positive self-talk that enhances performance. In this context, imagined actions can be speeded up, slowed down, or stopped, while affect can be muted or accentuated as clients watch their actions on imagined television screens, computers, or videos, for example.

Imagery-based projective techniques can promote insight and the identification of problem areas and treatment issues yet to be resolved. For instance, in her treatment of an anorectic client, Hornyak (chapter 3, this volume) describes a projective theater technique in which the client expresses or projects the unconscious meaning of her problem in symbolic form into a play she views in an imaginary theater, giving the material a "concrete form" that can be explored and understood.

The hypnotist can suggest that the client have a dream during hypnosis, which resembles a daydream or nightdream, that serves a therapeutic purpose (e.g., "Have a dream about "X" in which its meaning to you is revealed in direct or symbolic form"). Such dreams can serve as vehicles to learn about personally meaningful life themes, problems, and conflicts (e.g., Barrett, 1979; Brown & Fromm, 1986, Sheehan & Dolby, 1979; Spanos, Nightingale, Radtke, & Stam, 1980) as well as about the parameters of interpersonal relationships and hypnotic rapport (Frauman, Lynn, Hardaway, & Molteni, 1984; Sheehan & Dolby, 1979).

Age-progression techniques, in which clients project themselves into the future (e.g., "after you solve your problem") can stimulate creative thought and solution-focused attempts to cope in the present (and near future) to achieve a more distal goal. Clients can be asked to reflect on what small, attainable steps they took on the path to achieving their goals. Green, in describing his technique for smoking cessation (chapter 11, this volume), invites participants to visualize two roads, a high road in which a future is imagined if the person quits successfully and a low road in which a future is imagined if the person is not truly motivated to quit. Clients are simply asked to choose which road they will walk down on the basis of the future they envision.

"Ego-State" Metaphors

The hypnotist can also suggest to the client that it is possible to communicate with discrete "parts of the personality," "ego states," or "hidden observers" that are ordinarily not accessible. For instance, Hornyak (chapter 3, this volume) informs her clients that it is sometimes "helpful to think of our self as a collection of parts, like a picture puzzle. Each part has its own characteristic feelings, behaviors, and motives. The goal is to know these parts of herself better."

Ego states have been described as "cognitive structural systems that are covert, but are organized segments of personality, often similar in content to true, overt multiple personalities." (Watkins, 1993, p. 235). Hilgard (1973b, 1986) introduced the concept of the hidden observer to describe the phenomenon by which a person registers and stores information in memory, without being aware that the information had been processed. In a typical study, highly hypnotizable subjects are able to recover concealed experiences or memories during hypnotic suggestions when they are informed that they possess a hidden part that can be contacted by the hypnotist with a prearranged cue. Although the clinical use of the procedure to recover repressed memories should be avoided, it can be used to stimulate the creative development of psychological insight.

Mare and her colleagues (Mare, Kvaal, Segal, & Sivec, 1994; Mare, Lynn, Kvaal, Segal, & Sivec 1994) showed that hidden observer suggestions can elicit additional personal information about subjects' experience of hypnotic dreams and age regression beyond ordinary repeated recall attempts. Indeed, the great majority of high-hypnotizable participants in hypnotic and nonhypnotic contexts were able to respond to suggestions they had a hidden part that could comment on various aspects of their experience. Mare and her associates argued that "parts of the personality," "ego states," and "hidden observers" are useful therapeutic metaphors that are suggested by the hypnotist (see Spanos & Hewitt, 1980), rather than independently existing dissociated entities. Nevertheless, hidden observer suggestions can be used to facilitate commentary and interpretation of events, experiences, and motives; to encourage clients to adopt multiple perspectives about their feelings and behaviors; to foster distance and dissociation from painful thoughts and feelings; and to enhance hypnotic amnesia (e.g., the hidden part can remain hidden).

Ego-state therapists have highlighted the ways in which hidden observer suggestions or suggestions for discrete ego states can be framed in terms of an "inner advisor" (see Comstock, 1991; Gainer & Torem, 1993) or a higher or strong self (Frederick & McNeal, 1993) that possesses special awareness and wisdom that can be accessed and exploited to assist the client to make decisions and to cope with stressful life events. Caution, however, must be used in administering hidden observer suggestions to highly dissociative, highly suggestible clients who would be prone to reifying the metaphor of the hidden observer and incorporating it into a presentation of multiple personality.

Hypnotic Desensitization

Hypnotic techniques can be used to desensitize clients to fears and provide an optimum level of exposure to anxiety-eliciting stimuli in a gradual, safe, and controlled manner. When graduated tasks are administered and calibrated to the clients' readiness to move forward in treatment, a sense of personal efficacy can be cultivated or enhanced. Schoenberger (chapter 2, this volume) demonstrates how hypnosis can be used to enhance the effectiveness of a standard, empirically validated, cognitive–behavioral treatment for phobia. Kirsch and Coe's (chapter 17, this volume) description of their treatment of a woman with a phobia of using restrooms in public places illustrates how hypnotherapy can begin with easy tasks and progress to more difficult ones only after the easier ones have been mastered. Approaching the same case from an Ericksonian perspective, Matthews, Lankton, and Lankton (chapter 18, this volume) discuss how personal resources can be gradually accessed, developed, and associated with present and future life situations. Lynn, Rhue, Kvaal, and Mare (1993) have described a graded series of suggestions that can be used in the treatment of anorexia nervosa that range from relatively low to high difficulty, personal and interpersonal focus, complexity, degree of structure imposed by the therapist, affectivity, conflict-evoking potential, and imaginative versus behavioral rehearsal.

Self-Hypnosis

Hypnotic procedures can be defined as "self-hypnosis" to enhance perceptions of treatment success and the likelihood that what is learned during the therapy hour will be implemented in every-day life (Barber, 1985). Often, perhaps in the majority of the cases in which hypnosis is used clinically, hypnotic procedures are framed in terms of self-hypnosis (Orne & McConkey, 1981). Many clinicians inform clients that all hypnosis (even heterohypnosis) can be thought of as self-hypnosis insofar as clients are ultimately responsible for generating suggestion-relevant imagery, experiences, and behaviors. Self-hypnosis is most frequently taught by first introducing the client to heterohypnotic techniques and related experiences and then encouraging the client to assume increasingly greater responsibility for devising suggestions appropriate to achieving treatment goals.

In self-administering therapeutic suggestions, the client replaces the therapist as the active agent in the therapeutic proceedings. Barber (1985) noted that labeling procedures as self-hypnosis minimizes many fears often encountered when the situation is labeled as hypnosis (e.g., fear of being under the control of another, fear of not coming out of hypnosis, and fear of being unaware or unconscious). Working with trauma survivors, who might be threatened by an intrusive therapist, Smith (chapter 6, this volume) defines his role as a coach or a guide. In self-regulation therapy, described by Amigó and Capafons (chapter 8, this volume), the client actively participates in treatment by choosing and improving on strategies and suggestions proposed by the therapist. Self-hypnosis, rather than heterohypnosis, may be the treatment of choice in certain cases, such as with obsessive–compulsive clients.

Therapists often make customized tapes for clients to listen to at home or at work (see Ellis, chapter 16, this volume) that capture the essentials of the hypnotic session and crystallize important learnings to be taken home. This is done to minimize dependency on the therapist, generalize treatment gains, and encourage mastery of self-suggestions that can be implemented in a variety of situations without the tape or the hypnotist. When instructions for self-hypnosis are given, therapists instill the idea that suggested responses will get easier with practice and that additional resources will become available to cope with problems in living.

Posthypnotic Suggestions

Posthypnotic suggestions can also be used to generalize treatment gains. It is often helpful to administer posthypnotic suggestions for relaxation, ego enhancement, and mastery that are linked with a physical movement or gesture such as touching the thumb and forefinger together. When a particular feeling state or sense of mastery regarding a situation is achieved during hypnosis, clients can be instructed, for example, to touch thumb and forefinger together, and to do so in an actual life situation in which they would like to replicate the feelings or sense of mastery (e.g., "later, when you are taking the test, you will feel particularly relaxed yet alert when you touch your thumb and forefinger together").

This technique of cue-controlled relaxation, or "anchoring" as it is sometimes termed, is widely used. Many therapists use cue-control techniques that pair an image or verbal cue with a well-practiced or conditioned response to relaxation or other suggested experiences. Key phrases (e.g., relax completely, safe, and secure) can be used to trigger or elicit specific feelings and cognitions. Typically, key phrases are first suggested by the therapist or developed by the client during hypnosis and then later self-administered in relevant situations. In treating public-speaking anxiety, Schoenberger (chapter 2, this volume) invites clients to associate feelings of relaxation with a word or a phrase they can think of when they wish to enter hypnosis or experience relaxation in public-speaking situations. To ease tension states in hypnotic and nonhypnotic contexts, Hornyak (chapter 3, this volume) suggests that her clients allow an image or thought to come to mind that represents a sense of control and inner strength.

Whereas our discussion highlights the fact that hypnotic procedures can benefit many clients, it is perhaps less obvious that they are not for everyone. Hypnosis should not be used without careful consideration. As a rule, the decision to use hypnosis should be preceded by a thorough evaluation of the client. This evaluation will often include not only an assessment of the client's psychological status and beliefs and motives to experience hypnosis, but also an evaluation of the client's ability to respond to hypnotic suggestions.

Psychological Assessment

At a minimum, the psychological assessment should include information pertinent to the client's mental and physical status, life history, and current psychological problems and dynamics. Important areas of inquiry include the client's treatment motivation, needs, character structure, life situation, history of dissociative and posttraumatic reactions, resources, perceived strengths and weaknesses, and beliefs and misconceptions about hypnosis.

Misconceptions about hypnosis may hamper the client's ability to trust the hypnotist and to participate fully in the events of hypnosis. It is therefore imperative to initiate hypnosis only with the participant's explicit consent, to demystify hypnosis and bolster positive expectancies, and to help the participant feel tangibly in control of the events that unfold during hypnosis. In short, it is essential that the decision to use hypnosis be informed by what is learned in the initial assessment, by the therapist's general theoretical orientation, and by the specific goals and objectives of psychotherapy. Just as important, therapists should establish a strong therapeutic alliance, know what they wish to accomplish, and have a clear idea about how hypnotic communications can facilitate treatment. Ideally, the therapist and client should have congruent perceptions and mutual goals in this regard.

When a client requests hypnosis, much can be gained from carefully assessing the client's motives. What does hypnosis represent to the client? What does the client hope to accomplish? Are the client's expectations realistic? Is the request for hypnosis a veiled message that the client is dissatisfied with the therapeutic work so far? Does the client request hypnosis as an evasive maneuver to sidestep issues that are emerging in therapy? Are there powerful secondary gains operative that diminish the likelihood of success with hypnosis? Could direct attempts at symptom removal backfire, given fears or ambivalent feelings about relinquishing familiar patterns? Will the client diminish the therapy, the therapist, and himself or herself if the outcome of hypnotherapy is negative or less than hoped for?

As Dowd (chapter 14, this volume) cautions, when hypnosis is viewed as "magic" or as a last resort where other treatments have failed (e.g., You're our last hope, doctor!), the hypnotherapist should be wary of being "set up" for possible failure.

Correspondingly, what are the therapist's motives? Do we wish to use hypnosis because we feel guilty that we are not doing more for the client? Are we bored or angry with the client and hungering for "fireworks" in therapy that only hypnosis can provide? In short, one or more issues may need to be examined and resolved before hypnotic treatment is initiated.

Assessment of the client is also necessary to screen out candidates who are inappropriate or less than ideal for hypnotherapy. Clients who are vulnerable to psychotic decompensation (Meares, 1961); those with a paranoid level of resistance to being influenced or controlled (Orne, 1965); unstabilized dissociative or posttraumatic clients; and those with borderline character structure for whom hypnosis may be experienced as a sudden, intrusive, and unwanted intimacy may all be poor candidates for hypnosis or require special attention or modification of typical hypnotic procedures to emphasize safety, security, and connectedness (see Murray-Jobsis, chapter 9, this volume). Horevitz's chapter provides many thoughtful observations on the special considerations and procedures that need to be invoked in the treatment of fragile clients with dissociative identity disorder. Ultimately, the pros and cons of hypnosis must be carefully weighed against those of nonhypnotic treatment.

Hypnotizability Assessment

It is well-known that certain people are more responsive to hypnotic suggestions than others. Hence, knowledge of a client's ability to respond to hypnotic suggestions may well factor into a decision to proceed with a treatment that relies heavily on hypnotic procedures. No doubt, most clients will be able to respond to relatively simple nondemanding suggestions. This is important because many of the suggestions used by the authors of this book can be so described and because much good therapeutic work can be done with suggestions for comfort, security, peace of mind, and imaginative rehearsal of specific events, for example. However, virtually every experienced therapist has encountered the rare client who cannot or will not respond to even simple suggestions. Given this, many therapists conduct a brief informal assessment by observing their clients' responses to simple suggestions such as eye closure or relaxation. Indeed, it is impossible to know precisely how a client will respond to a hypnotic intervention prior to inducing hypnosis itself.

Yet even when hypnosis is not entirely successful, much can be learned about the client. Examination of the reasons why a client fails simple suggestions may reveal that popular misconceptions about hypnosis were not truly modified by prehypnotic education (e.g., you do not lose control during hypnosis); that inadequate rapport was established; that the hypnotic communications were interpreted in an idiosyncratic manner or touched on conflictual issues; that the client did not expect he or she would be successful; and that there were, perhaps, powerful yet unconscious resistances to relinquishing symptoms. It is always advisable to carefully explore the reasons why the client failed to respond to suggestions in keeping with the treatment agenda. Whether and how this knowledge can be exploited depends in part on the therapist's acumen and the degree to which insights derived from clients' reactions to hypnosis are relevant to the therapist's particular brand of psychotherapy (Kirsch, Lynn, & Rhue, 1993).

Another reason to assess hypnotic responsiveness is if substantial costs are incurred with failure to hypnotize someone. Consider the case of a request to hypnotize a dental patient who is contemplating undergoing painful dental procedures without analgesia because of an allergic response to analgesiacs. It would be foolhardy to hypnotize such a patient in a dental situation who failed to demonstrate appreciable hypnotic analgesia, in a relatively less-demanding situation, prior to the dental procedure.

Assessment may provide indications regarding how to present and tailor "hypnotic" communications to particular clients to optimize treatment. For instance, experimental studies have shown that hypnotizability is related to pain reduction in situations that are labeled as *hypnotic* (see Lynn, Rhue, & Spanos, 1994). However, research has also demonstrated that if a person is low hypnotizable, he or she will not respond to hypnotic suggestions for analgesia but may respond to analgesia suggestions that are not couched in hypnotic terms. We could, for example, label what we are doing as *imagination* or *goal-directed fantasy* and, in all likelihood, still be just as effective (Bates, 1993; Kirsch, 1993). Amigó and Capafon's self-regulation therapy (chapter 8, this volume), in which clients learn to respond actively to suggestions without a trance induction and with their eyes open, has been shown to be effective in treating many problems.

Evidence is accumulating that a link exists between hypnotizability and successful hypnotic treatment of a number of disorders. Not all clients can benefit from hypnotic treatment (Brown, 1992; Wadden & Anderton, 1982). For instance, obsessive–compulsive clients are less hypnotizable than both other client groups and normal controls (Spinhoven, Van Dyck, Hoogduin, & Schaap, 1991). In the treatment of other disorders and conditions such as asthma (Collison, 1978), obesity (Levitt, 1993), nicotine dependence (see Lynn, Neufeld, Rhue, & Matorin, 1993), somatoform disorders (Wickramasekera, 1993), posttraumatic stress disorders (Spiegel, 1993), and phobias (see Crawford & Barabasz, 1993), there are good empirical or theoretical reasons to support a link between hypnotizability and treatment outcome, even though it may be mediated by imaginative processes.

A number of psychological disorders (e.g., phobias, eating disorders, and dissociative disorders) are associated with above-average hypnotizability (Rhue et al., 1993). Of course, just because a person is phobic, for example, is in no way a guarantee that he or she will be high hypnotizable or successfully treated with hypnotic methods. This is true because there is sufficient treatment variability within each one of the diagnostic categories noted above to warrant careful assessment of an individual client's hypnotic responsiveness and distinctive way of responding to hypnosis, regardless of diagnostic classification.

Hypnotizability assessment is invaluable when early trauma-resolution work is contemplated, given that moderate-to-high hypnotizability increases the risk of pseudomemory formation. It is worth noting that psychotherapists might wish to test for suggestibility even in nonhypnotic contexts in that hypnotizable participants evidence relatively high rates of pseudomemories in nonhypnotic conditions as well as hypnotic conditions (see Lynn & Nash, 1994).

Let us assume for a moment that a therapist decides to informally assess hypnotizability (i.e., without a standardized hypnotizability scale). What is the best way to proceed? It is essential that a therapist assess the client in a positive and, we hope, fail-safe way. As an initial assessment of potential responsiveness, particularly with clients who are reserved about experiencing hypnosis, clients can be introduced to hypnotic-like experiences such as the Chevreul pendulum[1] (see Bates, 1993) prior to hypnosis. These demonstrations are simple and powerful and increase the client's expectations of responsiveness in other situations defined as hypnotic (Kirsch, 1993). Of course, if the client continues to express reservations about hypnosis or finds responding to suggestion aversive, for some reason, the therapist and client may decide to pursue alternative nonhypnotic treatment methods.

Other procedures provide relatively risk-free assessment possibilities. For instance, Kirsch et al. (1993) suggest the use of simultaneous suggestions for heaviness in one arm and lightness in the other as a way of determining client responsiveness during an initial induction. If there is any overt response to the lightening suggestion (e.g., fingers twitching and arm movement), then further suggestions for lightness can be given. If there are no overt signs of response to lightness suggestions, then sugges-

---

[1] A Chevreul pendulum consists of a thread or light string approximately the length from elbow to fingertips, with a bob such as a key attached. The person rests the elbow on the resting surface and holds the loose end of the thread between the thumb and forefinger, with the wrist bent at approximately a right angle. The person is given instructions to focus on the bob and to think of the bob doing different things, such as making circles or swinging back and forth in predetermined directions (Coe, 1993). Clients' commonly reported experience is that the pendulum moves in conformity with the imagined or suggested movement but without awareness of intentional physical movements of the hand or arm. The experience can easily be self-generated without external suggestions.

tions for increased heaviness are pursued. Responses to lightness suggestions may be an indication of a higher level of responsiveness and can be followed up by more difficult suggestions. Whether or not the client responds to lightness suggestions, a gross measure of responsiveness is gained, while at the same time avoiding any sense of failure on the part of the subject.

Another approach is to administer a variety of suggestions in a waking context. Many studies now suggest that task-motivated or relaxed participants who are asked to think and imagine along with suggestions while awake can respond successfully to a variety of suggestions for responses as diverse as hypnotic dreams, age regression, hand levitation, trance logic, and analgesia (Lynn et al., 1994; see Spanos, 1986). If clients succeed in responding to these sorts of suggestions while awake, it can be virtually guaranteed that they will respond to equivalent suggestions during hypnosis. However, if they do not respond to such suggestions while awake, a number of options are available to the clinician. The clinician could either pursue an alternate nonhypnotic treatment approach or imply that the procedures did not work because the client was not hypnotized and retest responsiveness to the test suggestions during hypnosis. Taking this latter course of action would, of course, be somewhat risky and would depend on the client's expectancies and motivations concerning hypnosis.

If a therapist requires additional information about a client's responsiveness, he or she must decide whether to use formal, standardized tests of hypnotic responsiveness or nonstandard tests of responsiveness carefully tailored to the treatment at hand (Bates, 1993; Brown & Fromm, 1986). If the clinician decides to use a standardized test, then he or she must further decide about whether to use a relatively long formal test of hypnotizability or a shorter yet potentially diagnostic assessment of hypnotizability such as the "induction" (IND) score of the Hypnotic Induction Profile (HIP; Spiegel & Spiegel, 1978), for which moderate to high correlations with other hypnotizability scales have been shown (Perry, Nadon, & Button, 1992).[2]

The HIP is a sensible choice for a short yet informative multidimensional assessment. Nadon and Laurence (1994), however, strongly recommend the much longer Stanford Hypnotic Susceptibility Scale, Form C (SHSS:C; Weitzenhoffer & Hilgard, 1962) or a tailored version (Hilgard, Crawford, Bowers, & Kihlstrom, 1979) "primarily because of its stringency and its broad sampling of hypnotic suggestions" (p. 91). The advantage of a tailored version is that it can provide information about specific responses relevant to treatment. These standard measures are to be preferred in research settings or when reporting of clinical studies is anticipated.

---

[2]In contrast, the eye roll sign, which is also a part of the HIP, is very difficult to rate and does not seem to be correlated substantially with other measures of hypnotizability.

If treatment is brief and involves only relaxation or generic ego-strengthening suggestions, a thorough assessment of hypnotizability and an examination of responses to a variety of suggestions may not be required. Indeed, many of the chapter authors do not use formal tests of hypnotizability. Furthermore, if the therapist knows in advance which suggestions will be relevant to treatment, he or she may decide to limit hypnotizability testing to specific, treatment-relevant target suggestions. It may not be essential to test clients on a complete hypnotizability scale if therapists are only interested in determining the robustness of hypnotic amnesia, for example, or the response to an age-regression, analgesia, or hypnotic dream suggestion. Because there is variability in how even high-hypnotizable individuals experience and respond to suggestions, a high hypnotizability score does not obviate the need to evaluate clients' responses to specific suggestions that are germane to treatment. It is useful to assess not only observable hypnotic responses but also subjective responses. After all, most clinicians are as keenly interested in the client's internal or subjective experience of suggestion as they are in the client's ability to have a motoric response (e.g., hand levitation) in keeping with a suggestion.

In summary, hypnotizability assessment can provide the clinician with valuable data. Although each therapist must weigh the costs and benefits of any assessment procedure with each client, we would argue that some form of assessment of hypnotizability, whether formal or informal, brief or extensive, can be useful with perhaps the majority of clients.

HYPNOSIS IN PRACTICE: AN ILLUSTRATIVE SELF-HYPNOSIS SCRIPT

It is useful to think of suggestions as being divided into two phases—induction and application—although in practice they may not be entirely distinct. In the *Handbook*, we noted that a boggling variety of inductions (e.g., instructions to relax, fix gaze on an object or attention on an idea, suggestions of various images or automatic behaviors) have been used in the past, and we presented an illustrative example of a standard relaxation-based induction. Here we present an example of an induction that defines the methods as "self-hypnosis" and includes many of the techniques previously noted.

In this induction, the reader will recognize permissive and generic suggestions for comfort, security, and a wide range of alterations in experience; suggestions for imagining a safe place; suggestions for a key phrase and anchoring; suggestions for working with a metaphor of a "higher, deep, internal self"; and suggestions for generalizing gains outside the hypnotic context. The induction also contains many suggestions to deepen the experience and illustrates how a hypnotic session can be terminated. Lynn has used this induction with particular success with anxious and depressed clients as well as with clients who have posttraumatic reactions and who have survived physical and sexual abuse. It is relatively simple, nondemanding, and does not rely on movements such as hand levitation, which may lead to attributions of failure (e.g, "my hand did not rise completely" or "it did not feel involuntary"). The great majority of clients who have experienced this induction report that they felt comfortable, relaxed, empowered, and involved with the suggestions.

However, the reader should keep a few things in mind. First, the induction is really only a scaffolding for a more individually tailored induction that can be adapted to the unique needs of each client and type of psychotherapy. Second, we wish to reinforce the point that this induction is intended for professionals and graduate students and not for a lay audience. We caution readers against sharing this information with nonprofessionals and remind the reader that hypnosis should be used only by people with appropriate training and credentials.

The description below assumes that this is the client's first experience of hypnosis, that an adequate rapport has been established, that the nature of hypnosis has been explained, that fears and misconceptions have been discussed, that the client is seated in a comfortable chair or couch, and that permission to induce hypnosis has been granted.

> Please make yourself comfortable. In this session, I will help you to create a self-hypnotic experience for yourself . . . one that you can use on your own. So, if you will, let us begin by your simply closing your eyes. Please close your eyes and take a deep breath. And as you breathe out you can begin to feel a sense of calm, feel the calmness spreading. You will not fall asleep, although just how relaxed or awake you are really doesn't matter because there are always lessons to be learned, and in learning . . . growing, and in evolving as a person, reminding yourself that you are in charge now, you can do or not do, think or not think, as you wish. And whether your mind drifts or wafts or whether thoughts break up or flow like a stream, you can always listen to my voice and talk if you have the desire to do so. I wonder whether you would like to experience what it might be like to move to an even deeper state of calm, moving and moving and moving, you doing it, you creating it, in your own mind, in your own body, in your own way, peace, easy, comfortable, at ease, as deep as you like into your experience, nothing to disturb, nothing to bother, lots of time, lots and lots of time to experience what you need to, what you want to, with no one to make decisions for you, to tell you just how to be the person you are or can be, or what you need to know to do what needs to be done or exactly when and how you will go even deeper into your experience of who you are and what you can be, with freedom to write the story more and more as you wish, you the author, your hand writ-

ing, in your own hand, taking with you, from this experience, what interests and absorbs you, what piques your curiosity, even surprises you, noticing what you need to, discovering what is really important . . . what you want . . . in your own time, in your own way, with you the author, you the creator of it all.

I wonder if you have the experience of time slowing down . . . time slowing down to a most comfortable pace. Are you aware that your breathing has altered, perhaps slowed down, perhaps speeded up slightly; it just doesn't matter at all . . . not for now . . . at any rate . . . at any speed. No matter how you breathe, no matter whether you might wish to move around to adjust your position, what matters is that you are aware of what you can experience. And are you willing to experience a certain level of comfort, a level that is good enough for you? Just enough, if not a little more, to have an experience of safety and security? Wouldn't it be nice to feel at perfect peace? Wouldn't it be nice to be quiet inside? Wouldn't it be wonderful to experience body, mind, at ease . . . safe . . . secure . . . comfort . . . for now . . . as if enveloped by some sort of protective bubble, in charge of what comes in and goes out, able to write the script as you choose? Would you like to modify your experience in some way? Do you give yourself permission to do so? Go ahead and do so, if you wish, make yourself comfortable.

Perhaps even images and thoughts are slowing down to a trickle . . . but can you perhaps . . . experience a place where you are complete, whole, where you begin to move closer and touch your deep inner self, increasingly aware of your higher self of strength and goodness, of kindness and caring for others, and of caring for yourself? Can you take a minute or two to be aware of this? What is your experience of it? How can you enhance it?

I don't know whether this place really exists in your past, in your present, in your future, in your memory, in your fantasy, it really doesn't matter, for what matters for now is a certain level of comfort, of willingness to experience that higher self, that deep internal self . . . that self that is good, whole, clean, fresh, and perhaps even childlike in some refreshing ways . . . born to grow and learn . . . good and whole . . . that transcends your experiences . . . that still learns and grows and informs, as any concerns you have that get in the way of this sense of perfect peace are moving farther and farther away, breaking up like clouds in the wind. And there's lots of time . . . time to feel connected . . . to approach your inner self, to feel oneness with it, at all levels of your being. This self is full of life within you, it is fresh, spontaneous, and wise.

If you are not yet there in your experience, would you be willing to get even closer to this inner self, until all aspects of your being begin to merge with it and become one, and you become whole, fresh, and alive in this place? With each step you take toward this goal, you may notice that you become more centered, grounded, focused. I wonder, can you feel waves of gentle relaxation? Or are you just feeling open and receptive? Do you feel more heavy and warm or an easy floating feeling? I don't know, it is your experience.

To help us move toward this goal, I will count from one to five. And with each step, you can remember to take a deep breath and move closer to that part of yourself. If you are there already, your conscious mind does not even need to listen fully to what I say, as I count from one to five, as you move and flow with this sense of self.

One. Take your first step. More and more focused on your experience of what you are and can be as you gain a sense of inner peace. And wouldn't it be nice to really let go to the point where you feel this sense of serenity enveloping you? Is this all right?

Two. And with your second step, are you more relaxed than when you are asleep or would you rather not think at all? Are you willing to go deep and deep and deeper into your own experience as you move toward that part of yourself? Your breathing is so relaxed at this point. Would you like to go even deeper? When will you know that you are there? Or do you somehow know? Nothing to bother, nothing to disturb.

Three. And with your third step you discover a pull toward your inner self like a magnet, gently drawing you toward it, if you are willing to approach even closer. Let yourself learn and discover and sense even more aspects of it, and the space around your inner self, where there are all these different parts becoming integrated, interwoven, your caring for yourself, your curiosity, your ability to sense, to be aware, to experience, to love and be kind and to care, your wisdom, and more, much more.

Four. You are almost there. Touching that inner part of yourself, almost one with it, even as you breathe. You don't really have to do anything, nothing to bother, nothing to disturb as you turn inside, more and more at peace, serene.

Five. And with that fifth step, all those different parts of yourself are merging with your inner self, connecting, becoming one, becoming a new, creative, alive, wonderful, whole sense of yourself. Can you let this wholeness give you a sense of strength to draw on? Would you be willing to draw on this strength when you need to, to draw on your wisdom and power?

In times when you need to, would you be willing to call on that part of yourself, to experience its strength fully, to perhaps even be surprised by its ability to help you get through it, to continue, to provide you with wisdom, to add depths of appreciation and understanding to your perceptions? To make this part of you real?

Would you be willing to say "strength is within" as a key phrase, a beacon that shines outward and touches you at all levels of your being, radiating from your inner self, bringing you in contact with the very core of you that is good, so good and whole? Can you, at some level, remind yourself not to forget to look deep, deep within, to be aware of what is good for you, be aware of that part that nourishes and restores you, that part that transcends your past, even your experiences, that transcends your doubts and fears, that helps you work through whatever you need to, that is there, deep within, that reminds you that you are in control, in control.

You can access this key phrase in your mind, "strength is within." And when you need it, you can use your key phrase as a beacon. "Strength is within." It will bring you right back to where you are now. You can access this sense of being grounded, of strength, of inner peace.

Now I will suggest a way for you to access your inner strength. You will do three very simple things to anchor yourself, to access that inner part of yourself. One, you will take a deep breath. Two, as you breath in, you will think of your key phrase. "Strength is within." And three, you will make a fist, drawing on all your inner strength and will and determination and love and caring for yourself.

When I say the word *anchor*, you will breath in, think of your key phrase, and make a fist, all at the same time. Then, you will breathe out, release your fist, and think of your key phrase again. "Strength is within." And now, anchor: Breathe, phrase, fist . . . and release, "Strength is within."

Experience a sense of inner peace, of deep calm. This is a place to remember when you are stressed or disturbed or simply wish to feel good. And you can use this anchor any time you need it. Once again, anchor and release. Feel the calmness spread as you breathe out.

In a minute, I will suggest another anchor you can use. You will bring your thumb and forefinger together, creating a circle or a ring. That circle stands for strength, for wholeness, for serenity, for determination. The circle represents your inner self. You will anchor in the same way you did when you made a fist. You will do three things at once. You will bring your thumb and forefinger together, breathe in, and think of your key phrase, "strength is within." Then breathe out and think of your key phrase again. "Strength is within." Once again, anchor.

You can use this anchor at times when you need to focus on strength, when you want to go deep inside. You can access your inner self this way.

Feel yourself so relaxed, notice how comfortable and peaceful you are now. You have a sense of peace, of being at one with yourself, of being at one with your inner self. You can return to this place anytime you want. You can come back to this state of calm at even the most distressing times. Remember to use your anchors when you are distressed or upset, as well as any other times. And remember that your inner self is more than your experiences, more than your thoughts, more than your feelings, more than your past.

And in a minute, you will begin to leave this special place, but you will bring your inner self with you. And you will come back slowly. You will bring your strength, your renewed sense of self, coming together, more whole and complete, your inner calmness, and you will bring all of your tools, all of your ways of coping with you. I will count back slowly from five to one. You will gradually come back, so that, by the time I say two, you will open your eyes. When I reach the count of one, you will be wide awake, alert, no longer hypnotized.

And now, I am counting back . . . five . . . You are getting a sense of moving away very, very slowly. You are very calm. Four . . . You're moving a little further away. Your inner self is coming with you, and you feel so safe and secure. Three. You're becoming more aware of your body. You're more aware of your surroundings. Maybe you are aware of light beyond your closed eyelids. You're more aware of sensations in your body, that you might not have been aware of before. Two . . . You are slowly opening your eyes. Can you continue to feel very calm and relaxed? Have a sense of wholeness, of completeness? It can feel so good, and it can stay with you. You're becoming reoriented to where you are right now. Your inner self is coming with you. One . . . You are becoming wide awake again. Fully alert. Let yourself move your body . . . begin to move slowly. Stretch and let it come back to a state of wakefulness. Your inner self is with you. You can come back to this hypnosis exercise again and again, when you wish, when you want to. You can develop even more skills and abilities to calm and sooth yourself as you practice using your self-hypnosis. The idea here is that practice makes perfect. Practice at night, the morning, and the afternoon, at least once or twice a day, or more, as you choose, as you wish, at any time you need to, want to. If you wish, you can also keep a record of what works best for you as you learn and grow, learn and grow. Let's practice using the anchor now.

Place yourself in self-hypnosis. Use your anchor now, be sure to breathe and say your keyphrase. Take a minute or so.

Wide awake. How do you feel?

A simple, basic induction such as this can serve as an initial assessment of a person's responsiveness to suggestions for relaxation and other alterations in experience and as the cornerstone for the application of additional therapeutic suggestions. To build on this induction, answers to the following questions can provide the therapist with invaluable information: What did you like about your experience? At what point were you most deeply involved? What was particularly helpful? Did anything get in the way? How did the experience square with what you thought you would experience? How could the experience be made even more pleasurable, meaningful, or therapeutic? Do you have any specific suggestions you would like to add to your experience of self-hypnosis? Are there parts you would like to leave out? How do you feel about practicing your hypnotic skills? What are your plans to do so?

At the conclusion of the hypnosis session, it is important to ask clients how they are feeling. Negative aftereffects are not common, but they are sometimes reported. Although there is no evidence that these are due to the use of hypnosis (see Frauman, Lynn, & Brentar, 1993; Lynn et al., 1995), they require clinical attention whatever their cause.

Novice hypnotists sometimes worry about not being able to bring a client out of hypnosis. This is a holdover from conceptions of hypnosis that are no longer held by professionals but that continue to influence the public through inaccurate portrayals in the media. The state of consciousness produced by typical hypnotic inductions is similar to meditative or relaxed states. Asking "What if my client doesn't come out of hypnosis?" is like asking "What if my client doesn't stop relaxing?"

It can happen that a particular subject seems to be "stuck" in hypnosis, but this is extremely rare, especially in clinical settings in which a good therapeutic relationship has been established. On those rare occasions in which it does occur, it may indicate that the client is enjoying the experience and does not want it to end. In nonclinical settings, it may be a provocation aimed at seeing what the hypnotist will do. The motive for remaining in hypnosis can be ascertained by simply asking the client, and the answer is likely to provide the therapist with the cues needed to resolve the problem. If all else fails, clients can be told that they will come out of hypnosis when ready, but that they will be charged for the time they remain in the therapist's office.

At this point, we conclude our introduction to clinical hypnosis. In the concluding chapter, we will discuss a number of issues introduced here, as well as other issues such as pseudomemory risk in clinical hypnosis, which are broached in the chapter that follows. We will conclude with recommendations and steps that clinicians can take to minimize resistance and maximize treatment gains.

REFERENCES

American Psychological Association, Division of Psychological Hypnosis. (1993). Hypnosis. *Psychological Hypnosis*, 2, 3.

Banyai, E. (1991). Toward a social-psychobiological model of hypnosis. In S. J. Lynn & J. W. Rhue (Eds.), *Theories of hypnosis: Current models and perspectives* (pp. 564–598). New York: Guilford Press.

Barber, T. X. (1969). *Hypnosis: A scientific approach*. New York: Van Nostrand Reinhold.

Barber, T. X. (1985). Hypnosuggestive procedures as catalysts for all psychotherapies. In S. J. Lynn & J. P. Garske (Eds.), *Contemporary psychotherapies: Models and methods* (pp. 333–376). Columbus, MO: Merrill Press.

Barrett, D. (1979). The hypnotic dream: Its relation to nocturnal dreams and waking fantasies. *Journal of Abnormal Psychology, 88*, 584–591.

Bates, B. L. (1993). Individual differences in response to hypnosis. In J. W. Rhue, S. J. Lynn, & I. Kirsch (Eds.), *Handbook of clinical hypnosis* (pp. 23–54). Washington, DC: American Psychological Association.

Brown, D. P. (1992). Clinical hypnosis research since 1986. In E. Fromm & M. R. Nash (Eds.), *Contemporary hypnosis research* (pp. 427–458). New York: Guilford Press.

Brown, D. P. & Fromm, E. (1986). *Hypnotherapy and hypnoanalysis.* New York: Guilford Press.

Chaves, J. F. (1994). Hypnosis: The struggle for a definition. *Contemporary Hypnosis, 11*, 145–146.

Coe, W. C. (1993). Expectations and hypnotherapy. In J. W. Rhue, S. J. Lynn, & I. Kirsch (Eds.), *Handbook of clinical hypnosis* (pp. 73–94). Washington, DC: American Psychological Association.

Collison, D. R. (1978). Hypnotherapy in asthmatic patients and the importance of trance depth. In F. H. Frankel & H. S. Zamansky (Eds.), *Hypnosis at its bicentennial: Selected papers* (pp. 261–274). New York: Plenum Press.

Comstock, C. (1991). The inner self helper and concepts of inner guidance: Historical antecedents, its role within dissociation, and clinical utilization. *Dissociation, 4*, 165–177.

Crawford, H. J., & Barabasz, A. F. (1993). Phobias and intense fears: Facilitating their treatment with hypnosis. In J. W. Rhue, S. J. Lynn, & I. Kirsch (Eds.), *Handbook of clinical hypnosis* (pp. 311–338). Washington, DC: American Psychological Association.

Frauman, D. C., Lynn, S. J., & Brentar, J. P. (1993). Prevention and therapeutic management of "negative effects" in hypnotherapy. In J. W. Rhue, S. J. Lynn, & I. Kirsch (Eds.), *Handbook of clinical hypnosis* (pp. 95–120). Washington, DC: American Psychological Association.

Frauman, D. C., Lynn, S. J., Hardaway, R., & Molteni, A. (1984). Effect of subliminal symbiotic activation on hypnotic rapport and susceptibility. *Journal of Abnormal Psychology, 93*, 481–483.

Frederick, C., & McNeal, S. (1993). From strength to strength: "Inner strength" with immature ego states. *American Journal of Clinical Hypnosis, 35*, 250–256.

Fromm, E., Hilgard, E. R., & Kihlstrom, J. F. (1994). APA definition of hypnosis: Endorsements. *Contemporary Hypnosis, 11*, 144.

Fromm, E., & Nash, M. R. (1992). Contemporary hypnosis research. New York: Guilford Press.

Gainer, M. J., & Torem, M. S. (1993). Ego-state therapy for self-injurious behavior. *American Journal of Clinical Hypnosis, 35*, 257–266.

Gfeller, J. (1993). Enhancing hypnotizability and treatment responsiveness. In J. W. Rhue, S. J. Lynn, & I. Kirsch (Eds.), *Handbook of clinical hypnosis* (pp. 235–250). Washington, DC: American Psychological Association.

Gorassini D. R., & Spanos, N. P. (1986). A social–cognitive skills approach to the successful modification of hypnotic susceptibility. *Journal of Personality and Social Psychology, 50,* 1004–1012.

Gravitz, M. (1991). Early theories of hypnosis: A clinical perspective. In S. J. Lynn & J. W. Rhue (Eds.), *Theories of hypnosis: Current models and perspectives* (pp. 19–42). New York: Guilford Press.

Hilgard, E. R. (1965). *Hypnotic susceptibility.* New York: Harcourt, Brace & World.

Hilgard, E. R. (1973a). The domain of hypnosis: With some comments on alternate paradigms. *American Psychologist, 28,* 972–982.

Hilgard, E. R. (1973b). A neodissociation interpretation of pain reduction in hypnosis. *Psychological Review, 80,* 396–411.

Hilgard, E. R. (1986). *Divided consciousness: Multiple controls in human thought and action* (expanded ed.). New York: Wiley.

Hilgard, E. R., Crawford, H. J., Bowers, P. G., & Kihlstrom, J. F. (1979). A tailored SHSS:C, permitting user modification for special purposes. *International Journal of Clinical and Experimental Hypnosis, 27,* 125–133.

Kirsch, I. (1993). Cognitive-behavioral hypnotherapy. In J. W. Rhue, S. J. Lynn, & I. Kirsch (Eds.), *Handbook of clinical hypnosis* (pp. 151–171). Washington, DC: American Psychological Association.

Kirsch, I. (1994). Defining hypnosis for the public. *Contemporary Hypnosis, 11,* 142–143.

Kirsch, I., & Lynn, S. J. (1995). The altered state of hypnosis: Changes in the theoretical landscape. *American Psychologist, 50,* 846–858.

Kirsch, I., Lynn, S. J., & Rhue, J. W. (1993). Introduction to clinical hypnosis. In J. W. Rhue, S. J. Lynn, & I. Kirsch (Eds.), *Handbook of clinical hypnosis* (pp. 3–22). Washington, DC: American Psychological Association.

Kirsch, I., Montgomery, G., & Sapirstein, G. (1995). Hypnosis as an adjunct to cognitive behavioral psychotherapy: A meta-analysis. *Journal of Consulting and Clinical Psychology, 63,* 214–220.

Kirsch, I., Silva, C. E., Carone, J. E., Johnston, J. D., & Simon, B. (1989). The surreptitious observation design: An experimental paradigm for distinguishing artifact from essence in hypnosis. *Journal of Abnormal Psychology, 98,* 132–136.

Kraft, W. A., & Rudolfa, E. R. (1982). The use of hypnosis among psychologists. *American Journal of Clinical Hypnosis, 24,* 249–257.

Levitt, E. E. (1993). Hypnosis in the treatment of obesity. In J. W. Rhue, S. J. Lynn, & I. Kirsch (Eds.), *Handbook of clinical hypnosis* (pp. 533–554). Washington, DC: American Psychological Association.

Lynn, S. J. (1994). The interface of hypnosis research and clinical practice. Guest editorial in the special issue of the *American Journal of Clinical Hypnosis, 37,* 81–83.

Lynn, S. J., & Garske, J. P. (1985). *Contemporary psychotherapies: Models and methods* (2nd ed). Columbus, MO: Merrill Press.

Lynn, S. J., Mare, C., Kvaal, S., Segal, D., & Sivec, H. (1994). The hidden observer, hypnotic dreams, and hypnotic age regression: Clinical implications. *American Journal of Clinical Hypnosis, 37*, 130–142.

Lynn, S. J., Martin, D., & Frauman, D. C. (1996). Does hypnosis pose special risks for negative effects? *International Journal of Clinical and Experimental Hypnosis, 44*, 7–19.

Lynn, S. J., & Nash, M. R. (1994). Truth in memory: Ramifications for hypnotherapy and psychotherapy. *American Journal of Clinical Hypnosis, 36*, 194–208.

Lynn, S. J., Neufeld, V., & Mare, C. (1993). Direct versus indirect suggestions: A conceptual and methodological review. *International Journal of Clinical and Experimental Hypnosis, 41*, 124–152.

Lynn, S. J., Neufeld, V., Rhue, J. W., & Matorin, A. (1993). Hypnosis and smoking cessation: A cognitive-behavioral treatment. In J. W. Rhue, S. J. Lynn, & I. Kirsch (Eds.), *Handbook of clinical hypnosis* (pp. 555–586). Washington, DC: American Psychological Association.

Lynn, S. J., & Rhue, J. W. (Eds.). (1991a). *Theories of hypnosis: Current models and perspectives.* New York: Guilford Press.

Lynn, S. J., & Rhue, J. W. (1991b). An integrative model of hypnosis. In S. J. Lynn & J. W. Rhue (Eds.), *Theories of hypnosis: Current models and perspectives* (pp. 397–438). New York: Guilford Press.

Lynn, S. J., Rhue, J. W., Kvaal, S., & Mare, C. (1993). The treatment of anorexia nervosa: A hypnosuggestive framework. *Contemporary Hypnosis, 10*, 73–80.

Lynn, S. J., Rhue, J. W., & Spanos, N. P. (1994). Hypnosis. In I. Ramachadran (Ed.), *Encyclopedia of human behavior* (pp. 555–566). New York: Wiley.

Lynn, S. J., Rhue, J. W., & Weekes, J. R. (1990). Hypnotic involuntariness: A social cognitive analysis. *Psychological Review, 97*, 169–184.

Mare, C., Lynn, S. J., Kvaal, S., Segal, D., & Sivec, H. (1994). The dream hidden observer: Primary process and demand characteristics. *Journal of Abnormal Psychology, 103*, 316–327.

McConkey, K. M. (1986). Opinions about hypnosis and self-hypnosis before and after hypnotic testing. *International Journal of Clinical and Experimental Hypnosis, 34*, 311–319.

Meares, A. (1961). An evaluation of the dangers of medical hypnosis. *American Journal of Clinical Hypnosis, 4*, 90–97.

Nadon, R., & Laurence, J-R. (1994). Idiographic approaches to hypnosis research: Or how therapeutic practice can inform science. *American Journal of Clinical Hypnosis, 37*, 85–94.

Nash, M. R. (1987). What, if anything, is regressed about hypnotic age regression? A review of the empirical literature. *Psychological Bulletin, 102*, 42–52.

Nash, M. R., Minton, A., & Baldridge, J. (1988). Twenty years of scientific hypnosis in dentistry, medicine, and psychology: A brief communication. *International Journal of Clinical and Experimental Hypnosis, 36*, 198–205.

Orne, M. T. (1965). Undesirable effects of hypnosis: The determinants and management. *International Journal of Clinical and Experimental Hypnosis, 13,* 226–237.

Orne, M. T., & McConkey, K. M. (1981). Toward convergent inquiry into self-hypnosis. *International Journal of Clinical and Experimental Hypnosis, 29,* 313–323.

Perry, C., Nadon, R., & Button, J. (1992). The measurement of hypnotic ability. In E. Fromm & M. R. Nash (Eds.), *Contemporary hypnosis research* (pp. 459–490). New York: Guilford Press.

Rhue, J. W., Lynn, S. J., & Kirsch, I. (1993). *Handbook of clinical hypnosis.* Washington, DC: American Psychological Association.

Sheehan, P. W., & Dolby, R. M. (1979). Motivated involvement in hypnosis: The illustration of clinical rapport through hypnotic dreams. *Journal of Abnormal Psychology, 88,* 573–583.

Sheehan, P. W., & McConkey, K. M. (1993). Forensic hypnosis: The application of ethical guidelines. In J. W. Rhue, S. J. Lynn, & I. Kirsch (Eds.), *Handbook of clinical hypnosis (pp. 719–738). Washington, DC: American Psychological Association.*

Simon, M. J., & Salzberg, H. C. (1985). The effect of manipulated expectancies on posthypnotic amnesia. *International Journal of Clinical and Experimental Hypnosis, 33,* 40–51.

Smith, M. L., Glass, G. V., & Miller, T. I. (1980). *The benefits of psychotherapy.* Baltimore, MD: The Johns Hopkins University Press.

Spanos, N. P. (1986). Hypnotic behavior: A social psychological interpretation of amnesia, analgesia, and "trance logic." *Behavioral and Brain Sciences, 9,* 449–467.

Spanos, N. P. (1991). A sociocognitive approach to hypnosis. In S. J. Lynn & J. W. Rhue (Eds.), *Theories of hypnosis: Current models and perspectives* (pp. 324–361). New York: Guilford Press.

Spanos, N. P., & Chaves, J. (1991). History and historiography of hypnosis. In S. J. Lynn & J. W. Rhue (Eds.), *Theories of hypnosis: Current models and perspectives* (pp. 43–82). New York: Guilford Press.

Spanos, N. P., & Hewitt, E. C. (1980). The hidden observer in hypnotic analgesia: Discovery or experimental creation? *Journal of Personality and Social Psychology, 39,* 1201–1214.

Spanos, N. P., Nightingale, M. E., Radtke, H. L., & Stam, J. J. (1980). The stuff hypnotic "dreams" are made of. *Journal of Mental Imagery, 4,* 99–110.

Spiegel, H., & Spiegel, D. (1978). *Trance and treatment: Clinical uses of hypnosis.* New York: Basic Books.

Spinhoven, P., Van Dyck, R., Hoogduin, K., & Schaap, C. (1991). Differences in hypnotizability of Dutch psychiatric outpatients according to two different scales. *Australian Journal of Clinical and Experimental Hypnosis, 19,* 107–116.

Wadden, T. A., & Anderton, C. H. (1982). The clinical use of hypnosis. *Psychological Bulletin, 91,* 215–243.

Watkins, H. H. (1993). Ego-state therapy: An overview. *American Journal of Clinical Hypnosis, 35,* 232–240.

Weitzenhoffer, A. M., & Hilgard, E. (1962). *Stanford Hypnotic Susceptibility Scale: Form C.* Palo Alto, CA: Consulting Psychologists Press.

Wickramasekera, I. (1993). Assessment and treatment of somatization disorders: The high risk model of threat perception. In J. W. Rhue, S. J. Lynn, & I. Kirsch (Eds.), *Handbook of clinical hypnosis* (pp. 587–622). Washington, DC: American Psychological Association.

II

HYPNOTHERAPY WITH ADULTS

2

COGNITIVE–BEHAVIORAL HYPNOTHERAPY FOR PHOBIC ANXIETY

NANCY E. SCHOENBERGER

Extreme fear and avoidance of a particular object or situation characterize phobic anxiety. Such phobias are common and can interfere with the daily functioning of people who suffer from them. For example, people with phobic anxiety of public speaking endure substantial distress, or avoid situations in which public speaking is required, or both. Many careers and social functions require the ability to communicate in groups. Thus, avoidance of public speaking interferes with occupational functioning, social activities, and relationships (American Psychiatric Association, 1994).

Cognitive–behavioral therapies are currently the treatments of choice for phobic anxiety disorders, with emphasis placed on the use of in vivo exposure to a graduated hierarchy of feared situations. In this chapter, I present the use of hypnosis in treating a case of public-speaking anxiety, a frequently reported fear. Although this treatment was designed to address a specific phobia, treatment principles from this case can easily be extended and adapted for use with simple phobias, generalized social phobia, and other anxiety disorders.

BACKGROUND INFORMATION

I have chosen to present the case of J. H. because I found her an interesting and engaging woman who had severe phobia of public speaking.

Her response to treatment, however, reflects the experience of other group members. At the time of treatment, J. H. was 33 years old, married, the mother of two children, and a graduate student in English literature. Ms. H. sought treatment for her extreme fear of public speaking. She avoided all situations that would require her to speak before a group and experienced substantial anxiety at the mere thought that she might be asked to do so. Her phobic anxiety interfered with her education because she would not take courses that involved oral presentations and would not contribute to class discussions. She felt quite embarrassed by her fear and had had no prior treatment. Ms. H. recalled being severely anxious about public speaking since junior high school, and at the time of treatment she had not made a presentation to a group of people for the past 12 years.

Assessment and treatment occurred in the context of a research project involving the use of hypnotherapy; therefore, detailed assessment information was available, including self-report and behavioral measures, in addition to an initial interview. At pretreatment assessment, Ms. H. completed the Personal Report of Confidence as a Speaker (PRCS; Paul, 1966), which asks about reactions to public-speaking situations; the Fear of Negative Evaluation scale (FNE; Watson & Friend, 1969), which gauges people's reactions when others hold negative opinions of them or criticize them; and the Public Speaking Anxiety Expectancy Scale (PSAES; adapted from Krugman et al., 1985), which asks people to predict the extent to which several anxiety-related events will occur during an upcoming speech. Ms. H.'s scores on the anxiety measures were 28 out of 30 on the PRCS scale, 19 out of 30 on the Fear of Negative Evaluation scale, and 44 out of 60 on the Anxiety Expectancy Scale. Thus, she was severely anxious about public-speaking situations and moderately fearful of negative evaluation in general. Also, Ms. H. expected to be quite anxious during an upcoming speech.

She then received the topic "the most interesting person I've ever met" and spent 4 minutes preparing a 4-minute impromptu speech, to be given before two observers and a video camera. However, she became agitated and quite upset and stated that she could not perform the speech. I immediately met with her; she was tearful and said she felt embarrassed that she was so upset. We talked about the history of her anxiety and its impact on her life, and she agreed to call if she wished to enter treatment. She called less than a week later and joined a treatment group that included three other people, two men and one woman.

CONCEPTUALIZATION

I conceptualized Ms. H's. phobic anxiety as a negative cycle involving thoughts, affect, physiological reactivity, and behavior. Theories of simple phobias, social phobia, and agoraphobia reflect this view. For Ms. H., the cycle began in junior high school, which is not uncommon in public-speaking anxiety. Ms. H.'s fear of public speaking related to her general sensitivity to others' opinions of her. She feared being negatively evaluated and, when asked to speak before a group, felt that her classmates would scrutinize and criticize her. When she attempted to speak, she felt that she looked stupid and made a poor presentation.

On the basis of these past experiences, Ms. H. labeled herself as someone who was phobic of public speaking and who was unable to speak before groups of people. She experienced physiological reactions such as increased heart rate, trembling, and nausea in public-speaking situations; became overwhelmed with anxiety; and escaped or avoided the situation (including the pretreatment speech) to relieve her anxiety. Avoidance had the immediate effect of reducing Ms. H.'s anxiety, but in the long run it undermined her feelings of confidence, entrenched her beliefs that she could not cope with the anxiety-provoking situation, and prevented her from discovering that she could overcome her fears. Thus, Ms. H.'s beliefs about herself were confirmed, and when public-speaking situations arose she continued to feel terrified and to avoid them.

Ms. H.'s thoughts when she contemplated public speaking or was confronted with such situations fed into this negative cycle. Most instances of social phobia, including public-speaking anxiety, involve fears of being negatively evaluated by other people, and this was true for Ms. H. When asked to imagine giving a class presentation, she experienced a variety of negative thoughts about herself, her ability, and others' reactions to her, including, "I can't do this," "My classmates will think I'm stupid," and "There's something wrong with me." When Ms. H. noticed her physiological reactions such as a rapid heartbeat, trembling, and perspiration, she feared that others would realize how anxious she was and evaluate her more negatively as a result. This served to increase her anxiety and worsen her symptoms. These and other negative thoughts further increased her anxiety, which led to avoidance of public-speaking situations. Avoidance, in turn, produced more anxiety and more negative thoughts when she was asked to speak before a group.

TREATMENT RATIONALE

The goals of treatment were to reduce Ms. H.'s feelings of anxiety, modify her maladaptive thoughts, enable her to perform in public-speaking situations (particularly class presentations and class discussions) with manageable levels of anxiety, and increase her self-confidence in speaking situations. Cognitive–behavioral therapies have emerged as treatments of choice for a number of anxiety disorders, including simple phobia, social phobia (Heimberg, 1989), and agoraphobia (Barlow, 1988). Integrative approaches are increasingly popular in the treatment of phobic anxiety because they address the three major components of anxiety: physiological reactivity, maladaptive cognitions, and avoidance behavior. Ms. H.'s treatment included relaxation, cognitive modification, and in vivo exposure; it was based on an integrated, cognitive–behavioral group treatment for social phobia (Heimberg, 1991), which has been successful in the treatment of public-speaking phobia (Heimberg, Becker, Goldfinger, & Vermilyea, 1985).

Adding hypnosis to cognitive–behavioral treatments can increase the effectiveness of treatments for anxiety, obesity, insomnia, and chronic pain with some clients (Kirsch, Montgomery, & Sapirstein, 1995). I used hypnosis in treatment with Ms. H. because it provides a powerful context for relaxation and because I thought it would be particularly useful in conjunction with cognitive modification. Changing maladaptive cognitions is an important part of treatment for social phobia, including public-speaking phobia. However, one of the difficulties of cognitive therapy is that adaptive thoughts such as "I am intelligent and well prepared," "It's OK to be nervous," and "I'm just as good as anybody else" may be logically accepted by the client without being felt true at a gut level. Hypnosis is particularly useful for "helping the head convince the heart of what the head knows to be true" (Kirsch, 1993).

Prior to treatment, Ms. H. had a moderately negative attitude toward hypnosis. The use of hypnosis in treatment is contraindicated if clients strenuously object to the procedure and their fears are not allayed by discussing the technique with the therapist. Also, if clients believe hypnosis to be a "sham" and powerless to help them, other treatment techniques should be used. However, hypnosis may be used effectively with clients who have neutral attitudes or even some doubts and fears about hypnosis, if their concerns are addressed prior to the first use of hypnosis, as I did with Ms. H. The decision to use hypnosis further or to modify it in some way can then be made on the basis of clients' experiences in treatment.

DESCRIPTION OF TREATMENT

Ms. H. participated in a five-session group treatment; the other group members had also reported phobic anxiety of public-speaking situations. The first treatment session began with introductions structured to build group cohesiveness; clients shared their particular feelings and reactions to public-speaking situations and their goals for treatment. I presented a cognitive–behavioral model of anxiety, similar to the case conceptualization described above, to help Ms. H. and other group members better understand their anxiety. They discussed their physiological reactions, negative thoughts, and avoidance of public-speaking situations. Ms. H. emerged as a group leader, making others feel more comfortable and encouraging group interaction. Although embarrassed, she openly described her fears and was extremely warm and supportive when others were speaking.

I then presented the components of treatment, focusing specifically on how each intervention targeted thoughts, feelings, or behaviors related to clients' anxiety. I introduced hypnosis at this point and took special care to prepare each group member adequately for hypnosis. I explained the cognitive–behavioral view of hypnosis, and misconceptions about the nature and experience of hypnosis were discussed and corrected, as elaborated by Kirsch (1993). I emphasized that hypnosis is not something done to people but is something they learn to do to themselves. Ms. H. learned that she would remain in control of her own reactions, and I as the hypnotherapist could do nothing to her against her wishes. I elaborated that hypnosis does not work like magic. Hypnosis can make it easier for people to experience suggestions, but it is up to each person to decide to accept the suggestion and to make it happen. I informed Ms. H. and the other group members that they needed to be actively involved in hypnosis, rather than waiting passively for change to occur. If they decided to experience the suggestions for changes in their anxiety reactions and behaviors, hypnosis would make it easier for them to do so. We discussed all questions and concerns about hypnosis thoroughly before proceeding with treatment.

There were four major components of treatment: (a) hypnosis, (b) cognitive modification, (c) exposure simulations, and (d) homework assignments. Table 1 contains an outline of the five treatment sessions.

Inducing Hypnosis and Teaching Self-Hypnosis

The hypnotic induction was taken directly from *The Handbook of Clinical Hypnosis* (Kirsch, Lynn, & Rhue, 1993). Following that induction, I gave general suggestions for improvement in feelings of anxiety, negative or irrational thoughts, and avoidance behavior. I then taught Ms. H. self-hypnosis, which would allow her to use hypnosis on her own for relaxation and to prepare herself for real-life public-speaking situations. The hypnotic suggestions and instruction in self-hypnosis were added to the induction, following the 10-count deepening of hypnosis, according to the following script:

> And as you come to later group meetings, perhaps you will find yourself more ready and able to learn new ways to cope with your anxiety . . . more and more ready and more and more able to use the new things you learn and to discover resources within yourself . . . so that you will gain more and more control over your public-speaking anxiety. Your feelings of anxiety will decrease—whether quickly or

TABLE 1
Outline of Treatment

Session 1

    Introduction and discussion of misconceptions about hypnosis
    Description of treatment
    Hypnotic induction and posthypnotic suggestions
    Training in self-hypnosis

Session 2

    Self-suggestion modification techniques
    Practice challenging and modifying negative self-suggestions
    Hypnotic induction and posthypnotic suggestions
    Homework: Self-suggestion modification exercise, including self-hypnosis

Sessions 3 and 4

    Self-suggestion modification and self-hypnosis
    Performance-based exposures
    Homework: Self-suggestion modification exercise, including self-hypnosis

Session 5

    Self-suggestion modification and self-hypnosis
    Performance-based exposures
    Review and termination

---

slowly over time. You will feel less and less anxious and more and more confident in yourself.

Now, bring your peaceful scene into your mind one more time, and imagine you are really there. And as you focus on the image, you feel totally and completely relaxed.

Pay close attention to the feelings you are having right now . . . because you can learn to enter hypnosis by yourself. You can begin to learn right now how to enter hypnosis by yourself. The first step is to pay attention to your feelings, your sense of relaxation and well-being. Now, associate that feeling with a word or a phrase you can think to yourself whenever you want to enter hypnosis. Whatever word or phrase you choose—when you think it to yourself, it will help you enter hypnosis even without me present. You will be able to enter hypnosis on your own. It might be a phrase as simple as "hypnosis now" or any other word or phrase that you choose. Pick your own cue word now to help you enter hypnosis on your own in the future.

When you want to enter hypnosis, whenever it is appropriate for you to enter hypnosis and you want to do it on your own . . . find a comfortable place, close your eyes, take a deep breath, let your body relax, and think your cue word to yourself. And as you think that word, you can begin to enter hypnosis. And you can do all kinds of things to deepen your experience, like those we have done today. You can focus on an image, or focus on your body and let the different parts relax, or repeat your cue word to yourself. You can think of your cue word, imagine your special place, or do whatever works best for you, and find yourself going deeper and deeper into hypnosis.

When you enter hypnosis on your own, I don't know if you will be as deeply hypnotized as you are now or even more deeply hypnotized. Perhaps you will enter a deep trance or perhaps a very light one. However deeply hypnotized you become will be enough. Fortunately, we don't need very deep trances to do our work here . . . even a light trance . . . even light hypnosis . . . will enable you to do the things you need to overcome public-speaking anxiety. A light trance or a deep one will be enough to help you overcome your anxiety. So you will enter the depth of hypnosis that works best for you.

Now I will teach you how to bring yourself out of hypnosis. In just a moment I will count backwards from five to zero, and with each count you will think the numbers to yourself and imagine energy flowing into your body. You will feel more and more alert, and less and less hypnotized. You will be wide awake and feel good. At the count of one you will open your eyes and at the count of zero you will be completely awake and out of hypnosis. You can do this any time you want, and you can come out of hypnosis any time you decide.

Now, I will count backward from five to zero, and as I do you will become more alert and awake, but still feel relaxed. Five . . . four . . . three . . . feel the energy flowing in . . . two . . . one . . . open your eyes . . . zero . . . wide awake.

After all questions were answered, Ms. H. was instructed to practice self-hypnosis:

Now, why don't you try to put yourself into hypnosis as deeply as you want. Go ahead, close your eyes . . . take a deep breath . . . relax your body . . . think of your cue word . . . imagine your special place, or whatever works for you so you can enter hypnosis by yourself. (I waited 3 to 4 minutes). Now you will enter more and more deeply into hypnosis as I count from one to five. One . . . two . . . deeper and deeper . . . three . . . four . . . more and more deeply hypnotized . . . five . . . as deeply hypnotized as you want to be. (I waited 2 minutes). And now you can bring yourself out of hypnosis. Count backward from five to zero, thinking the numbers to yourself and imagining yourself filled with energy. Open your eyes when you reach the count of one, and by the count of zero you will be fully alert and out of hypnosis.

Cognitive Modification

I introduced the cognitive component of treatment—modification of irrational and maladaptive thoughts about public speaking—in the second session. When confronted with public-speaking situations, Ms. H. and other group members experienced a barrage of negative thoughts about themselves, which we labeled negative self-suggestions. I instructed Ms. H. to imagine a feared public-speaking situation (she chose making a class presentation) and to report any negative self-suggestions that occurred to her. These included thoughts that she would fail the presentation, that others would notice how anxious she was, that she would be unable to continue and stand paralyzed in front of the class, and that others would see her as stupid and incompetent.

I gathered more detailed information about each of her negative thoughts. What did it mean to fail? Did it mean a poor grade from the professor, having other students look bored, or doing a less than perfect job in her own opinion? Many people with social phobia are excessively judgmental of themselves, setting standards that are unreachable and then berating themselves for failing to reach the standard. This is a form of illogical, maladaptive thinking.

Using a Socratic method, I then taught Ms. H. to challenge the poor logic present in her thinking, to more realistically estimate the probability of negative consequences, and to generate positive alternatives to her negative self-suggestions. No exact script is available from Ms. H's treatment, but the following is a re-creation of one intervention for which Ms. H. imagined giving a presentation to an undergraduate English class of 75 students. The format is consistent with Heimberg's (1991) treatment manual. She began by reporting negative self-suggestions.

> Ms. H.: I'll stand up there, and I won't be able to say anything. [This thought was recorded on an easel.]
>
> Therapist: What is the probability—realistically—that you'll be able to say absolutely nothing?
>
> Ms. H.: I don't know. I haven't spoken to a class before. I'm afraid of it.
>
> T: Will you have notes to guide you?
>
> Ms. H.: Definitely.
>
> T: So, if you have notes, will you be able to say something?
>
> Ms. H.: Probably, but I still think I'll mess up. [Recorded on easel.]
>
> T: What do you mean by "mess up"?
>
> Ms. H.: I'll do a bad job.
>
> T: That's still pretty vague. What would you need to do in order to do a good job?
>
> Ms. H.: Give correct information and not say anything wrong.
>
> T: So you want to be absolutely perfect?
>
> Ms. H.: Yeah, not very realistic, huh?

T:	Let's start with wanting to do a good job. What grades do you get in this class?
Ms. H.:	As and Bs, mostly As.
T:	So you know the material and are well-prepared for tests. Will you prepare for your presentation?
Ms. H.:	Are you kidding?
T:	OK. If you're that well-prepared, can you stand up and say enough to get your point across?
Ms. H.:	Probably.
T:	Now, is it so bad to make a mistake, even a small one?
Ms. H.:	It seems bad to me.
T:	Does the professor ever make a mistake?
Ms. H.:	Yes.
T:	What did she or he do?
Ms. H.:	He corrected himself the next time.
T:	It wasn't so bad for him.
Ms. H.:	No.
T:	So, what are more realistic self-suggestions to make to yourself during your speech?
Ms. H.:	I can probably say something. [Recorded on easel.]
T:	And get your point across?
Ms. H.:	Yes. [Recorded on easel.] Also, I'll be prepared enough to do a good job.
T:	That's a good one. I'd like to add, "I don't have to be perfect."
Ms. H.:	OK
T:	Let's start with those.

It is important to note that negative self-suggestions are rarely corrected on the basis of one such intervention by the therapist. It takes time, repetition, and new experiences to modify cognitions. This intervention represents the beginning of the modification process. Ms. H. was given a list of questions (taken from Heimberg's, 1991, manual) to test the logic of her thinking, taught to use cognitive modification procedures by herself, and assigned them as homework. First, she performed self-hypnosis, imagined herself in a feared situation, and noticed her thoughts and feelings. After bringing herself out of hypnosis, she wrote down her negative self-suggestions, analyzed them, and wrote down more realistic alternatives. She then entered hypnosis again, imagined the feared situation, and repeated more positive thoughts as suggestions to herself as a way to reduce her anxiety. In this way, clients use hypnosis to internalize more rational self-suggestions.

Note that this procedure is different from playing Pollyanna and looking only at the positives. It is more than the simplistic replacement of negative thoughts with positive ones. The power of the process lies in Ms. H.'s evaluating and questioning her negative self-suggestions rather than accepting them as hard facts about herself. Self-hypnosis is then used to repeat and reinforce these new self-suggestions to modify her beliefs about herself. Her alternative self-suggestions were not overly positive or unrealistic. Rather, they represented a realistic assessment of herself and the situation (e.g., I can get through this; It's OK to be nervous; I know the material well and can get my point across.) Ms. H. practiced self-hypnosis and cognitive modification each week as homework assignments.

Real-Life Exposure

In group sessions three through five, cognitive modification was integrated with hypnosis and exposure to public-speaking situations. When severe anxiety and avoidance have persisted for years as with Ms. H., the thought of entering the feared situation even in the safety of a therapy group can be terrifying. I introduced the idea of speaking before the group at the end of the second session. I assured Ms. H. that hypnosis and cognitive modification were valuable coping skills that she could use to reduce her anxiety in the situation. Group members discussed their concerns and provided support for each other. I emphasized that no matter how anxious she became, Ms. H. should get herself to the next meeting.

The next sessions were divided into segments that were devoted to each group member, as presented in Heimberg's (1991) manual. We arranged the room to simulate a relevant situation, such as making a class presentation, with the therapist and other group members acting as other players (e.g., instructor and class members). Ms. H. was the second member of the group to speak. During the previous session, she had decided to make a presentation to the group on a topic familiar to her and prepared an outline ahead of time. Prior to speaking, Ms. H. imagined the situation, and her negative self-suggestions were recorded on an easel. Then, she questioned these thoughts, with input from other members, and developed more adaptive self-suggestions. These were written where she could see them during her presentation. Ms. H. also set reasonable goals for her presentation (i.e., to speak for 5 minutes and to finish her talk without trying to leave the room). Then, she engaged in a period of self-hypnosis, using the newly generated positive self-suggestions. She commented that she was very anxious and was not sure she could complete the presentation, but with encouragement from other group members and me, she stood and made her presentation, reading the self-suggestions written on the easel when necessary.

Following her presentation, Ms. H. described her experience, assessed whether she had met her goals, and received feedback from other group members. This, her first attempt at public speaking in years, was a turning point in treatment for Ms. H. She was able to speak for almost 5 minutes, although anxious, and felt a personal triumph for doing so. She admitted, after her presentation, that she had been severely anxious during the week, was unable to sleep the night before, and felt nauseated for most of the day. However, she had used hypnosis and adaptive self-suggestions to cope with the situation and had succeeded in doing something she had avoided for years. This success experience served to reinforce the accuracy of the new, positive self-suggestions, to increase her confidence in her ability to cope with difficult situations, and to reduce her anxiety more over time. Her pride in herself was obvious and infectious, and other group members felt encouraged as they prepared for their own exposure simulations.

We designed Ms. H.'s second and third presentations before the group to be more difficult, based on her fears and negative self-suggestions. Ms. H. thought that if she made a presentation on a topic new to her, but familiar to the professor, she would be more likely to make mistakes. She described "mistakes" as making erroneous statements and being corrected by the professor or classmates or being unable to answer questions about her presentation. Cognitive modification for these thoughts included (a) questioning the probability that she would say something totally incorrect (highly unlikely because she was intelligent and would be well-prepared), (b) questioning the probability that the professor or a classmate would disagree with her (unlikely but possible), and (c) examining the consequences of such a disagreement (not so bad—she has the right to her own opinion, and people can learn new things when they disagree). She also decided that she could be prepared for most questions, and if she did not know an answer she would say so and offer to look it up before the next class.

Again, Ms. H. engaged in a period of self-hypnosis using her newly generated self-suggestions: I am well prepared and can do a good job; I don't have to know everything; I have the right to my own opinions. The room was then arranged as a classroom, and other group members agreed to ask questions after her presentation. We decided that I would ask one question for which Ms. H. would be unlikely to have an answer. Thus, one of the consequences she feared would actually occur, and Ms. H. could attempt to cope with it and decide if it was as disastrous as she expected. Ms. H. made her presentation on a topic taken from a psychology textbook, deliberately chosen so that I would be an "expert" on the subject. After her speech, Ms. H. fielded questions and offered to look up the answer to my question. She met her goals for the presentation, stated that she was much less anxious than during her previous talk, and decided that not knowing the answer to every question was no big deal. Ms. H.'s third exposure proceeded as the previous ones but involved an impromptu speech. She deemed this most difficult because she would be unable to prepare. The group helped her set goals reasonable for the situation. Because she had no time for preparation, she reduced her expectations of herself. Again, she completed the speech, met her goals, and received helpful feedback from other group members.

I encouraged Ms. H., following her first exposure, to engage in public speaking outside the group as opportunities arose. I recommended that she practice self-hypnosis prior to these attempts if at all possible. She began by asking questions and contributing to class discussions and reported that she was less and less anxious the more she did so.

Therapeutic Outcome

Following the final exposure simulations, group members reviewed their progress in treatment and discussed how to handle setbacks when they occurred and how they might use hypnosis and cognitive modification to cope with relevant situations in the future. Ms. H. felt that she had made tremendous progress because she could now imagine making a presentation to a class of 200 students. She admitted that she would feel quite anxious but felt that a great number of possibilities were open to her now because she would no longer avoid public-speaking situations. She believed that she had the tools to cope with her remaining anxiety and could continue to decrease it over time. Moreover, her success in confronting her anxiety seemed to enhance her global evaluation of herself (i.e., her self-esteem). The other group members also described treatment and their progress in positive terms. Ms. H.'s first exposure seemed a turning point for the whole group; her improvement and enthusiasm were a catalyst, and change continued for everyone in a synergistic way.

Follow-up information confirms Ms. H.'s report of her improvement. Table 2 shows her pre- and posttreatment scores. At posttreatment assessment, Ms. H. scored 6 out of 30 on the PRCS, 9 out of 30 on the FNE, and 21 out of 60 on the PSAES. These values represent large reductions in Ms. H.'s anxiety. In addition, her attitude toward hypnosis became quite positive. More important, Ms. H. completed the 4-minute impromptu speech at posttreatment (given before two observers and videotaped) and reported only mild anxiety while doing so. Other group members also showed substantial decreases in anxiety at posttreatment.

Ms. H.'s level of hypnotizability was also formally assessed during a separate session following treatment. She passed only 2 of 12 suggestions

TABLE 2
Pre- and Posttreatment Scores on Measures of Treatment Outcome

Measure	Pre	Post	Maximum
Confidence as a Speaker (PRCS)	28	6	30
Fear of Negative Evaluation (FNE)	19	9	39
Anxiety Expectancy (PSAES)	44	21	60
4-minute impromptu speech	no	yes	—
Anxiety during speech	—	25 (mild)	100

on the Waterloo-Stanford Scale of Hypnotic Susceptibility (Bowers, Laurence, & Hart, 1982), a standardized measure of hypnotizability. Nonetheless, she improved dramatically in a hypnosis-based treatment program.

THERAPEUTIC ISSUES

In group treatment, the therapeutic relationship exists not only between therapist and client but also between group members. The feelings that members have for one another and their interactions are integral parts of treatment. In this group, members shared the same phobic anxiety, which formed the base for building group cohesiveness. Ms. H. and the others in this group expressed their feelings more readily, were more supportive of one another, and were more invested in one another's progress than some other groups I have facilitated. This likely contributed to treatment outcome.

When hypnosis is used in a group setting, some difficulties can arise. People have a wide range of feelings about hypnosis, from enthusiasm to fear to derision. It requires effort from the therapist to address each person's concerns while maintaining a "group" approach to treatment. In this group, two members were open to the use of hypnosis and two were somewhat more skeptical; no one was particularly enthusiastic about the process. Ms. H.'s attitude was somewhat negative, but she was willing to give hypnosis a try in the interest of relieving her anxiety. However, after her initial exposure simulation, she became more confident in the process, faithfully practiced self-hypnosis outside treatment, and used it to reduce her public-speaking anxiety.

Ms. H. was not highly hypnotizable; therefore, she did not experience hypnosis as an altered state of consciousness. As she had been prepared to expect this and viewed hypnosis as a state of enhanced focus and concentration, hypnosis and therapeutic suggestions were successful for her. Highly hypnotizable clients are likely to have a different, and potentially more powerful, experience with hypnosis.

Because Ms. H. was not highly hypnotizable, one could argue that hypnosis did not contribute to treatment effectiveness. However, hypnotizability is not always correlated with improvement in hypnotic treatments (Wadden & Anderton, 1982). In fact, among participants in the treatment of public-speaking anxiety, correlations of hypnotizability and improvement tended to be nonsignificant and negative in direction (Schoenberger, Kirsch, Gearan, Montgomery, & Pastyrnak, 1996). In addition, Ms. H. reported that hypnosis was most helpful to her in conjunction with cognitive modification. She found that using self-hypnosis and making self-suggestions helped her to focus her attention in a new way and to believe more readily positive statements about herself.

CONCLUSION

Hypnosis is a valuable adjunct to cognitive–behavioral treatment of phobic anxieties. Hypnosis is not a form of treatment in itself, rather it is a technique used to enhance the outcome of other treatments. Cognitive–behavioral techniques are widely used in the treatment of anxiety as well as other disorders. When hypnosis is added, relaxation training can be replaced by a hypnotic induction. Clients who have a paradoxical reaction to traditional relaxation training often have more success with hypnotic relaxation. Also, hypnosis is uniquely useful for improving the cognitive-modification component of treatment.

A treatment outcome study involving phobic anxiety of public speaking (Schoenberger et al., 1996) compared the use of cognitive–behavioral treatment alone with the same treatment supplemented by hypnosis. Although both treatments produced substantial improvement, the hypnotic treatment was more effective. Specifically, hypnosis produced greater anxiety reduction and a faster drop in anxiety during posttreatment speeches than nonhypnotic treatment. This is important because relief from anxiety reduces avoidance, which allows for further improvement and increased self-confidence. These results are consistent with Ms. H.'s experience in treatment.

Using self-hypnosis and imagery of feared situations, Ms. H. rehearsed positive self-suggestions repeatedly prior to in vivo exposure to public speaking. Ms. H. was quick to see the illogical and irrational aspects of her thinking but had more difficulty changing negative thoughts. Hypnosis made it possible for her to repeat the same thoughts over and over without feeling foolish. With the use of hypnotic suggestions, she came to feel more deeply within herself that positive thoughts about herself and her abilities were true. This represents a substantial change in her beliefs about herself. These new beliefs and new success experiences in public-speaking situations helped reduce her feelings of anxiety. Thus, relaxation and positive self-suggestions used in self-hypnosis are powerful coping skills that Ms. H. continues to have available for confronting other situations. Learning self-hypnosis decreases her dependence on a therapist and empowers her for the future.

The method of using hypnosis in conjunction with cognitive–behavioral techniques can easily be applied to other anxiety disorders as well as to individual treatment. With an individual client, hypnotic inductions can be modified on the basis of the client's reactions, and hypnotic suggestions can target specifically the feelings, thoughts, and behavior causing the most distress to the client.

Although hypnosis can be integrated successfully into a group-treatment context, extra effort is required from the therapist to ensure that all members are adequately prepared for the use of hypnosis and to tailor suggestions to each member of the group. I recommend keeping a record of thoughts and symptoms particularly troublesome to each client and including as many as feasible during hypnotic suggestions.

Problems such as public-speaking phobia and generalized social phobia include substantial fear of negative evaluation from other people. Many clients believe that they are the only person who has such difficulties or that their problem is worse than anyone else's, and they feel embarrassed and ashamed. Group treatment is an excellent way to confront these feelings. Each member learns that there are others who have the same thoughts and fears, and a supportive environment is created. Support and feedback coming from people with the same difficulties are often more powerful than from the therapist. Evaluative concerns are also addressed directly when other group members observe behavioral simulations. Even this audience typically evokes clients' negative self-suggestions, which are then questioned and modified to be more realistic. If clients become comfortable with the members of their group so that these concerns are not evoked, bringing in strangers (well-briefed about issues of confidentiality) to observe behavioral simulations is usually effective.

Ms. H. benefited substantially from hypnotherapy even though her initial attitudes toward hypnosis were somewhat negative and she was not highly hypnotizable. Although it seems reasonable to assume that clients who have positive attitudes toward hypnosis or are highly hypnotizable would benefit most from hypnotherapy, this is not always the case. When clients strongly object to the use of hypnosis or believe it to be useless, other methods of treatment are indicated. However, among clients who have neutral feelings or even some doubts and fears about hypnosis, participation in hypnotic treatment produces positive attitudes (Schoenberger et al., 1996). Thus, hypnotherapy can benefit many clients with a range of attitudes and levels of hypnotizability.

Finally, this relatively brief course of therapy, five 2-hour group sessions, was sufficient to produce substantial improvement in Ms. H. Apart from her severe anxiety about public-speaking situations, she was a psychologically healthy individual. Her extremely negative thoughts were not generalized to other areas of her life; she thought herself a good student, wife, and mother. In addition, she was socially skilled and facilitated interactions among group members. Other clients may not respond as quickly to this treatment. When a client's anxiety is less circumscribed, as in generalized social phobia, or is associated with other psychological difficulties, longer treatment is necessary. Assuming the therapist finds each client appropriate for a group setting and for the use of hypnosis, this treatment can be used successfully with more anxious, less socially skilled clients who evaluate themselves negatively in a wider range of situations.

REFERENCES

American Psychiatric Association. (1994). *Diagnostic and statistical manual of mental disorders* (4th ed.). Washington, DC: Author.

Barlow, D. H. (1988). *Anxiety and its disorders. The nature and treatment of anxiety and panic.* New York: Guilford Press.

Bowers, P. G., Laurence, J. R., & Hart, D. (1982). *A group scale of hypnotic susceptibility: Revision and expansion of Form C.* (ASIS-NAPS Document No. 04632). New York: National Auxiliary Publication Service.

Heimberg, R. G. (1989). Cognitive and behavioral treatments for social phobia: A critical analysis. *Clinical Psychology Review, 9,* 107–128.

Heimberg, R. G. (1991). *Cognitive behavioral treatment of social phobia in a group setting: A treatment manual.* (2nd ed.).

Heimberg, R. G., Becker, R. E., Goldfinger, K., & Vermilyea, J. A. (1985). Treatment of social phobia by exposure, cognitive restructuring, and homework assignments. *Journal of Nervous and Mental Disease, 173,* 236–245.

Kirsch, I. (1993). Cognitive-behavioral hypnotherapy. In J. W. Rhue, S. J. Lynn, & I. Kirsch (Eds.), *Handbook of clinical hypnosis* (pp. 151–171). Washington DC: American Psychological Association.

Kirsch, I., Lynn, S. J., & Rhue, J. W. (1993). Introduction to clinical hypnosis. In J. W. Rhue, S. J. Lynn, & I. Kirsch (Eds.), *Handbook of clinical hypnosis* (pp. 3–22). Washington DC: American Psychological Association.

Kirsch, I., Montgomery, G, & Sapirstein, G. (1995). Hypnosis as an adjunct to cognitive behavioral psychotherapy: A meta-analysis. *Journal of Consulting and Clinical Psychology, 63,* 214–220.

Krugman, M., Kirsch, I., Wickless, C., Milling, L., Golicz, H., & Toth, A. (1985). Neuro-linguistic programming treatment for anxiety: Magic or myth? *Journal of Consulting and Clinical Psychology, 53,* 526–530.

Paul, G. L. (1966). *Insight vs. desensitization in psychotherapy.* Stanford, CA: Stanford University Press.

Schoenberger, N. E., Kirsch, I., Gearan, P., Montgomery, G., & Pastyrnak, S. L. (1996). Hypnotic enhancement of a cognitive behavioral treatment for public speaking anxiety. Manuscript submitted for publication.

Wadden, T. A., & Anderton, C. H. (1982). The clinical use of hypnosis. *Psychological Bulletin, 91*, 215–243.

Watson, D., & Friend, R. (1969). Measurement of social-evaluative anxiety. *Journal of Consulting and Clinical Psychology, 33*, 448–457.

3

HYPNOSIS IN THE TREATMENT OF ANOREXIA NERVOSA

LYNNE M. HORNYAK

The syndrome of anorexia nervosa, characterized by significant weight loss, willful pursuit of thinness, body image disturbance, and an intense fear of gaining weight or becoming fat, has the reputation of posing complex treatment challenges and of treatment failures. Although many essential features of anorexia nervosa are manifestations of starvation, the disorder is predisposed and precipitated by a variety of psychosocial factors (Garner, Rockert, Olmsted, Johnson, & Coscina, 1985). Furthermore, the nature and degree of psychological impairment among patients with anorexia nervosa vary considerably and are best understood within a developmental framework (Johnson & Connors, 1987). Consequently, treatment may be most effective when goals and techniques consider the patient's particular developmental deficits and capacities.

A host of treatment modalities has been developed to address the problems inherent in anorexia nervosa, based on different theoretical understandings and in response to the complex, multifactorial nature of the disorder. Such approaches include psychodynamic, cognitive, behavioral, family, and multidimensional treatments (Garner & Garfinkel, 1985). Although not extensive, there is a growing literature on the use of hypnotherapy in treating various aspects of anorexic symptomatology (Lynn, Rhue, Kvaal, & Mare, 1993; Nash & Baker, 1993). In addition to using hypnosis to treat core symptoms, this literature suggests that hypnotic interventions designed to address psychodynamic issues pertaining to autonomy, identity, and interpersonal conflict; to address the defensive use of denial and dissociation; and to promote developmental growth may serve as a useful component to a multidimensional treatment program for this challenging disorder.

Working with a range of eating-disordered patients in an outpatient setting, I have been particularly intrigued by a subgroup of patients restricting food intake who initially present as intelligent, competent, and presumably struggling with life-adjustment problems. As treatment proceeds, however, a marked unevenness in their psychological functioning emerges. On the basis of prevailing theories and research on eating disordered patients (Johnson, 1991),[1] I categorized my patients as seeming to fit the subgroup of eating-disordered patients referred to as restrictors with false-self organization.

I offer this case presentation to illustrate common therapeutic issues in working with anorexic patients with false-self adaptation from a self-developmental, object relations framework. Certain identifying elements of the case material have been altered to protect confidentiality, but the therapeutic issues and course of treatment remain intact. In addition, I chose to present a case representing this particular subgroup because these patients can easily be undertreated, and subsequently relapse or maintain a sublevel of psychological functioning, as a result of their particular adaptive style. Finally, female pronouns are used throughout the chapter because the majority of eating-disordered clients are women, although I acknowledge that male patients can present with false-self adaptation as well.

BACKGROUND INFORMATION

Amy was 22 years old, single, and had recently moved to the city to take her first job after graduation from college. She sought therapy because she was "miserable" and "regressing to old behavior" of severe food restriction, intense preoccupation with food and body size, and compulsive exercising. Amy was 5'7" tall and weighed 104 lb when she began treatment.

---

[1]Johnson (1991; Johnson & Connors, 1987) has reviewed the work of Winnicott (1965), who coined the term *false self-organization*, and Kohut (1971), who developed the theory of self psychology and extended these theoretical foundations to the understanding and treatment of developmental difficulties among eating-disordered patients. I refer the reader to other rich references such as Goodsitt (1985) and chapters by Lerner, Stern, and Strober in Johnson's (1991) volume, which present current views on developmental deficits in eating disorders. Chapters by Fleming, Hudgins, and Woodall and Anderson in Hornyak and Baker's (1989) volume present various experiential approaches to the treatment of anorexia nervosa based on developmental considerations.

History of the Problem

Amy had been diagnosed as anorexic during the fall semester of her senior year in college. She lost 20 lb in 2 months' time, dropping from 124 to 104 lb. With treatment, Amy graduated at a weight of 114 lb, but promptly lost 10 lb after moving back to her mother's house.

Amy reported that food was not an issue for her through high school, seemingly because her athletic activities and natural metabolism kept her slender. She gained 7 lb during freshman year in college, which was a blow to her self-esteem, yet she maintained her weight at 124 lb until that summer.

Two events were significant precipitants for her weight loss. Her boyfriend broke up with her when he moved to another city for his career, and her life-long best friend permanently moved overseas. Amy began spending several hours each day at her fitness club and withdrew from friends and regular activities. Given her serious weight loss, moodiness, and overexercise, several close friends took her to the student health center in early fall.

Treatment History

Because she continued to lose weight, Amy was referred to a more structured eating-disorders program in the community. Despite initial resistance, she agreed to work on an outpatient basis, attending weekly group therapy that emphasized a cognitive–behavioral approach, weekly individual therapy, and biweekly nutritional counseling. Treatment continued for approximately 6 months, terminating before graduation. Amy's individual therapist gave her my name as a referral in her hometown area, and eventually Amy called for an appointment.

Family History

Amy was the eldest of three daughters. Her relationship with Betsy, 15 months younger, was competitive yet intensely protective. Amy described her relationship with sister Kim, 6 years younger, as more parental than sisterly.

Amy's parents divorced when she was in her early teens. She described their relationship as conflictual, with frequent confrontations about her father's handling of money. Amy lived with her father, to whom she felt quite attached, for a year after the divorce, and then lived with her mother until college. Amy described her father as a fun-loving person who lavished her with material items but "had a hard time relating." Her father remarried soon after Amy moved back with her mother. Amy described her mother in global terms, providing little detail other than to say she was "her best friend." She mentioned that her mother always worried about her own weight and shape and was concerned about aging. Her mother had never remarried, although she had a steady companion.

Assessment Results

Medical results indicated that Amy was in good health. Her lab tests and electrocardiograph results were basically normal. Amy's internist interpreted her low glucose, white blood cell count, and thyroid indexes as side effects of starvation. He predicted that they would return to normal range with adequate nutrition.

Amy completed an eating-disorders questionnaire adapted from Johnson (1985). Supporting the intake interview information, the eating questionnaire indicated a significant relationship between weight loss and self-esteem, moderate body image dissatisfaction, strict dieting behavior, infrequent episodes of overeating accompanied by fears of being out of control, a loss of menstruation, and denial of purging other than burning off calories through exercise.

Amy exercised 1 to 3 hours daily, including an hour of running in the morning and 1 to 2 hours of aerobics or working out on fitness equipment after work. Amy reported that she rarely felt hungry, yet was intensely aware of and preoccupied with food when it was around her. She would avoid situations that involved food as an attempt to control the preoccupation. Although Amy was bothered by this hypervigilance, she acknowledged that she felt very proud of her "self-discipline," indicating that food restriction and exercising were the sole arenas in which she felt special and superior to others.

Amy had distortions about the size and shape of her stomach, hips, and thighs yet also complained of "looking too bony" around her shoulders and upper torso. She had an indistinct mental representation of her body and was globally terrified of "becoming fat."

CONCEPTUALIZATION OF THE PROBLEM

Amy's symptoms are common among women with eating disorders. They may also be observed in women who do not have a diagnosable eating disorder but who diet, exercise, and are weight- and appearance-conscious. It was the ego deficits that became apparent in the first few sessions, however, that significantly influenced the form and course of Amy's treatment.

Conceptualization of Restrictors With False-Self Organization

There are several common features that reflect an underlying false-self organization that Amy manifested. Individuals with false-self organization have an air of self-sufficiency, typically have good social skills, and consequently present a veneer of adequate integration and achievement. However, once a therapeutic alliance is established, these patients may reveal, directly or indirectly, pervasive feelings of nonexistence and fraudulence. They tend to devalue or discount accomplishments because they feel like frauds. Consequently, it is difficult to enhance self-esteem because such esteem-building experiences are negated or diminished. These feelings of fraudulence may coexist with narcissistic reactions and unintegrated grandiose feelings or fantasies. Finally, interpersonal sensitivity, mistrust, hypervigilance to others' reactions, and seeking out of others' guidance contradict the stance of self-sufficiency. (For more in-depth discussion, see Johnson, 1991; and Johnson & Connors, 1987.)

I often have certain subjective experiences with patients that I have come to identify as "signals" of an underlying false-self organization. Most prominent is a sense of "distant closeness." Our interactions feel pleasant, and I could be lulled into believing that the patient is "doing just fine." The reality is that something is truly missing—her authentic presence.

Underlying the patient's false-self adaptation and the willful, active manipulation of food and the body, there are a number of corresponding ego deficits. I find it conceptually helpful to think about these psychological impairments in three broad categories: self-regulation, agency, and self-integration. These deficits are thought to be the result of early experiences through which the child learns to adapt to her environment by complying and accommodating. This accommodating stance leaves the patient's capacity for self-regulation highly dependent on others' cues to determine how to feel and behave. She learns to assume a reactive rather than a proactive stance, which compromises the authentic experience of self in terms of thoughts, feelings, and actions. Although patients with false-self organization have attained self and object permanence and the capacity for self and object constancy is established, integration of various self experiences into a cohesive sense of self is not complete. As a result, the self-concept—including self-esteem and body experience—is vulnerable to external events and emotional disruptions. Such psychological disruptions often get expressed physically in eating and body-related symptomatology.

Self-regulation

Disruption of interoceptive awareness—which refers to the capacity to identify, discriminate, and articulate various internal states, including hunger, fullness, and affective states—has been viewed as a central feature of anorexia nervosa (Bruch, 1962). Goodsitt (1985) points out that the self-regulatory structure includes the capacity to maintain self-esteem, cohesiveness, vitality, and narcissistic equilibrium (sense of well-being and security), as well as to regulate tensions, moods, and impulses.

Agency

Agency refers to self-directed experience, which is the awareness that thoughts, feelings, and actions originate from within one's self, and to a secure sense that a person can effectively act in her own behalf. Restricting behavior may be viewed as an attempt to assert some sense of control, competency, or independent identity and to counter underlying feelings of powerlessness, helplessness, passivity, frustration, and shame when genuine autonomy has not been developmentally attained. Relationships tend to be ambivalent, alternating between engaging others who are still required to provide necessary self functions and retreating to maintain separateness.

Self-integration

A mature sense of self includes healthy attachments to others as well as healthy connections among various aspects of the self. In contrast, false-self organization may best be described by the metaphor of a jigsaw puzzle, with the frame put together but various pieces not yet in place to complete the picture. There is a lack of integration, with various aspects of the self hidden or split off. In anorexia nervosa, body self is most obviously split off from the psychological self. Basic narcissistic needs for empathic responding and encouragement as well as for connecting and relying on others are also disavowed.

Assessment of Amy

Amy's clinical presentation closely resembled that of restricting patients with false-self organization described above, particularly the self-sufficient facade and "distant closeness." Her self-regulatory capacities were deficient in terms of awareness of feelings and body sensations such as fatigue and pain; tolerating and modulating a range of feelings and tensions, particularly frustration, sadness, and disappointment, which were expressed through physical behaviors rather than words; discriminating hunger and fullness from affects; and maintaining self-esteem and vitality when alone or unoccupied. Regarding her sense of agency, Amy's hyperactivity seemed to express an underlying fear of passivity. Her descriptions of interpersonal situations communicated a sense of ineffectiveness and helplessness. Amy frequently contacted her parents and relied on their advice even though she acted otherwise. Her lack of self-integration was particularly noticeable in the variability of her "self states," which ranged from agitated drivenness to deflation, as well as in her treatment of her body as an object to be manipulated rather than as herself.

The losses and separations in Amy's history were significant. Although her parents were not intrusive, their emotional needs and conflicts seemed to dominate the family environment. Her "good girl" adaptation to her family's emotional needs covered substantial early narcissistic losses in terms of necessary empathic mirroring, caretaking, and support for authentic self development by her parents.

TREATMENT

When working with restricting patients with false-self adaptation, the therapist must anticipate compliance, sensitivity to engulfment, and disengagement based on separation concerns, as well as ambivalence about relating and about change leading toward greater autonomy. The treatment approach described in this case integrates elements of self-developmental and object relations theory. From the self-developmental perspective, therapeutic goals include helping the restricting patient attend to her own experience, to recognize her true strengths, and to reestablish the developmental course that has been arrested. From the object relations perspective, therapeutic goals include helping the restricting patient learn about her relationship patterns, that relationships can be more satisfying, and specifically, that she can express herself and get her needs met in a relationship without damaging the interpersonal connection.

The therapist's role is to provide an environment in which this learning is possible. The therapist needs to balance being attentive and interested in the restricting patient's experience, while being genuine and real within the relationship. Given her separation and autonomy concerns, it is important not to intervene too quickly or actively, yet to be responsive and provide opportunities for the patient to test out new experiences of self and other. Anticipating the patient's ambivalence, the therapist must keep these opposing dynamic tensions for autonomy and relatedness in mind and help the patient tolerate them in herself and find appropriate resolutions. As in all psychotherapy, the therapist must be sensitive to the patient's growth and changing developmental needs and must adjust his or her role accordingly.

Course of Treatment

Amy was in treatment for 20 months, which ended when she left the area for graduate school. Her therapy can be conceptualized in several phases based on her changing developmental needs, noting that her improvement was not a steady progression as might be implied by the term *phases*. Regressions occurred, particularly when Amy most seemed to be making progress, reflecting her ambivalence about autonomy and separation.

Initial Phase: Self-Regulation

Establishing the Therapeutic Frame

I discussed with Amy a framework for conceptualizing her eating disorder and her therapy during the initial evaluation. To summarize briefly, I acknowledged her past efforts to deal with her anorexia, conceptualized her eating problems as a desperate attempt to cope with life experiences that are overwhelming, and addressed her fears about becoming fat and the role anorexia had played in her identity. Observing that control seemed to be a very important concern for her, to which Amy agreed, I reframed her eating disorder as actually being out of control. This observation turned out to be quite powerful for her and served as a theme throughout her subsequent therapy. Our goals would be to understand what was so overwhelming for her that she returned to restricting and overexercising, to help her to develop more effective coping resources, and to manage her eating and exercise most effectively. The treatment process was described as a collaboration, including the use of "experiments" between sessions to find the solutions that would be best for her.

Introducing Hypnosis

The opportunity to introduce hypnosis occurred in the second month of treatment. We were discussing her mistrust of people in the context of a work-related incident. As part of the discussion, I asked Amy how she thought her mistrust might come up in our relationship. Amy did not respond directly but began talking about her lifelong friend, stating that she had been the only trustworthy person in her life. As she spoke, Amy seemed to disengage and emotionally withdraw. I realized that my comment may have evoked anxiety about closeness. I asked Amy, "Where did you go?" She looked at me and gradually reoriented, stating that she was thinking about times with her friend. As we continued to talk, Amy seemed to reengage, so I inquired about her "slipping away." Amy stated that she did that at times and was concerned that others saw her as a "space cadet." We then talked about "spontaneous dissociation," and I explained that people sometimes dissociate, or go someplace else in their minds, at times of stress or strong emotions. Later I mentioned that dissociation was actually a capacity, introducing hypnosis as a therapeutic method that makes use of dissociation. I suggested that we could discover her capacity to experience hypnosis and use it to help her feel more in control. Amy said "Maybe" and asked me to "tell her what to do about her food." Realizing that I had probably been experienced as intrusive again, I followed her lead, storing this observation for the future. We spent the remainder of the time developing a homework plan for the coming week.

Somewhat to my surprise, Amy reported at her next session that she felt better after the previous session even though she did not do the homework. She attributed her improved mood to my "catching her slipping away" and feeling reassured that there was a label (dissociation) for her experience. She turned quickly, however, to complaints about food and exercise. Over time, Amy's pattern of shifting abruptly to discussion of food-related issues was identified as her way of creating an emotional boundary when anxious about self-disclosure or interpersonal closeness.

Introducing Mastery and Control of Tension States

One week later Amy arrived highly agitated, complaining about her job, and "totally upset" about her eating. She had spent the weekend alone and withdrawn. Her initial enthusiasm and effort had quickly deflated and were replaced by an intense sense of frustration and agitation. Noticing her rapid, agitated speech and detachment in the moment, I decided to intervene experientially, starting with "Amy, are you breathing?" This captured her attention. As she looked at me, I said "Breathe" and blew out a full breath. This was enough of a suggestion that she began blowing out through her mouth, and I noted that "it looked like you stopped breathing." I suggested that it might be useful to do some relaxation to feel less tense. Amy agreed, and I invited her to sit back in the chair and to take a few full breaths. I proceeded in the following manner:

> . . . and you can just continue to take those breaths, in and out, that's right . . . finding a pace that is right for you . . . just as you do when you're running, or pacing yourself in aerobics class . . . your lungs moving the air in and out, your heart beating regularly, your blood flowing through your veins . . . your body knows how to pace itself naturally, without even having to really think about it. . . . And if it's comfortable to close your eyes, you can do that right now and just focus on your breathing . . . in and out . . . in and out, . . . and you can feel a bit calmer with each exhale . . . that's right. . . . Feel the tension in your chest, easing with your breath . . . just noticing what that feels like . . . [her breathing was regulating to a slower, rhythmic pace; I followed her pace with my words for a while] . . . Sometimes, we can lose touch with knowing when our body is tense and when it is relaxed. . . . And one way to become more aware again is to practice tensing various muscles, and then relaxing them . . . just as you learned to do when lifting weights at your fitness club. [I then led her in a classic

tension–relaxation exercise. The suggestions included focusing on a particular muscle group and tensing the muscles, then noticing how she experienced the sensations of tension. After holding the tension, it was suggested to release the muscle group and notice the difference between the sensations of tension and of relaxation. The approach was structured, yet permissive.] . . . And now, as you sit, you can be aware of the way that your muscles can be firm enough to support you in the chair yet able to release any unnecessary tension. . . . As you notice this, you can also be aware of the wholeness of your body . . . [I did a brief scanning from head to toe] . . . and now, an image or thought can come to mind, that reminds you of this sense of control and inner strength that you are feeling right now . . . just allow that image or phrase to come to mind, and when it does, your head can nod yes . . . . that's fine. And it's very important to know, Amy . . . that, just as you exercise your body's muscles, you can exercise your mental muscles. . . . And you can count on your sense of control and comfort developing more and more, bit by bit, easier and easier each time you exercise these muscles . . . letting your mind lead your body to comfort and control. . . . And, there are many more ways . . . waiting to be discovered . . . to feel more at ease, more comfortable, more in control as you work in your therapy to bring feelings of release and relief.

This intervention was designed to enhance Amy's experiential awareness of body sensations, of her capacity to ease acute tension states, and of the cohesiveness of her body. Although I did not label the intervention as *hypnosis* to Amy at the time, the relaxation exercise served as an induction. Suggestions were incorporated that emphasized mastery and control and predicted enhanced self-control over time. Given Amy's limited tolerance for frustration, the concept of taking small steps to achieve her goals was an essential message. At this time, we decided to increase therapy sessions to twice weekly, in response to Amy's difficulty in retaining a therapeutic benefit over the course of a week. Amy expressed a willingness to do more hypnotic work, and we began recording audiotapes of the hypnotic portion of sessions for her to use between sessions to strengthen her developing capacities.

Self-regulation: Affect Identification and Symptom Management

These two goals were addressed simultaneously as we worked with her food records, devised experiments, and discussed everyday situations. Amy would typically describe her experience in global terms such as "it was a miserable weekend" and focus externally on others' behaviors and reactions in a rather plaintive, complaining tone. At other times she would focus on her food and exercise in obsessive detail.

The goal was to begin translating "food talk" into "feeling talk." Initially, my role was to offer labels to Amy's affective states, saying something such as "You sound sad." I then taught her the acronym HALT to "check in" and identify internal states. HALT stands for Hungry, Angry/Anxious, Lonely, Tired. Her food logs initially provided material for determining internal events that triggered her symptoms. For example, if Amy had not eaten all day, we inferred that her food preoccupation was a response to feeling hungry.

Amy often seemed mildly dissociated as she obsessively talked about eating and exercise situations. Typically, I would respond by pacing myself to her physically and making brief comments to communicate that I was following her. Then I would state something such as:

> That was a difficult situation for you. . . . I wonder what might have been going on for you right then . . . let's see how we can slow that scene down, like a film in slow motion . . . and take a look at what was making it so hard for you to eat.

Over time, this routine became automatic. My words were an induction for Amy to settle back in the chair, take a few full breaths, and look down at her lap. I would continue with

> as you settle back into the chair, your inner mind can focus on (that situation) right now, just like a movie camera zooms in. . . . And as the tape slows down a bit, you can zoom in closer . . . and see, hear, notice what is happening, noticing the details. . . . And, as you continue to focus on the details, the question can come to mind: What's eating you right now? Is there an uncomfortable feeling there? . . . Your inner mind can notice the details as you hear the question.

This intervention, designed to make use of Amy's obsessive style, facilitated associations between content and affect and helped her to shift from a distant to a more engaged position.

Typically, ego-strengthening suggestions were included in such interventions. General ego-strengthening suggestions for increased feelings of comfort, contentment, self-acceptance, and increased self-efficacy were interspersed. For illustration, if Amy reported a "lousy food day" and was discouraged, I would ask her to also notice what she had done well. This material was then used to develop specific suggestions regarding her inner resources and qualities. An ego-strengthening suggestion might sound like:

> while you skipped dinner Thursday night, you *were* able to regain your footing on Friday, eating your breakfast . . . breaking that chain of deprivation . . . getting back on track . . . and the ability to get back on track is a sign of your persistence and control . . . that can allow you to move forward . . . and to experience greater stability, and confidence, each time you persist.

When a hypnotic intervention was planned, that portion of the session was taped so that Amy could listen to it between sessions.

Phase Two: Working With Self States

It became apparent that Amy's eating and exercise symptoms often reflected various states of distress, for which she did not have the capacity to identify and self-regulate. Specifically, Amy had difficulty soothing tensions, maintaining a sense of well-being and vitality ("narcissistic equilibrium"), tolerating separations, and modulating feelings of omnipotence and grandiosity ("healthy pride"). While continuing the symptom-focused work, I incorporated work with various self states into the treatment.

I find it useful to provide patients with a "parts metaphor" taken from Federn's (1952) and Watkins's (1978, 1992) work on ego states. The opportunity arose one day when Amy arrived in an agitated, irritable state. She reported that she had been "stuck in that feeling" for the past two days and had been exercising intensely. It became apparent that she had felt thwarted at work and frustrated with her boss's perceived lack of responsiveness. Amy responded to empathic listening, visibly calmed, and seemed more present. Referring to her agitated self state, I discussed the concept of "parts of the self," explaining that sometimes it is helpful to think of our self as a collection of "parts," like a picture puzzle. Each "part" has its own characteristic feelings, behaviors, and motives. The goal is to know these "parts of herself" better and what they are expressing through her eating and exercise. I also proposed labeling each "part," so that we would have common language for identifying the self states. Amy decided to call this her *frustrated* part, stating that only exercise seemed to relieve the physical tension and "hyperness." Amy later relabeled this as her *defiant* part because she would willfully defy her commitment to reduce her exercise when in this self state.

Three other self states became apparent over time. Amy labeled these as her *deflated* part, her *lonely* part, and "the part that wants to be *special*."

Over time, we worked with each self state during hypnosis to enhance Amy's capacity to regulate them, which allowed for a greater sense of autonomy, control, and eventually integration. I will describe an intervention for the frustrated self state that reflects the substance of many such working-through sessions over the course of treatment.

Frustrated, Defiant Part

The following intervention developed during a session in which Amy was stuck in a typical agitated, obsessing pattern. She repeatedly stated that she could not stop obsessing about food, exercise, and what other people were thinking of her. Plaintively, she said, "I feel like I'm floundering but I can't stop pushing myself—I don't know what else to do." She then waited for me to do something.

In addition to reflecting her limited capacity to soothe tensions, her behavior seemed to reflect a conflict between her desire to be effectively in control and a fear of being overwhelmed by her own neediness and passivity if she "slowed down." Dynamically, this sense of passivity may relate to unmet idealizing needs for a competent, idealized parent figure with whom the child experiences gradually increasing independence and learns how to define reasonable goals and how to be proactive. Amy's hyperactivity, extreme approach to food and exercise, and rigid determination can be viewed as compensatory mechanisms for these underdeveloped capacities.

On the basis of this understanding, it seemed important for Amy to experience reducing her immediate agitation without becoming passive. Given that she already seemed internally focused and detached from the present surroundings, I began with "Amy, you swim, don't you?" She nodded. "Perhaps you can imagine along with me. . . . Do you remember ever having the experience of swimming a long, long time . . . and you're out in the ocean and the shore is still a far way off . . . but you're getting *really* tired?" She nodded.

> And as you realize you're *so* tired, you get more and more scared . . . but the harder you try to swim, the more you go under . . . swallowing water . . . the water clogs your ears and nose . . . and you begin to cough, and flounder . . . and you worry, "maybe I won't make it" . . . and there's no one around to see you or help you.

Amy nodded, seemingly absorbed in the experience.

> And then the thought occurs to you . . . "there *is* something I can do" . . . and it's the very thing you need . . . to do . . . and that's to *tread water* . . . you know, extending your arms, gently paddling the water with your hands, just pedalling a bit with your feet . . . and as you paddle, you begin to feel a little stronger, . . . and you can take a breath . . . then another . . . and another . . . and your breathing slows down. . . . You can blow the water out of your nose, and take a look around you. . . . Gradually, you notice that your arms and legs are less fatigued, you're breathing easier . . . and you head for shore. . . . Finally, you feel your feet on the sand, you're on ground again. . . . And it's the same kind of thing, Amy . . . that perhaps you need to just *tread water* right now . . . and that's the very thing and the only thing you truly *need* to do right now . . . to feel some release, some relief.

Constant activity had become Amy's way of experiencing a sense of aliveness and autonomy. Experiencing herself slowing down in this intervention allowed her to begin altering her all or nothing belief that decreasing her hyperactivity was equivalent to being passive. The experience highlighted that she had the capacity to change within her, gratified her dependency needs through the implicit permission to slow down, and assisted in teaching her to do so. Amy gradually was able to re-create the experience of treading water for herself when she needed to manage her tensions in everyday situations.

Formal hypnosis was not used later in treatment with Amy's defiant part. This decision followed a brief but educative experience. Amy was quite cool and distant, yet polite, for two sessions. I remarked to Amy that she did not seem present and asked what she was experiencing. She denied that anything was the matter. Interestingly, I found myself beginning to "work hard," becoming more active in a way that signals to me that something is occurring in the relationship. At the following session, the same pattern began to occur. I shared the observation of my own experience with Amy (i.e, that I found myself "working hard"), and she smiled slyly, saying "Good." Apparently, Amy had felt hurt and offended in a previous session when she was in a defiant state. I had suggested some hypnosis, and Amy felt that I had done so because I "did not want to deal directly with her" when she was feeling defiant. We agreed that it was important for her to engage with me directly when she had such feelings because she typically submerged them out of fear of endangering relationships.

Initially, the hypnotic "parts work" served to concretize and validate the existence of these various self experiences. I placed emphasis on mastery and control. Gradually, I emphasized modulation of affect intensity and integration of these experiences.

Phase Three: Agency: Autonomy and Separation Concerns

Amy gained 10 lb within 8 months of treatment, with substantial anxiety and trepidation, and stabilized at 114 lb for a period of time. She was more aware of feelings and could discriminate sensations of hunger. Symptom management became less central, and her treatment focused on issues of personal authority and developing better relationships. Sessions were reduced to one per week. Symptoms did reemerge periodically when Amy experienced significant distress or anxiety about changes she was making during this phase. Typically, the reemergence of symptoms was addressed by both structured eating interventions and insight, in a manner similar to earlier interventions.

For the first 6 months in treatment, Amy had spent most weekends with her family. At this point Amy was socializing more with her female housemates and coworkers. Her accounts of less-frequent family visits indicated that Amy was disagreeing and getting exasperated with her mother more overtly than in the past, suggesting that differentiation was occurring. Amy typically resisted deeper exploration of this relationship, however.

Three events occurred during the following 8 months that provided opportunities to deal with separation and autonomy issues: Amy began dating, a crisis precipitated around her father's spending habits, and she quit her job. The work on her relationship with her father will not be elaborated in this chapter other than to note its significance in her progress toward greater individuation.

Dating

Amy arrived at her session smiling sheepishly. Tom, a manager in another department, had asked her out. Amy was pleased; however, her concerns about getting close to a man quickly emerged. She had not dated since breaking up with her college boyfriend. Amy was certain that she could "look good," meaning she would dress well and be appropriately responsive to Tom's remarks, but worried that she would have nothing of interest to share of herself. Her words conjured up the image of a china doll. Amy also worried that Tom would want physical intimacy. Her worst fear was that she would go blank and would respond by pushing him away in a panic or else passively complying "to get through it." Either option seemed humiliating. Her concerns about inadequacy and emptiness led to work on healthy boundaries and inner substance to replace the false-self facade with a sense of personal authority.

We worked with an experiential intervention adapted from Baker's (1988) work. During hypnosis, Amy was invited to "now open your eyes, and you can look over at me *through your own eyes* while remaining comfortably in hypnosis . . . and you can experience the space between us accurately and comfortably . . . just notice what this is like for you." This intervention, designed to accentuate the experience of separateness and a "self perspective," was practiced repeatedly until Amy was able to "be in touch with herself" simply by closing her eyes as she took a few breaths then opening her eyes and gazing around her.

This self-centering experience was then used within a desensitization paradigm over a number of sessions to reduce her anxiety with Tom. After identifying several situations, Amy ranked each situation from the least anxiety-provoking to the most terrifying to her. A variety of mental rehearsal techniques were used to imagine the scenarios. First, it was suggested to "let the scene unfold, *just as if it were happening today.*" After the scene, she returned to her self-centered, calm position. Once this experience was reestablished, it was suggested that

> in a few moments you can return to that scene. But this time, it can be different. In your secure, centered position, you become aware of a resource that you can carry back with you into the scene. Just notice that resource right now.

Suggestions for the scene were then repeated. Whenever Amy felt anxious, she signalled me with her index finger, and I reintroduced suggestions for her self-centered experience. When reconnected with that secure position, and sometimes identifying another coping resource, she would return to the scene.

Issues about body image also arose in the context of her dating experiences. Amy still did not have a clear picture of her body size and shape. She continued to ask, on occasion, if she "looked normal." Amy had gained an additional 5 lb over approximately the same number of months, now weighing 119 lb. One day Amy indicated, with some embarrassment, that she had worn her aerobics leotard underneath her dress. She walked quickly into the bathroom and called to me to look with her at herself in the mirror, which I did. I invited her to share her thoughts aloud as she looked at various parts of her body. Starting from head to toe, we looked at her body, listening to her self talk. This in vivo situation was ideal for exploring the differences between judgments and observations. For example, in response to her judgment "My shoulders stick out too much," the modeled observation was "I have straight, well-defined shoulders, with pale skin and sandy freckles on my shoulders." Afterwards, we discussed the experience. In her anxiety, Amy had not considered how she would feel doing this intimate exercise with me. Amy felt pleasantly surprised that I seemed to be unperturbed about her request, was not critical of her, and spoke factually yet caringly about her body. She valued the modeling and was able to relate her judgmental approach to her mother's judgments about her own body and her appearance-based competition with her sister Betsy. The situation was also a fruitful opportunity to talk about emotional boundaries and closeness issues evoked by this experience.

In later sessions we used a hypnotic, imaginary-mirror exercise in which Amy observed herself in a three-way mirror "with the eyes of an observer." During hypnosis, she repeated to herself the observational statements, and we made associations among these remarks, a sense of comfort, and an accurate, enduring, secure sense of her body boundary and body experience. Useful ideas for imaginary-mirror scripts can be found in Orbach (1982) and Hutchinson (1985). In following sessions, we discussed what she had learned from her family about her body, particularly with regard to messages from her mother and the competition with her sister, Betsy.

Quitting Her Job

Amy's decision to leave her job was intended as an act of autonomy. However, the defiant manner in which she did it and her defensiveness suggested that underneath the confident appearance, Amy had doubts about her capacity to succeed in finding a more satisfying job situation for herself. After the first week her delight turned to depression, and Amy began to obsess about food in a way that she had not done for some time. Hypothesizing that her symptoms were an attempt to reorganize her sense of self by returning to familiar symptom patterns and her anorexic identity, I suggested that we use hypnosis to help her regain a sense of equilibrium. The script went as follows:

> Amy, take a few moments to close out the world around you, knowing that there is nothing you *really* need to do right now . . . other than to listen to the sound of my voice. . . . Notice your own experience as you enter that particular state called trance . . . and go to that *special* place where you can just be open to some thoughts and ideas in a safe way . . . where you can discover and rediscover some very interesting things. . . . Perhaps you are already curious about what you will think, hear, feel, experience. . . . And all of us have had experiences of discovering something . . . finding a new way to walk to work . . . a bookstore that you've never been in before . . . a different way to wear your hair . . . opening up a door and seeing what's in the room . . . opening a package to see what's inside . . . many ways of discovering. . . . Just as you can discover in therapy the many ways that you can more truly be yourself. . . . And as you already know so well, movies are a familiar and enjoyable way to discover and learn about one's self. . . . [Amy often talked about movies, and the material typically had something to do with her own issues.] . . . And perhaps you can imagine yourself seated right now in a favorite theater, in a seat with a clear view. Other people may be present, and if they are, you can feel a comfortable sense of anonymity . . . as you watch the movie that unfolds on the screen. It will let you know something important about an interest or goal of your own. And as you watch with curiosity, or perhaps a detached interest, you can observe all the details of this picture. And when the movie is completed, your head can gently nod. [Amy nods.] And you can remember the scenes, Amy, feeling interested and curious about the meaning for you . . . and how this meaning will develop for you over the coming days . . . perhaps in a brief daydream as your thoughts wander during a break at work . . . or at night, securely asleep in your bed . . . and you can discover things about yourself, in ways that are safe, good, dependable . . . just like unwrapping gifts on your birthday, with a sense of anticipation and pleasure . . . uncover, discover, recover . . . that will help you move forward step by step, bit by bit, over the days and weeks ahead.

The purpose of the intervention was to help Amy reconnect with aspects of her self to support her independent strivings and to tolerate the uncertainty and unpredictability of unstructured time. Her job had been an important external organizer, though often resented and resisted. During this session, Amy was able to access her athletic talents and her affection for animals as longstanding, consistent positive resources. She then used this information to plan enjoyable activities, including volunteer work at the animal shelter, to structure her free time.

Amy used the audiotape from this session frequently during her job search. It served as a transitional object, bridging the gap between her growing but not yet secure sense of autonomy and competence and her need to rely on others, including me, to remind her of her capacities through mirroring and modeling of a confident expectation that she would find her way.

Phase Four: Wrapping Up

The themes mentioned above continued to be addressed over the following 4 months. During this time, Amy decided to apply to graduate school, was accepted at a university in another part of the country, and moved there several weeks prior to fall semester. Since her treatment was ending for external reasons rather than as a decision based on her internal progress, sessions focused on acknowledging and integrating the progress she had made and identifying unfinished issues.

Not surprisingly, Amy avoided addressing her impending separation from me until the last few sessions. She also missed two sessions, which was unusual for her. I wondered with her if the missed sessions had anything to do with her upcoming departure from therapy. Amy protested my "interpretation" and then became tearful. She was terrified that she would regress after leaving therapy as she had after her first treatment. Discussing her concerns, we planned to tape a hypnotic session for Amy to take with her.

The hypnotic session addressed internalization and integration issues. Amy described all that she had learned from her therapy, including statements such as "Is there a feeling there that needs to be expressed?" and "You have choices" as well as the images representing aspects of her self. After an induction, I repeated all the statements and images that Amy had identified, with the suggestion that these beliefs and awarenesses were part of her and that they would always be with her, even when she was not consciously aware of them. I then used the metaphor of a tapestry:

> Have a sense of some connections being made and some threads woven between thoughts and feelings, thoughts and actions, actions and your sense of yourself . . . coming together, connecting, like threads that develop into a lovely piece of fabric. . . . Bit by bit, each thread is chosen . . . and each thread has its own unique color, brightness, texture. . . . There are some long, continuous threads that go from beginning to end, as well as those that crisscross back and forth . . . each thread adding in its unique way to the total picture, bit by bit, thread by thread . . . unique and connected, forming a lovely fabric . . . just

as you are doing now, in your therapy, connecting your thoughts and feelings and actions ... your past memories, present experiences, and future wishes ... moving toward a sense of secure anchoring, a sense of wholeness.

To address our separation, I proposed that we could actively speak to and honor this ending, which would be different from other losses and separations in her past. Amy shared her experiences, including her disappointment that she "did not feel totally finished." With some reluctance, Amy stated that she would miss me and quickly asked me to share my perceptions. After exploring her feelings about directly expressing her caring to me, I shared my perceptions of our work and her progress. Finally, Amy decided that she would like to end in hypnosis, simply with the suggestion that she could "now review in her mind all that we had just shared."

Follow-Up

Amy recently contacted me, almost 3 years later. She had completed her graduate degree and wanted to resume her therapy on returning to the local area. Amy reported that she had initiated therapy at one point during graduate school when she lost five pounds but terminated because she did not feel a connection with the therapist.

As of this writing, Amy is working and has regained the weight that she lost but has not been in a significant dating relationship since leaving for graduate school. She is continuing her therapy, focusing particularly on her poor body image, unresolved dependency needs, and intimacy concerns. Her capacities to engage emotionally, tolerate her anxiety, and confront her fears and defenses have substantially deepened since our earlier work. Consequently, Amy is better able to look at her relationship with me and examine her reactions and behavior with less criticalness and even at times with a healthy sense of humor. I have no doubts that, with committed effort, she will progress toward reclaiming her full, true self.

CONCLUSION

This case presentation illustrates the use of hypnosis as an integral component of the outpatient psychotherapy of a young woman with anorexia nervosa. Hypnotic interventions were used throughout the course of treatment to address the psychological impairments underlying the anorexic symptoms and to help Amy resume her arrested psychological development. Hypnosis was used particularly because the nature of the method provides the patient with essential experiential learning, both in terms of self experiences and relationship experiences. At times, the interventions were planned, and I used a formal induction. At other times, they spontaneously developed from the experiential material in the moment. I found it challenging to communicate in written words the qualitative nature of our interactions, the moment-to-moment attunement and reciprocal influencing that occurs and is amplified in the hypnotic context. This was a primary reason for including scripts rather than providing more analytic accounts of the hypnotic interventions.

Given that control is a central issue in anorexia nervosa, the timing and manner of introducing hypnosis were critical to its acceptance by the patient. My clinical experience with Amy and other restricting patients, consistent with the literature (e.g., Baker & Nash, 1987; Gross, 1984; Nash & Baker, 1993; Yapko, 1986), is that hypnosis is best introduced as a method to help the patient regain her sense of personal control and mastery. In addition, hypnosis was introduced to Amy in response to her spontaneous dissociation in an early therapy session, thereby linking the method to her dissociative skills. In this manner, her dissociative capacity was viewed as a strength, with hypnosis being the method to harness her capacities in a therapeutic way.

It is essential to keep in mind that symptoms serve not only a defensive function but also an adaptive function for patients with significant psychological impairments. The patient needs to experience hypnosis as safe and self-strengthening before the therapist applies hypnotic interventions to core features of the symptomatology.

This case illustrates the way in which hypnotic interventions can strengthen the self structure by providing needed self-experiences within the context of a supportive relationship. Audiotapes of the hypnotic interventions were also used to facilitate internalization between sessions. Amy's psychological impairments were typical of restrictors with false-self organization for whom the development of the authentic-self has been arrested. Amy needed to experience the identification of various self states; the modulation of disrupted self states, thereby enhancing a sense of mastery and control; and the exploration of aspects of herself in new and different ways. Strengthening Amy's sense of self was an essential step in reducing symptomatology and resuming her developmental growth toward greater autonomy and separateness while maintaining vital relationships. It is my clinical impression that the primarily cognitive–behavioral focus of her first treatment, while valuable and providing a base from which Amy made progress with symptom management in her treatment with me, did not address her arrested character development and consequently left her vulnerable to regression when challenged by a major life transition.

Amy also needed to experience different and more functional patterns of relating. Her facade of self-sufficiency and compliance effectively disguised her true needs in many relationships and interfered with healthy, genuine connections. Indeed, Amy's experiences of other people were quite ambivalent. She longed for nurturance and attention yet expected neglect and feared being overwhelmed by others' or her own needs. With a few individuals, she developed an idealized dependency, and separations from and individuation within these relationships—including ours—were difficult for her.

As her therapist, my goal was to be aware of the transference pulls and provide Amy with a different experience. It was important to be interested, to be available, and to keep the focus on attending to her experiences yet not be too active as a countertransferential reaction to "compensate" for Amy's past neglect. In situations such as noticing her spontaneous dissociation, my responses communicated an awareness of her psychological self and that she was missed when she was not fully present. The hypnotherapeutic interventions also emphasized collaboration within the relationship. Amy generated the material, and I guided her in exploring or experiencing this material in a therapeutic way. It was my impression that the hypnosis work not only gratified her but also validated her desire for connection. As noted earlier, hypnosis was not used when Amy was enacting a defiant role because Amy felt more engaged when issues of conflict were addressed directly in the relationship.

Amy made significant progress in her therapy. Because the treatment approach incorporated dynamic and cognitive–behavioral elements in addition to hypnosis, it is difficult to determine which elements were directly responsible for Amy's improvement, whether hypnosis contributed uniquely to the treatment effect, and whether hypnosis expedited the course of treatment. Nash and Baker (1993) report research results that, although preliminary, suggest that the introduction of hypnosis into their treatment paradigm improved treatment responses. Controlled studies with outpatient groups in a treatment paradigm that includes cognitive–behavioral, dynamic, and hypnotherapeutic methods would be relevant to answer the above questions. Furthermore, research on the adaptation of specific hypnotic interventions to suit the restricting patient's particular characterological makeup, including modification of technique or method, would address the hypothesis that such therapeutic matching enhances treatment effectiveness and efficiency.

It is my clinical impression, however, that the hypnotic work was particularly potent for Amy on a relational level. Banyai (1991) writes about this relational dimension in her social–psychobiological theory of hypnosis, for which she reviews the supporting research and provides a model for further study of the interactive processes of hypnosis. In my view, the relational aspects of the hypnosis enhanced Amy's experience of empathy and rapport. The hypnotic relationship provided a safe, secure, gratifying environment in which to explore and claim her self within the context of a relationship that could respond to her changing needs for autonomy and closeness. Although unfortunately there was not time to explore Amy's subjective experience in the last session, her request to end therapy in hypnosis constituted a strong statement about the value of the hypnotic component in her psychological growth and our work together. Her recent contact with me suggests that we will have the opportunity to explore these speculations and clarify her subjective experience of this therapeutic work.

REFERENCES

Baker, E. L. (1988). Use with severely disturbed patients. In G. J. Pratt, D. P. Wood, & B. M. Alman (Eds.), *A clinical hypnosis primer*. La Jolla, CA: Psychology and Consulting Associates Press.

Baker, E. L., & Nash, M. R. (1987). Applications of hypnosis in the treatment of anorexia nervosa. *American Journal of Clinical Hypnosis, 29*(3), 185–193.

Banyai, E. I. (1991). Toward a social-psychobiological model of hypnosis. In S. J. Lynn & J. W. Rhue (Eds.), *Theories of hypnosis*. New York: Guilford Press.

Bruch, H. (1962). Perceptual and conceptual disturbances in anorexia nervosa. *Psychosomatic Medicine, 24*, 187–194.

Federn, P. (1952). *Ego psychology and the psychoses* (E. Weiss, Ed.). New York: Basic Books.

Garner, D. M., & Garfinkel, P. (Eds.). (1985). *Handbook of psychotherapy for anorexia nervosa and bulimia*. New York: Guilford Press.

Garner, D. M., Rockert, W., Olmsted, M. P., Johnson, C., & Coscina, D. V. (1985). Psychoeducational principles in the treatment of bulimia and anorexia nervosa. In D. M. Garner & P. E. Garfinkel (Eds.), *Handbook of psychotherapy for anorexia nervosa and bulimia*. New York: Guilford Press.

Goodsitt, A. (1985). Self psychology and the treatment of anorexia nervosa. In D. M. Garner & P. E. Garfinkel (Eds.), *Handbook of psychotherapy for anorexia nervosa and bulimia*. New York: Guilford Press.

Gross, M. (1984). Hypnosis in the therapy of anorexia nervosa. *American Journal of Clinical Hypnosis, 26*, 175–181.

Hornyak, L. M., & Baker, E. K. (Eds.). (1989). *Experiential therapies for eating disorders*. New York: Guilford Press.

Hudgins, M. K. (1989). Experiencing the self through psychodrama and Gestalt therapy in anorexia nervosa. In L. M. Hornyak & E. K. Baker (Eds.), *Experiential therapies for eating disorders* (pp. 234–257). New York: Guilford Press.

Hutchinson, M. G. (1985). *Transforming body image*. Trumansburg, NY: Crossing Press.

Johnson, C. (1985). Initial consultation for patients with bulimia and anorexia nervosa. In D. M. Garner & P. E. Garfinkel (Eds.), *Handbook of psychotherapy for anorexia nervosa and bulimia*. New York: Guilford Press.

Johnson, C. (1991). *Psychodynamic treatment of anorexia nervosa and bulimia.* New York: Guilford Press.

Johnson, C., & Connors, M. E. (1987). *The etiology and treatment of bulimia nervosa: A biopsychosocial perspective.* New York: Basic Books.

Kohut, H. (1971). *The analysis of the self.* New York: International Universities Press.

Lerner, H. D. (1991). Masochism in subclinical eating disorders. In C. Johnson (Ed.), *Psychodynamic treatment of anorexia nervosa and bulimia* (pp. 109–127). New York: Guilford Press.

Lynn, S. J., Rhue, J. W., Kvaal, S., & Mare, C. (1993). The treatment of anorexia nervosa: A hypnosuggestive framework. *Contemporary Hypnosis, 10*(2), 73–80.

Nash, M. R., & Baker, E. L. (1993). Hypnosis in the treatment of anorexia nervosa. In J. W. Rhue, S. J. Lynn, & I. Kirsch (Eds.), *Handbook of clinical hypnosis.* Washington, DC: American Psychological Association

Orbach, S. (1982). *Fat is a feminist issue* (Vol. 2). New York: Berkley Books.

Stern, S. (1991). Managing opposing currents: An interpersonal psychoanalytic technique for the treatment of eating disorders. In C. Johnson (Ed.), *Psychodynamic treatment of anorexia nervosa and bulimia* (pp. 86–105). New York: Guilford Press.

Strober, M. (1991). Disorders of the self in anorexia nervosa: An organismic-developmental paradigm. In C. Johnson (Ed.), *Psychodynamic treatment of anorexia nervosa and bulimia* (pp. 354–373). New York: Guilford Press.

Watkins, J. G. (1978). *The therapeutic self.* New York: Human Sciences Press.

Watkins, J. G. (1992). *Hypnoanalytic techniques: The practice of clinical hypnosis* (Vol. 2). New York: Irvington.

Winnicott, D. W. (1965). *The maturational process and the facilitating environment: Studies in the theory of emotional development.* New York: International Universities Press.

Woodall, C, & Andersen, A. E. (1989). The use of metaphor and poetry therapy in the treatment of the reticent subgroup of anorexic patients. In L. M. Hornyak & E. K. Baker (Eds.), *Experiential therapies for eating disorders* (pp. 191–206). New York: Guilford Press.

Yapko, M. D. (1986). Hypnotic and strategic interventions in the treatment of anorexia nervosa. *American Journal of Clinical Hypnosis, 28*(4), 224–232.

4

A BRIEF THERAPY APPROACH TO THE USE OF HYPNOSIS IN TREATING DEPRESSION

MICHAEL D. YAPKO

Our knowledge of depression has dramatically improved in recent years, rendering obsolete many of the beliefs commonly held about its etiology and course. As a result, the role of psychotherapy has been firmly established as vital, not only to overcome episodes of depression but also to minimize the likelihood of later relapses (Antonuccio, Danton, & DeNelsky, 1994, 1995). Whenever psychotherapy is indicated, so are specific identifiable patterns of hypnotic influence, because the two are fundamentally inseparable.

The use of formal hypnotic interventions in the treatment of depression has been both actively and passively discouraged over the years. The reasons for this are many and have been discussed in detail in an earlier work, *Hypnosis and the Treatment of Depressions* (Yapko, 1992b). A review of the relevant literature reveals a bias stemming from outdated misconceptions, such as hypnosis stripping away the patient's defenses and rendering him or her suicidal or even psychotic. On the contrary, hypnosis—when skillfully applied—holds great potential for empowering the helpless and hopeless patient. The following case example may illustrate this point well.

The author would like to acknowledge Linda Griebel for her help in the preparation of this chapter.

75

BACKGROUND INFORMATION

The patient was a 42-year-old White man who I'll call Tim. Self-referred for psychotherapy, Tim presented the problems of experiencing moderate depression, moderate anxiety, and concerns about his escalating consumption of alcohol, which he viewed as a coping mechanism for managing his uncomfortable levels of depression and anxiety. Tim was employed in the construction field. He was a general contractor and was capable of performing all major aspects of construction, including building, plumbing, and electrical. Tim was not married, but he lived with a woman who he had been involved with for several years. He was ambivalent about the relationship.

Tim's family history was significant. His mother had been in and out of psychiatric hospitals numerous times throughout Tim's childhood for what appeared to be severe depression that sometimes involved psychotic depressive episodes. Tim described his father as highly detached from his wife and very aloof with his children. Consequently, Tim believed he had little parental support and involvement in his life. Tim was the youngest of three children. He described his older siblings as "reasonably supportive and helpful" in his formative years; as adults, they were geographically separated. They maintained friendly though superficial relationships with one another.

Tim described himself as always having been prone to high levels of anxiety and moderate levels of depression. He was a deeply philosophical man by nature and a "searcher of truth." In his late adolescence and early 20s, when he was in college, his philosophical interests led him to intensive study of Eastern religions. Around that same time, he sought psychotherapy for the first time for help with depression. He soon quit, however, because he saw the therapy as irrelevant to his life concerns. When asked about this previous psychotherapy, he characterized it as "psychoanalytic in nature." He described it as "useless" because he was "not given any meaningful feedback" in his interactions with his analyst and because he was "not given any specific tools to work with in order to better manage" his depression.

No formal psychological-assessment tools were used in working with Tim. He was a very bright and articulate man who was intensely curious about many things. He asked me many direct questions about my perspectives about psychotherapy, and he was particularly interested in hypnosis and brief therapy methods. In fact, Tim specifically sought me out on the basis of my emphasis in treatment of providing specific skill-building tools and my emphasis on working in an active brief therapy format (Tim had read my self-help book, *Free Yourself From Depression*, 1992a). Tim made it clear from the outset that this was going to be a time-limited therapy and that he wanted to accomplish as much as possible in up to but no more than half a dozen sessions. His focus was entirely on acquiring alternative perspectives and practical tools. Tim professed and appeared to be open and willing to engage with whatever ideas or methods I thought might best fit him.

Tim's intellectual curiosity, his extensive readings of psychological and philosophical literature, and his history of exploring various consciousness-raising movements over the past couple of decades made Tim a very critical and active participant in the treatment process. Despite his intelligence and curiousity, however, he also demonstrated a rigid preoccupation with finding "the truth." He experienced a great deal of depression and anxiety as he attempted to find answers to complex life questions and to control aspects of his life that he had not yet recognized were beyond his range of control (such as how his girlfriend felt about spirituality). His low self-esteem resulting from his ongoing self-criticism for the lack of success in certain areas of his life, most notably conquering his own depression, was considerable.

CONCEPTUALIZATION OF THE PROBLEM

We have learned in recent years that depression is not exclusively or even primarily a biological illness. It cannot be viewed only as anger turned inward, as a reaction to loss, or as a condition that exists simply because the person is rewarded for it through associated secondary gains (Seligman, 1990). Each such perspective may hold true in some cases, but none of them truly represents the essence of the disorder (Yapko, 1992b). Rigid viewpoints of depression that emphasize a specific psychodynamic or behavioral contingency have proven to be so limited as to be potentially destructive frameworks for attempting diagnosis and treatment (Akiskal, 1985; McGrath, Keita, Strickland, & Russo, 1990; Yapko, 1988).

Emerging in the treatment literature in recent years has been a welcome shift away from analyzing the abstract issues of a person's life in favor of developing a focus on specific patterns the individual uses to organize and respond to his or her perceptions of life (deShazer, 1991; Fisch, Weakland, & Segal, 1983). Epidemiological, cross-cultural, and treatment studies have made it clear that any of a variety of patterned ways of responding to life's circumstances can lead to the phenomenological experience of depression (Schwartz & Schwartz, 1993). Thus, there is no single cause for depression.

In describing depression as a product of various self-organizing patterns that can cause and maintain the experience of depression, I am also emphasizing that there are identifiable patterns that may be appropriate targets for therapeutic intervention. Tim clearly manifested some of these identifiable patterns. Specifically, Tim showed what I call "a present temporal orientation" (Yapko, 1989, 1992b), a relationship to time that places greatest value on the immediacy of one's experience, often at the expense of a detailed and realistic representation of eventual consequences. In other words, individuals with the "now" orientation tend to become so selectively focused on immediate experience (e.g., instant gratification, avoidance of unpleasant obligations, and an inability to fully grasp cause–effect relationships) that there is too little attention paid to making realistic and meaningful projections about the future. As a result, such individuals are often poor at planning, poor at anticipating consequences for current courses of action, and highly ambivalent because of their intense focus on whatever mixed feelings they have in the present moment. Tim manifested a marked lack of long-term goal planning; he had no specific ambitions or long-term goals. As a result, Tim's focus was simply on getting through each day, making his goals extremely short-term and clearly unsatisfying. Tim described his ongoing experience as "merely coping with whatever each day brings." As a result, each day was a struggle, despite the fact that he did not usually face any particularly difficult or overwhelming external challenges. In fact, much of Tim's anxiety and depression was a product of his repeatedly asking himself global and complex questions such as, "Where is my life going? What do I want out of life? What is the meaning of my life? What should I do with my life? Will I ever be happy? When will I be happy? What will give meaning to my life?"

Anxiety is frequently associated with depression. It is not uncommon for depressed individuals such as Tim to ask themselves a seemingly endless stream of questions that are certainly not immediately answerable and, in fact, may never be answerable. To ask serious questions that can profoundly affect the quality of one's life and then be unable to answer them can easily stimulate anxiety and a sense of hopelessness in any individual. Consider questions such as: "Is there a God? What is the right occupation for me? What is the best use of a day off? What is the smartest use of $10,000?" To ask such unanswerable questions (i.e., unanswerable in any definitive or objective sense) is to raise serious doubts about any course of action one takes if one is wanting to be "correct." The depressive's typical "all or none" thinking (Beck, 1967, 1973) usually leads to being either right or wrong, with no comfortable place to be in the middle. In Tim's case, his focus was a short-term one on just getting through the day. He had no longer-term specific plans for his future. Meanwhile, in the course of each day, Tim asked himself countless unanswerable, yet seemingly sensible, introspective questions that neither he nor anyone else could answer in any definitive sense. This left him feeling very unhappy, frustrated, and without any apparent potential, in his view, for his current circumstances to change.

In previous writings (Yapko, 1988, 1989, 1990, 1991, 1992a, 1992b), I have described some of the most common patterns underlying depression. In the same way that a present temporal (i.e., "now") orientation can preclude a well-developed and realistic sense of future orientation, there are other potentially depressogenic patterns, including low frustration tolerance, internal orientation, low compartmentalization, and diffuse attentional style. These specific patterns were evident in Tim's narrative when he initially described his problems.

Tim's low frustration tolerance led him to make quick short-term attempts to find other more satisfying job opportunities. It also led him to often feel frustrated with the apparent lack of progress in his relationships with women when interpersonal problems could not be immediately resolved. It further led him to use a short-term coping strategy of excessive consumption of alcohol, despite knowing this was a potentially hazardous practice in the long run. His frequent "giving up" when he could not find immediate solutions to his difficulties was further evidence of his low-frustration tolerance.

Tim's internal orientation style led him to be highly introspective about and sensitive to each emotion he felt. Thus, no matter what he was feeling, good or bad, he would ask "Why?" and then ruminate seemingly endlessly about the meaning of his feelings. By being so internally oriented, he was considerably less "tuned in" to people and circumstances around him. As a result, his relationships with others were brief and unsatisfying.

The final, salient depressogenic pattern Tim manisfested was his diffuse attentional style. His attentional style led Tim to focus on factors that were often irrelevant in the course of his dealings with others (i.e., they shared his interest in philosophy but they were exploitive of his resources). Thus, he often found others frustrating when they did not immediately provide what he was looking for.

I thought about Tim's problems in terms of the various skills Tim was clearly lacking that are necessary to succeed in the arenas that concerned him. Tim was a very intelligent, articulate, motivated man whose experiential deficits precluded him from accomplishing the very things that he most wanted to accomplish. This is highly typical of depressed individuals. I do not believe I have ever encountered someone who enjoys or wants his or her depression. I have encountered depressed individuals routinely, however, who do not have the necessary skills to overcome their problems. It is unfortunate that clinicians have focused so intensely on people's motivation, hypothesizing about people's fear of failure or people's fear of success, without fully considering the lack of necessary skills that would enable an individual to succeed in whatever arena(s) he or she is attempting to succeed in. Motivation without ability can be very depressing.

It seemed apparent to me that Tim would benefit from experiencing some meaningful hypnotic age-progression work with the goals of evolving a longer-term goal orientation and greater frustration tolerance to work more patiently toward goals that could only be realized over time. I further decided that Tim would likely benefit from using hypnosis to access the necessary resources for greater impulse control to reduce his drinking. I also elected to use hypnosis for the purposes of anxiety reduction and, in a general sense, to increase Tim's sense of clarity about what is and is not controllable in various life experiences.

TREATMENT

The treatment goals in working with Tim were to help him (a) develop a positive and optimistic orientation toward the future, (b) develop greater frustration tolerance and an enhanced ability to exercise impulse control by making current choices on the basis of their consistency with future goals rather than the feelings of the moment, (c) develop the ability to take deliberate steps to actively and independently reduce anxiety without the use of alcohol, (d) recognize his ongoing experience of life as changeable and malleable in contrast to his current view of his circumstances as fixed and unyielding, and (e) shift from a reactive to a proactive position for responding to both external life experiences and internal personal perceptions. All of these goals reflect the development of specific skills that would enhance Tim's ways of managing his life. Each goal was discussed with Tim clearly and directly in each of the sessions. Such discussions clarify the session goals and establish a framework for giving the hypnosis sessions meaning. Thus, even the indirect and metaphorical approaches were used in the context of agreed on goals.

There are some excellent reasons to use hypnosis in psychotherapy in general and with depressives in particular: (a) Hypnosis amplifies portions of subjective experience thereby making it easier to recognize where the patient's patterns of perception, thinking, relating, and so forth are causing or maintaining his or her experience of depression; (b) it serves as a potent method of therapeutic pattern interruption; (c) it facilitates experiential learning; (d) it helps associate and contextualize desired responses; (e) it models flexibility, encouraging a variety of ways to relate to one's self; and (f) it helps build focus (Yapko, 1992b).

Tim had as a part of his general philosophical orientation a heavy reliance on a conscious and intellectual framework for interpreting his own experience in particular and life experience in general. Despite the premium Tim placed on conscious understanding and an intellectual analysis of experience throughout his life, he did not improve over time but, in fact, deteriorated over time. Thus, it seemed important in his therapy to expand Tim's perspective of himself and his experience by having him "step outside" his usual framework. In other words, it could be said that Tim was already absorbed in a "symptomatic trance" in which he was selectively focused on dimensions of experience that were self-limiting and hurtful (Gilligan, 1987, 1988; Yapko, 1992b). The idea of redirecting his focus in a positive direction and thereby facilitating a therapeutic hypnotic state seemed a desirable way of interrupting Tim's usual experience of himself. All of the ways that hypnosis can be used in the treatment of depression described above were highly relevant in Tim's case.

Hypnosis was introduced to Tim in a formal manner (i.e., openly discussed and implemented) in our second therapy session. Hypnosis was described as a valuable therapeutic ally that could help Tim shift depressogenic perceptions and redefine his experience of himself. Tim readily agreed to hypnotic treatment and even found the prospect of working hypnotically intriguing.

In the hypnosis sessions with Tim, I used direct and indirect suggestions, metaphors, truisms, affective reassociational suggestions, ratifications of trance responses, process and content suggestions, positive and negative suggestions, and posthypnotic suggestions. I suggested the following classical hypnotic phenomena as part of the hypnotic interventions: age regression, age progression, dissociation, and sensory alterations. I used these to facilitate the kinds of therapeutic experiences that would most likely be of help to him in overcoming his problems.

Tim was seen five times, in keeping with his original request to have only a few sessions. Each of the sessions involved direct discussion of relevant issues as well as discussion about learnings gleaned from the previous session. I used hypnosis with Tim in sessions two, three, and four, following discussion of his current needs and interests and the session's goals. The unedited transcripts of each of the three hypnosis sessions are provided below, along with commentary and analysis.

SESSION TRANSCRIPTS

Hypnosis Session One

Prior to the first hypnosis session, I elaborated on points made in the first session regarding the need for goals and a future orientation, as well as specific life-management skills such as anxiety management and an ability to be more flexible and objective in one's thinking. I then used hypnosis to facilitate these possibilities.

All right Tim. . . .	Orienting first to the notion of experiencing trance as a means for facilitating eventual responsiveness.
you can begin by taking a few deep, relaxing breaths and just orient yourself now to the idea of being able to get absorbed internally . . . being able to experience yourself differently . . . little by little . . .	Building internal focus. Defining the purpose of the trance.

now you have lots of different experiences . . . visualization, meditation . . . that very closely parallel the experience of comfort . . . the relaxation of trance . . .

Accessing previous experiences that parallel and suggest trance as a means of induction.

and yet at the same time, it is a different enough experience as you focus your thoughts . . . generating deeper understandings, different awarenesses. . . .

Orienting to the notion for making finer distinctions between experiences in contrast to a simple "all or none" perception.

In a sense, what I am encouraging you to do is to take the time to explore within yourself. . . .

Using his curiosity and tendency to search for answers, but redirecting him to begin to search internally rather than externally.

you know as well as I, how very . . . ritualistic experience can get . . . doing many of the same things . . . thinking many of the same things . . . the same feelings. . . .

Building rapport through defining ourselves as collaborators, while raising the issue of rigidity. Describing rigidity as repetitive and thereby beginning to create a negative affective association to it.

I think what's most interesting about going into trance . . . and by that I mean that state of focused comfort . . .

Directing his attention to building a trance state that is defined as interesting, comfortable, and focused.

is that you get to step outside your usual experience of yourself . . . initially . . . your thoughts can be all over the place . . . listening and not listening . . . paying attention . . . being distracted . . .

Redefining shifts of perception as comfortable rather than anxiety-provoking.

which is really quite normal and to be expected . . .

Feeding back and redefining the cognitive dimensions of anxiety as both acceptable and usable.

but at some point along the way . . . you really can't know just when . . . you start to notice shifts in your breathing . . . shifts in your musculature . . . subtle shifts . . . that start to gather momentum . . . and become more pronounced as time goes on . . .

Suggesting a shift in awareness from the cognitive to physical dimensions of experiences concurrent with unconscious shifts in sensory experience.
Amplifying unconscious and effortless shifts in awareness.

now there's a lot that you know about construction from the earliest stages of design . . . to the last moment's work . . . in completing a project . . .
you learn something about architects . . . when you do construction . . . you learn something about how much vision they really have . . . or don't have . . .

when they put something where it really doesn't belong . . . or where he didn't put something that should be there . . .
and times that . . . people have commented that the finished product isn't what they had envisioned . . .

and you discover . . . that sometimes people's vision . . . is really quite restricted . . .

now the skills that you have . . . the things that you know how to do . . . well . . . have evolved over years of pratice . . .

and each project has a sequence . . . from beginning to middle to end . . .
and the parallel is really quite clear, Tim . . . I don't think there is anything particularly hidden . . . or subtle about the analogy . . .
because right now you are the architect . . . designing the blueprints for the rest of your life . . .

Use of his professional identity as the basis for a metaphor indirectly suggesting a structured sequence for producing successful results.

Using his experience with architects as an indirect suggestion for recognizing the differences between plans that work and plans that don't, especially in regard to "vision"—a realistic and detailed plan for the future.
Encouraging a review of architectural blunders that reflect poor or inadequate planning as a basis for future.
Identifying the notion that dissatisfaction often occurs when expectations and hopes are not realized because they were unrealistic or lacking in detail.
Emphasizing the great potential value of developing realistic vision (i.e., future orientation) as a means for preventing disappointment.
Enhancing self-esteem and frustration tolerance by defining Tim as possessing skills that are complex and requiring years to develop, with no quick shortcuts.
Reemphasizing that any project has a fixed sequence to follow.

Shifting from indirect (metaphor) to direct suggestions.

Suggesting a shift from a reactive to a proactive position in making life choices and emphasizing that choices now are the "blueprints" for later experience, encouraging again a stronger future orientation.

and we want to make sure that everything is right where it should be ... so that when you start building ... it looks right ... feels right ... more importantly, it works ...

now the interesting thing is ... that when you have people ... who have a very strong sense of future possibilities ...

those things that happen in the moment ...

are just a *part* of experience ...

and so the *transient* bad moods ... or the *transient* episodes of anxiety ...

are scaled down ... because the moment passes ... and the larger goals remain ...

now I don't know if you have ever been around a little kid ... but my best friends have a little two-year-old girl ... and each night they read her a bedtime story ...

and she has a favorite story ... and each night mom ... and/or dad ... reads that story ...

and if they vary one word ... she'll stop them and indignantly say, "Read it right!" and if they change an inflection, she'll stop them and say, "Read it right!" ... the same story in the same way night after night ...

how many different ways are there ... of reading the same story ... how many different inflections ... changes of tempo ... changes of emphasis ...

Encouraging impulse control by suggesting pausing before acting to evaluate the appropriateness of a course of action. Emphasis is placed on it working as more important than looking or feeling "right."
Using his curiosity and intellectual interest.
Encouraging a strong sense of furture orientation.
Distinguishing between moment-to-moment experiences and a greater goal that overrides them.
Encouraging breaking global representations into component parts.

Distinguishing ongoing depression and anxiety from transient bad moods, thereby encouraging a more unstable attribution for internal experiences.
Reemphasizing that enduring goals supersede momentary fluctuations of mood or feelings.
Lead-in to metaphor regarding rigidity.

Orienting Tim to a child's version of repetitive experiences.

Exaggerated examples of perceptual rigidity to illustrate the point that flexibility is desirable.

Encouraging flexibility by asking rhetorically for Tim to identify how many ways there are to read a story and then suggesting possible ways to vary one's reading.

and over years of experience, Tim . . . of reading yourself the same story in the same way . . . until you start to realize . . . how many different ways are there . . . of responding to a worry . . . how many different ways of responding to an anxious feeling?

Some people when they get an anxious feeling . . . they sit down with a relaxation tape . . . and they *watch* it evaporate . . .

some people have an anxious feeling . . . and they sit down with a jar of soap suds and blow bubbles . . . I've always speculated that that's how Lawrence Welk got his start . . .

some people play air guitar to a favorite rock 'n' roll song . . . some people call a friend . . .

how many different ways are there . . . that allow the feeling to pass? . . . while maintaining the larger goal . . . of staying healthy . . . of staying clearheaded . . .

reinforcing . . . you're in control . . . YOU'RE IN CONTROL . . .

now we talked about constructing realities . . . blueprints and tools . . . and since you're obviously doing a remodel . . . on the reality you constructed many years ago . . .

Associating the metaphor directly to his own experience by suggesting he has told himself the same story without variation about himself. Tying into the metaphor's rhetorical questions to encourage variability and flexibility, suggesting that anxiety is not fixed and unchangeable but can change as his responses change.

Indirect suggestion to use the hypnosis tape of this session being provided to him and encouraging a shift from a kinesthetic to a visual representation of the anxiety (pattern interruption).

Introducing humor and lightheartedness as a means for reducing both anxiety and depression while reinforcing a representational shift from kinesthetic to visual regarding his feelings.

Encouraging flexibility in problem solving through diversity of examples while also suggesting connecting to others as a valuable tool in reducing depression.

Rhetorical question suggesting an infinite and diverse range of ways of managing feelings while simultaneously redefining them as transient, not permanent. Emphasis on larger goal of health and a clear head rather than focusing on alcohol directly.

Encouraging redefining self as in charge rather than a victim of unknown forces of the universe.

Reiterating the construction metaphor as a meaningful framing of the change work Tim intends to undertake. Letting him know it's a "remodel," not a tearing down and starting over.

one of the great benefits of being in the field that you are in . . . is you can do custom upgrades knowledgeably . . . and so to upgrade your thinking . . . to remodel your responses . . . to customize your interior . . . for	Using Tim's professional experiences as the basis for suggesting upgrading his quality of life while enhancing his self-esteem as a knowledgeable professional.
maximum aesthetic value . . . is a very different goal . . . than just getting through the day . . . and then just getting through another day . . . and then just getting through another day . . . so out of all the different things we spoke of . . . I'll be curious which words . . . which phrases . . . ricochet through your mind . . .	Encouraging higher and more appropriate goals using his skills rather than merely coping, building motivation to challenge himself and actively seek more for himself.

Encouraging Tim to review key concepts of session and to retain them in ways that can be helpful to him. |
| in evolving a different way . . . | Reinforcing flexibility and a shift in approach. |
| take your time, Tim . . . process your different thoughts and feelings . . . and then when you feel like you're ready to, you can bring the experience to a comfortable close . . . and start to reorient whenever you want to . . . gradually . . . so that when you are ready in a little while, you can reorient fully and allow your eyes to open. | Closure and disengagement. |

After hypnosis Tim reported significant reductions in anxiety and rumination, which was reinforced as evidence of the malleability of his experience. Discussion of the importance of effective problem-solving strategies preceded the hypnosis session's focus on developing and consolidating personal resources for improved self-esteem.

Hypnosis Session Two

Lean back get yourself comfortable . . . the chair goes back . . . there you go . . .	Encouraging assuming a comfortable position to begin.
and orient yourself now . . . to what is by now probably a very familiar experience . . . of being able to sit back and let your eyes close . . . and start to absorb yourself in a frame of mind . . .	Using his previous trance experiences from having listened multiple times to the tape made of the first trance session as the basis for the current induction.

you wanted to know what trance is . . . it's a frame of mind . . .

being immersed in a way of thinking . . . a way of being . . . so there are cultural trances, individual trances . . . trances of being a man . . . trances of being a builder . . . trances of personality . . .
and the more absorbed in a particular idea . . . the more exclusive a focus, the deeper the trance . . .
and how deep a trance is deep enough? What you're discovering . . . is that you have the ability to recognize value in a particular line of thinking . . .

you might even have surprised yourself that you have the flexibility to shift your thinking in certain specific ways . . .
so right here, right now . . . you have some time . . . to entrance yourself with a set of ideas, a set of images . . .
the things that you find . . . interesting enough . . . engaging enough . . . and that changes from time to time . . .

sometimes you'll be absorbed in trance . . . processing very important memories that really teach you something . . .
other times . . . you'll be far away from thinking . . .

and your way of being allowed you . . . to abuse yourself in the long-run . . . for short-term coping . . .

Using Tim's question posed earlier in the session about what constitutes a trance state.
Encouraging a flexible and broad view of trance to prevent it from being another construct Tim rigidly compartmentalizes. It further defines trance as a largely context-defined phenomenon.

Equates trance depth with depth of absorption, indirectly encouraging greater absorption.

Rhetorical question illustrating a relative appraisal rather than an all-or-none one. Feeding back to Tim his observation stated earlier in our session that he notices more flexibility, tasking himself to look at one thing from many perspectives. Reinforcing flexibility and the ability to shift perspectives.

Shifting locus of control from me to himself as the entrancing agent.

Encouraging multiple focal points rather than restricting himself to only one, allowing but using the inevitable "wandering mind" of anxious patients.
Raising the possibility of experiencing age regression by important memories surfacing.

Suggesting thinking (and analyzing) is not only not essential but also may be unnecessary in this context. Raising the issue of short-term coping and defining it as self-abuse, even though alcohol is itself never specifically mentioned.

Script	Commentary
and I can't really predict, Tim ... where you'll be, what you'll be doing ... what kind of job you'll be working ... when it occurs to you ... that you have moved so far past where you were ...	Use of past tense regarding how he was as a direct contrast to how he's becoming, evolving past old perspectives and limitations. Encouraging a break from the past by framing him as having outgrown old behaviors and perspectives that limited him.
in learning to manage ... all the parts of yourself ...	Emphasis is on managing self as situations arise rather than obtaining "the answer" to life questions.
whether they're bored parts or ... fearful parts ... anxious parts, doubtful parts ... certainly you know it at least as well as I ...	Redefining all parts of self (negative feelings especially) as manageable.
some parts feel differently than others ... some parts better ... some worse ... but you now know that they are all valuable ... some time, some place ...	Feeding back the reality that not all experiences may be pleasant, but all are manageable and valuable in some way at some point in time, an affective reassociated suggestion.
but what you and I have done, we've turned the spotlight on ... the parts of you that are ambitious enough ... and strong enough ... to want more for yourself ... than just another can of beer ... and when you turn the spotlight on ... the parts of you that you really value ... your sense of humor ... your quick grasp ... of things that you hear ... your curiosity ... and insightful questions ...	Defining our work as involving amplifying in his awareness the positive parts of himself to counteract his narrow focus on only his perceived weaknesses; by focusing on them he can want more than just coping day to day. Directly suggesting the development of an appreciation for characteristics he genuinely possesses but never notices or represents to himself in his self-image.
those are all things that you can't really teach somebody ... how do you teach somebody to be curious?	Self-esteem—enhancing suggestions.
and when you start to realize ... that there is a very important part of you that's been ... underutilized ... you can start to connect ... with that deeper part of you ... in more and more ways ...	Shifting focus from a pathology-based view to a view encouraging greater balance of personal characteristics. Encouraging greater appreciation of his deeper characteristics.

and then the very thought . . .
dulling parts of yourself . . . so
that you'll think slower . . .
speak less articulately . . . miss
important, but subtle things . . .
it's just an idea . . . with no
appeal . . . different things start
to occur to you . . . and where
you are now . . . outgrowing the
need . . . to hear the same old
story . . . in the same old way
. . . which means that you can
say to yourself . . .

read it different, Tim . . . tell it
different . . .

now over the course of the next
few days . . . weeks . . . months
and years . . .

there will be lots of experiences
. . . and every once in a while
. . . when it occurs to you . . .
that your response is different
. . . than it used to be . . .

the feelings different . . . the
choice that you make is different
. . .

it is very reinforcing . . . very
reinforcing . . .

and even though there aren't
any parades, bells or whistles . . .
neon lights that flash . . . there
really is a great feeling . . . in
feeling real solid . . . that you did
what you set out to do . . .

feeling more whole and
connected to yourself . . . aware
of yourself and valuing yourself
. . .

that isn't something that's
transient . . . it's a way of life, it's
a way of being . . .

Creating dissonant feelings about
alcohol, suggesting it can only
interfere with his feeling good about
himself, thereby breaking the
association to alcohol as an
acceptable coping tool.
Reiterating flexibility in responding
to his own feelings rather than
rigidly responding with alcohol by
referencing the metaphor from the
previous session regarding the young
girl.

Contrasting with "read it right" (i.e.,
the same).
Orienting to the future (age
progression).

Furthering a posthypnotic suggestion
for unconsciously behaving
differently in a manner consistent
with the suggested patterns.

Establishing directly the expectation
that things can and will change for
the better.
Encouraging, recognizing, and
enjoying the changes.
Encouraging a recognition that the
external world will not be a likely
source of feedback that he's doing
better, only his internal awareness
can let him know he's doing better.

Emphasizing greater self-awareness
and self-acceptance.

Suggesting that while moods and
situations may come and go, good
self-esteem can endure.

it's the guideline . . . for all that you do . . . judging a course of action . . . by how it will feel in the long run . . . what it says about you . . . what it highlights . . .

Emphasizing self-esteem is the basis for decision making. Reiterating the need for impulse control and a processing of options to weigh a course of action against what it will do and how it will feel in the long run, rather than what the short-term results might be.

now you and I talked about a lot of different things . . . from deeper philosophies of life . . . all the way to beer . . .

Emphasizing our collaborative relationship that exists on many levels to reinforce rapport.

now the interesting thing is . . . and you already know this . . . someone can say something or do something . . . that's very important at the time . . . moving you to a different level of awareness . . .

Suggesting the possibility that the things I talk to him about can evolve in importance beyond what he might currently realize.

then it becomes a way of life . . . where you really don't have to think about it . . . it's so automatic . . . so effortless . . . it's just a given that you handle it this way and not that . . .

Encouraging a transition from effortful to effortless change.

there's a lot to look forward to, Tim . . . all the things yet to be discovered . . . by you . . . about yourself . . .

Encouraging an optimistic and motivating view of future possibilities.

each time . . . that you don't read the same old story in the same old way . . .

Referencing again the contrast between flexibility and rigidity in the child metaphor of the previous session.

so over the course of time . . . you can absorb and integrate deeply . . . very deeply . . . all you're learning . . .

Suggesting integrating the relevant principles of our session.

take whatever time you'd like to now . . .

Closure

to process all your different
thoughts and feelings . . . so that
you can start to bring the | Suggesting the need to generate
experience to a comfortable | comfort beyond the trance
close . . . and bring back with | experience.
you the strongest feelings of
certainty . . . to carry with you
. . . and then when you've had
enough time . . . you begin the
process of reorienting yourself at
a rate that is comfortable and
gradual . . .

so that when you are ready in a | Disengagement.
little while . . . you can reorient
fully . . . letting your eyes open
whenever you're ready.

Hypnosis Session Three

Prior to the third hypnosis session, Tim reported a shift in his perceptions of himself, for the first time recognizing that he trapped himself
with his own intellect by making assumptions about himself and the world
that he had never challenged. We discussed the value of changing frames
of reference in some contexts from identifying what is "true" to identifying
what "works." Considerable emphasis was placed on thinking ahead pre-
ventively in making life choices and continuing to adapt to changing life
circumstances.

All right, Tim . . . you can begin | Shifting focus from trance induction.
by taking in a few deep . . . | Encouraging Tim to define his own
relaxing breaths . . . and orient | trance state.
yourself now . . .
to whatever that . . . frame of
reference is . . .
that allows you to build the state | Using his construction background
of mind . . . and I am very | as a metaphor for encouraging a
deliberate in saying . . . *build* a | proactive approach to establishing a
state of mind . . . that highlights | meaningful trance experience.
for you, amplifies in your
awareness . . . a different
experience of yourself . . .
each trance experience is | Encouraging flexibility and an ability
different . . . in some way . . . | to adapt to familiar yet changing
| circumstances.

each involves a different focal | Emphasizing the variability of trance
point, a different message, a | experience as a metaphor for
different theme . . . | flexibility.

and certainly there's the surface . . . content of what I describe to you . . . and simultaneously, there's a deeper . . . much deeper . . . message to absorb . . . to make use of . . . it's really . . . simply a choice . . . because at any given moment, you get to choose . . . how you distribute your energy . . .

Using his tendency to analyze by encouraging a multilevel view of the hypnosis sessions.
Encouraging learning at deeper levels than even he may be aware of.
Emphasizing he is in an active position, not a reactive one, in these sessions and in life in general.

whether you will attach more . . . or take away from . . . a particular aspect of your experience . . .

Suggesting awareness is not fixed but is negotiable even with himself.

emotional energy, physical energy, spiritual . . .

Identifying different elements of experience and directly suggesting their equal value.

the power of a thought of the trance suggestions . . .

Using his greater value for the cognitive portion of his experience and tying positive value to the hypnosis as a vehicle for better operating on that level.

the ripple through your consciousness . . . of even the most subtle shifts . . . within you . . .

Suggesting that each trance experience presents a chance to learn and grow even further.

so I am really quite aware . . . that each opportunity you have . . . to explore . . . to redefine . . . the different parts of yourself . . . sometimes it isn't until people . . . *have* to explore . . . to redefine . . . the different parts of themselves . . . sometimes it isn't until people . . . have a crisis that they move outside of themselves to discover what matters . . .

Orienting Tim to the notion that sometimes "necessity is the mother of invention," but that one need not wait until one is in crisis to act.

other times, it's the recognition of an opportunity . . . I am very aware . . . that you are exploring . . . and discovering . . .

Seeking good choices to pursue before a crisis brews to force one's hand.

and that you're investing the time and energy . . . in evolving new skills . . . developing parts of yourself that for whatever reason had been underdeveloped . . .

Defining Tim's work as growth-oriented and healthy rather than "curing pathology" to enhance his self-esteem and better motivate him to continue.

a shifting perception of time . . . that has allowed you the wisdom . . . that leads you to recognize every choice . . . has a consequence . . .

Reinforcing Tim's emerging ability to better anticipate consequences and avoid making bad choices he'll regret later. Encouraging Tim to realize he will always be responsible for making the best choices possible in his life, not just while he's in therapy.

and because you're making . . . more sensitive and perceptive choices . . . because you're tuned into sequences . . . knowing what's at the end of the line . . . well before you get there . . . allows you to choose powerfully . . .

Reinforcing Tim's perception (stated earlier in our session) that he is making better choices. Identifying how his increased ability to choose now on the basis of later consequences is a powerful skill.

what you're going to do in order to create a particular outcome . . . what you're not going to do in order to avoid a particular outcome . . .

Consolidating his awareness for thinking more in cause–effect terms, enhancing his impulse control, diminishing low frustration tolerance, increasing optimism and a sense of greater personal control.

and it means thinking . . . farther ahead . . . planning in more detail . . . and just a very simple . . . and practical approach to life . . . learning to do what works . . . being observant about what works . . . and so you continue . . . making good choices . . .

Reinforcing progress and generalizing results into the future as a more stable personal trait of greater future orientation.

what to say . . . what not to say . . . what to do . . . what not to do . . .

Choosing wisely according to desired results.

when to respond to your feelings, when to override them . . . which part of yourself to listen to . . . because you know . . . it has some vision . . .

Redefining his feelings as part of, not all of, his experience of himself and as a controllable part.

having taken the time . . . to learn at a deeper level . . . how much more resourceful . . . how much more capable you are than you might have given yourself credit for . . .

Praising his efforts in his own behalf as evidence of his growth. Building self-esteem and acknowledgment of his skills.

it forces you to redefine yourself . . . in the best of ways . . .

Suggesting directly an upgraded revision of self-image.

and whether you're living in Northern California . . . or Southern . . . New Mexico . . . or someplace else . . . There will always be sequences that work . . . resources within to draw upon . . .	Using Tim's plans to move in the near future while reinforcing that his awareness is in him wherever he goes to live.
and a refined ability . . . to distinguish . . . things that you make up . . . from things that are true . . . so even though you really don't know . . . the precise location of where you're going to be . . .	Reiterating from our sessions the need to better distinguish subjective beliefs from facts.
it can certainly be very comforting and reassuring to know . . . anywhere you go . . . you're taking with you all that you've learned, developed . . . and worked so hard . . . to learn how to use skillfully . . .	Reinforcing that despite uncertainty about where he will be moving to, Tim can be confident he has the skills to live well.
take some time, Tim . . . to process and absorb . . . and then when you're ready, you can bring the experience to a comfortable close . . .	Closure.
and start the process of reorienting gradually . . . so that in a little while when you're ready . . . you can reorient fully and allow your eyes to open . . .	Disengagement.

THERAPEUTIC-RELATIONSHIP ISSUES

It is in neither my theoretical nor my practical framework to consider or label such relationship dynamics as transference or countertransference. Instead, I would describe my therapeutic relationship with Tim in particular and with all my patients in general as collaborative. In virtually all instances, I align myself with the patient's therapeutic goal and strive to transmit the message overtly and covertly that "what you want is fine, now let's talk about how to get what you want." My patients almost invariably want things that I can easily and genuinely support, such as good relationships, satisfying careers, greater personal satisfaction, better self-esteem, and so forth. By aligning myself with the patient's therapeutic goal, it becomes clear to the patient that I am on his or her "side." As a result, we work

94   MICHAEL D. YAPKO

together on the problem, rather than placing me against the patient or the patient against me. In this context, it is generally (not always) inappropriate and unnecessary for us to focus on our feelings about each other. It is far more appropriate to focus on the desired outcomes as defined by the patient's therapeutic goals.

In line with this approach, the emphasis is not on the patient's "pathology." Rather, I believe the patient is simply lacking the necessary skills to do those things he or she wants to be able to do. Tim is a good example of how someone can get depressed and anxious when unable to effectively respond to and manage his or her own thoughts and feelings. When given the appropriate tools, patients can finally succeed (or start to) at whatever they have been trying to accomplish, and their symptoms often readily diminish or disappear. As with Tim, my first reframing of the treatment process is to say, in essence, "it isn't you, it's the way you've gone about it. Change your approach, and you'll get a different result."

OUTCOME

Tim quickly absorbed the deeper messages evident in each of our sessions. He rapidly evolved the skills of shifting focus and using the hypnotic tapes to better manage his anxiety, and he reduced his alcohol intake to nearly zero almost immediately following the first hypnosis session. This result continued throughout the treatment process. In the fifth and final session, Tim presented to me the transcripts he had made on his own initiative of each of our hypnosis sessions. He enthusiastically gave his own analysis of the meaning of the things that I had talked about during the hypnotic processes and the things that he was now able to put together. Tim accepted the notion that the specific skills that he was missing were the cause of his pain and distress. He also appreciated discovering that depression and anxiety were changeable experiences with the use of specific strategies to first acquire then use the necessary skills in his life. Tim became realistically optimistic and started developing longer-term goals for how he was going to accomplish the things that he had always felt too confined within himself to accomplish. Tim described the therapy as an entirely successful and invaluable experience for him.

CONCLUSION

I believe Tim was typical of many depressed patients. Tim was an intelligent, sensitive, articulate man who was so focused on mere survival that it never seemed possible to him that he could evolve the skills that would allow him to transcend mere survival and actually start to enjoy living. My experience has led me to observe repeatedly that depressed individuals are often seriously damaged by the questioning—by self and others—of their motivation to resolve depression. I find that questioning the patient's motivation to succeed is frequently a therapeutic dead end. I rarely question my patients' motivation to improve themselves or the quality of their lives. I do, however, question whether merely knowing what they want is enough. My firm belief is that it is not. I view it as my job to empower the patient by helping him or her evolve the specific skills that are missing and resolve a hurtful situation. I believe this point is represented well in Tim's case. Tim's inability to manage his anxiety and his inability to distinguish between useful, answerable questions to ask himself and those that are unanswerable led him to invest enormous amounts of emotional and intellectual energy in directions that held no potential for resolution. As a result, Tim's escalating anxiety and general dissatisfaction with the lack of apparent meaning in his life colored his perceptions about himself, his relationships, his career, and nearly everything else in his life.

Tim's case also illustrates how relatively unimportant a person's personal history often is in planning and implementing therapy. Despite Tim's background and the chronicity of his problems, Tim was able to rapidly develop the skills necessary to overcome his experiential deficits. Analyzing a patient's history may provide plausible and insightful explanations for the evolution of his or her symptoms, but such a backward focus does little to empower the patient to begin to do things differently. Such "psychological archaeology" may explain symptoms, but it does not teach the patient new possibilities. Milton Erickson once said, "Patients do not come in to change their unchangeable past, they come in to change their futures" (Zeig, 1980). I believe this to be an enormously valuable perspective to maintain, particularly in working with depressed patients. After all, depression is a disorder that typically features a strong preoccupation, usually with the past, but sometimes the present (Yapko, 1988, 1992b). This past orientation exists at the expense of being able to realistically anticipate consequences and plan a longer-term course of action that is more likely to yield success. It is as if the person's past is extended into the future, fueling hopelessness with such internal statements as "I'll never be (happy, successful, whatever) because I never have been." The future looks bleak simply because the past has been.

Tim's case certainly poses a challenge to some of the most common assumptions about depression and its treatment. We may want to reconsider our answers to questions such as What causes depression? Who gets depressed and why? What is the role of exploring and understanding personal history in the process of recovery? I would suggest that the most efficient ways of providing treatment to depressed individuals involve recognizing and correcting through experiential learning the depressogenic patterns that regulate the individual's experience of depression. This is very different from focusing on "issues" in a person's life, especially those originating in childhood.

Tim showed clearly that when patients are provided with new tools that will help them better accomplish what they are trying to accomplish, they will often integrate them readily and adjust to a better quality of life.

I hope and expect that future research on depression will address key questions about the success of those treatments that involve minimal exploration of the past and maximal consideration of the future. Future research on depression can explore the roles of hopefulness and realistic optimism on the rates of recovery and relapse. I also hope that future research will better clarify the relationship among depression, anxiety, and substance abuse such that clinicians can more readily recognize when substance abuse is merely a coping mechanism for an associated depression or anxiety that should be the central focus of treatment.

REFERENCES

Akiskal, H. (1985). The challenge of chronic depressions. In A. Dean (Ed.), *Depression in multidisciplinary perspective* (pp. 105–117). New York: Brunner/Mazel.

Antonuccio, D., Danton, W., & DeNelsky, G. (1994). Psychotherapy for depression: No stronger medicine. *Scientist Practitioner, 4*, (1), 2–18.

Antonuccio, D., Danton, W., & DeNelsky, G. (1995). Psychotherapy versus medication for depression: Challenging the conventional wisdom with data. *Professional Psychology: Research and Practice, 26*(6) 574–585.

Beck, A. (1967). *Depression: Causes and treatment.* Philadelphia: University of Pennsylvania Press.

Beck. A. (1973). *The diagnosis and management of depression.* Philadelphia: University of Pennsylvania Press.

deShazer, S. (1991). *Putting difference to work.* New York: Norton.

Fisch, R., Weakland, J., & Segal, L. (1983). *The tactics of change: Doing therapy briefly.* San Francisco: Jossey-Bass.

Gilligan, S. (1987). *Therapeutic trances: The cooperation principle in Ericksonian hypnotherapy.* New York: Brunner/Mazel.

Gilligan, S. (1988). Symptom phenomena as trance phenomena. In J. Zeig & S. Lankton (Eds.), *Developing Ericksonian therapy* (pp. 327–352). New York: Brunner/Mazel.

McGrath, E., Keita, G., Strickland, B., & Russo, N. (Eds.). (1990). *Women and depression: Risk factors and treatment issues.* Washington, DC: American Psychological Association.

Schwartz, A., & Schwartz, R. (1993). *Depression: Theories and treatments.* New York: Columbia University Press.

Seligman, M. (1990). *Learned optimism*. New York: Knopf.

Yapko, M. (1988). *When living hurts: Directives for treating depression*. New York: Brunner/Mazel.

Yapko, M. (Ed.). (1989). *Brief therapy approaches to treating anxiety and depression*. New York: Brunner/Mazel.

Yapko, M. (1990). *Trancework: An introduction to the practice of clinical hypnosis* (2nd ed.). New York: Brunner/Mazel.

Yapko, M. (1991, May/June). A therapy of hope. *Family Therapy Networker, 15*(3), 34–39.

Yapko, M. (1992a). *Free yourself from depression*. Emmaus, PA: Rodale Press.

Yapko, M. (1992b). Hypnosis and the treatment of depressions. New York: Brunner/Mazel.

Zeig, J. (Ed.). (1980). A teaching seminar with Milton H. Erickson. New York: Brunner/Mazel.

5

HYPNOSIS IN THE TREATMENT OF POSTTRAUMATIC STRESS DISORDER

DAVID SPIEGEL

It is no accident that interest in hypnosis revives in wartime. There is substantial overlap between the phenomena of hypnosis and those observed in individuals who suffer from posttraumatic stress disorder (PTSD). Indeed, there is growing evidence that trauma elicits dissociation (Cardeña & Spiegel, 1993; Spiegel & Cardeña, 1991) and that those who do dissociate are at higher risk for developing later PTSD (Koopman, Classen, & Spiegel, 1994; Marmar et al., 1994)

Trauma can be understood as the experience of one's being made into an object, a thing—the victim of someone else's rage or nature's indifference. It is a situation in which one entirely loses control of one's body for a period of time, and the theme of helplessness is a critical one in the psychotherapy of trauma victims.

PTSD involves three major classes of symptoms: intrusive symptoms, such as flashbacks, nightmares, and unbidden preoccupation with memories of the traumatic event; numbing, including loss of pleasure in usually pleasurable activities; and hyperarousal, an exaggerated psychological and somatic response to stimuli reminiscent of the trauma (e.g., a young woman who was raped in an elevator breaking into a cold sweat whenever she enters an elevator). Interestingly, there is an analogy between these three major components of PTSD symptoms and the three major components of hypnosis: absorption, dissociation, and suggestibility (Spiegel, 1994). Absorption (Tellegen, 1981; Tellegen & Atkinson, 1974) is a total and self-altering immersion in a central experience at the expense of peripheral awareness. Individuals who are more highly hypnotizable spontaneously have more absorbing experiences (Tellegen & Atkinson, 1974). Intense absorption in a central experience deprives it of its context. If such absorption is applied to memory of a traumatic event, it leads to reliving rather than remembering the event, with all of the ongoing uncertainty about the outcome that occurred at the time. Similarly, the numbing and avoidance typical of PTSD are reminiscent of hypnotic dissociation. Even though information in hypnosis is kept out of awareness, it still may affect consciousness. A rape victim who has no conscious recollection of the facts of the rape itself still feels demeaned and unable to joyfully engage in sexual activity with an appropriate partner.

The hyperarousal state of PTSD is reminiscent of suggestibility in hypnosis—in essence, a heightened responsiveness to cues. The empty elevator is imbued with the same sense of threat, now imagined rather than real, that the one that contained the rapist had.

Many trauma victims report entering dissociative or hypnotic-like states during trauma. For example, victims of hostage taking situations report feeling detached from their own bodies, observing with a kind of casual disinterest the suffering their bodies are going through (MacFarlane, 1986; Noyes and Slymen, 1978–1979; Sloan, 1988). Thus, it makes sense that hypnosis may be especially useful in accessing and altering these trauma-related states.

What follows is a case description of the use of hypnosis in the psychotherapy of a young woman with PTSD. Nancy came in for treatment at the age of 31 complaining of crying spells, depression, social withdrawal, and inability to form a stable, long-term relationship with a man. In addition, she had occasional suicidal ideation, although no specific plan or method had developed and she had made no suicide attempts. She reported having been somewhat rootless for the past 5 or 6 years, working part time as a waitress and part time in retail sales. From the age of 15 to 25, she had a period of moderate to severe drug and alcohol abuse. She had had a series of brief relationships with men, the longest lasting 3 months. She noted that she quickly came to feel exploited by men.

She reported that her earlier life was marred by sexual abuse from her maternal grandfather. She was uncertain when it began, but had memories of sitting on his lap and having him penetrate her with his finger. She also recalled times when her mother was away that he would force her to hold his penis. She reported that there was never any intercourse. This had gone on for a number of years prior to adolescence. At the age of 12 or 13, she finally told her mother about it. She reports that her mother told her to tell the grandfather to stop, which she said she did, but he became cool and distant and less supportive of the family as a whole. She described him as a prominent man with many intellectual pursuits and someone who most people would consider highly unlikely to abuse his granddaughter.

There was substantial alcoholism in her family. Both parents suffered from the disorder. Her father, an engineer, continued to drink. Her mother had stopped drinking. Her parents divorced when she was 5 years old. She currently reports being extremely close to her mother, and she seemed to continue to fluctuate between being in an abusive relationship with men and clinging to her mother. She denied amnestic episodes or other dissociative symptoms but ruminated about her relationship with her grandfather and had a general feeling of guilt. She found herself avoiding relationships with men or feeling exploited when she was in them and was very ambivalent about sexual contact. She was especially sensitive to having her privacy and her body invaded by a man, overtly fearing abandonment but covertly responding to sexual advances as if the man's interest were for his satisfaction rather than hers.

MENTAL STATUS EXAMINATION

Nancy presented as a casually dressed attractive woman, looking younger than her stated age. Her speech was fluent. There was no looseness of associations. There was evidence of depression, but the sadness was congruent with the content and there was range to her affect. She denied anxiety and phobic symptoms but admitted to occasional suicidal ideation. There was no evidence of delusions, and she was oriented to time, place, and person. The initial diagnosis was PTSD and dysthymic disorder.

She had had one prior episode of psychotherapy for 8 months with a clergyman counselor. She said he spent a good deal of time talking about himself rather than her and that she had gotten little benefit from it. She was open to the idea of psychotherapy.

She was tested with the Hypnotic Induction Profile (Spiegel & Spiegel, 1978/1987) and scored 9 of the possible 10 points, indicating high hypnotizability.

CONCEPTUALIZATION OF THE PROBLEM

Nancy came to feel that she had lost control of her life, drifting from relationship to relationship, avoiding intimacy, wanting sexual contact but feeling exploited by it, and immersing herself for a period of time in drugs and alcohol. Even having been off of substances for 6 years, however, she felt uncertain about her life's direction.

Nancy felt in particular that her development had been seriously contaminated by the sexual abuse inflicted on her by her grandfather. She talked tearfully about how she felt that he had robbed her of her own control of developing her sexuality and of her innocence. As she expressed these ideas in the therapy and started to experience anger, however, she wound up being angry at herself, blaming herself for, in essence, allowing herself as a child to be victimized by this adult. She felt that in some ways she still was a child, not having wanted to grow up. To her, growing up would mean embracing what her grandfather was doing to her, becoming like him in some way.

She saw this contamination as seriously impairing her ability to establish a loving relationship with a man. She initially talked about how unhappy she was that she was some 10 lb overweight. Although she had some problems in her eating behavior, the main issue for her was her fear of becoming too close and involved with a man, fearful of having her privacy and her body invaded. She recalled how one potentially promising relationship with a man had ended because he had tried to "get a rise out of her," and she refused to get angry and withdrew from him. Allowing herself to be angry at this man and, more important, at her grandfather would amount to an admission of how vulnerable she was: how much her new friend could hurt her and how much her grandfather had hurt her. Thus, she felt that her life continued to be contaminated by memories of and the aftereffects of this sexual abuse. She thus had the intrusive and persistent recollections of the trauma, loss of pleasure in usually pleasurable activities, and excessive sensitivity to stimuli reminiscent of the original sexual abuse typical of individuals with PTSD.

TREATMENT

I used hypnosis as a means of acknowledging, bearing, and putting into perspective these traumatic memories (Spiegel & Cardeña, 1990). Hypnosis could facilitate immediate access to traumatic memories and a context for restructuring them in such a way that Nancy could face the content of the memories but emerge with a different point of view about the roles she and her grandfather had played in the abuse. Through hypnosis I wanted to show her a means of controlling the appearance as well as the impact of these memories. Rather than feeling victimized by the intrusion of the memories, as she had by her grandfather himself, she could take control of them. She could choose to bring them on in hypnosis and by inference choose to put them aside at other times. Thus, the hypnosis was a means of accessing and working through traumatic memories while teaching her to enhance her sense of control over them.

She was taught a simple self-hypnosis induction:

> There are many ways to enter a state of self-hypnosis. One simple way is to the following. On one, do one thing; look up. On two, two

things; slowly close your eyes and take a deep breath. And on three, three things; breath out, eyes relaxed, but keep them closed, and let your body float. Then imagine one hand or the other floating up into the air like a balloon and that is your signal to yourself and to me that you are ready to concentrate.

Waiting until her hand floated into the air, I gave her the following instruction:

Feel your body floating somewhere safe and comfortable. It might be a bath, a lake, a hot tub, or just imagine floating in space, each breath deeper and easier. Enjoy this pleasant sense of floating.

After a pause for her to experience this, I said the following:

Notice how you can use your store of memories and fantasies to help yourself and your body feel better. Now picture in your mind an imaginary screen. It could be a movie screen, a TV screen, or a piece of clear blue sky. Picture on the screen a pleasant scene, somewhere you enjoy being. Again notice how you can use your store of memories and fantasies to help yourself and your body feel better. Now we are going to try something different. We are going to picture some memories related to the abuse by your grandfather on this imaginary screen, but with this rule: Do your thinking and feeling out there on the screen and leave your body out of it. Keep your body floating here safe and comfortable while you picture those memories on the screen.

I asked Nancy to picture on the left side of the screen a moment when her grandfather was abusing her. She began to twitch, and I said, "Are you losing that floating of your body?" She responded, "Yes." So, I said, "All right, freeze what is happening on the screen and reestablish the sense of floating," which she did. After several tries, she was able to picture her grandfather on the screen but keep her body floating comfortably.

This is important, in that it enables the subject to use hypnotic dissociation to separate somatic from psychological response. We then went back to this image of her grandfather on the screen. She talked about feeling guilty, and I asked her what she felt guilty about. She said that she realized for the first time that part of what she felt guilty about was that she had experienced some physically pleasurable sensations during the abuse. She had felt in her heart that it was wrong but had in some ways enjoyed it and had not been able to admit this to herself. I told her that this was perfectly normal, that part of her body was built to experience pleasure, and she was experiencing it even though she knew it was wrong. This did not mean that she had invited or wanted it, but rather that her body was responding to what her grandfather was doing.

I also had her take a hard look at her image of her grandfather in the act of abusing her. She could see him as having an almost malicious look on his face that indicated he did not care about her. As she looked at him, she thought of herself wanting to get it over with but deluding herself into believing that he really cared about her. At this point she had an image of how he lost interest in her when she was finally able to stop the abuse at age 13. She had an image then of the promising innocent child she felt she had been and how different she felt, guilty and critical of herself—a view of herself that continued to impair her life. I had her picture herself as the innocent child on the right side of the screen and picture what her grandfather did to her on the left side.

She emerged from this state of self-hypnosis saying "I feel clear." She elaborated on this, commenting that she felt the self-hypnosis was clarifying her feelings about herself and that she would feel less like a victim now because she had admitted more of her victimization in the past. She also thought the process would allow her to feel less conflicted about her sexuality and developing relationships.

In the 2 weeks after that session she said she had felt much better. She pursued a discussion of her relationships with men and recognized that she tended to treat them as though they were her grandfather and that this, consequently, prevented her from feeling good about anything that might happen. She would feel guilty instead. Nancy also noted that she expected rejection. She started dating a man who she felt she could really like. Her anxiety about this and other relationships had involved not just a sense of her being exploited, but also a sense that, if a man really got to know her, he would be repelled by her. Nancy related this, in part, to the rejection by her grandfather after she stopped the abuse. The idea that what she did with men mirrored this deep sense of guilt and ambivalence in relationship to her grandfather was novel to her. In the transference, she was using the relationship with me to see if she could feel better about herself and cared about without being abused. Her depression was decreasing at this time.

Nancy continued to feel that she was taking more charge of her life, both at work and personally. Her relationship with a man was developing, but she did not feel physically attracted to him, and she noted that she really could not feel deeply emotionally and physically about the same man. In some ways, she preferred sexual relationships that were more overtly exploitative to those in which she felt that she was taking the risk of wanting to be cared about. She had other ongoing problems, moreover, including her father's return to active drinking, which were followed by an increase in her depression. She recalled that her grandfather, who had previously favored her during the time that he was abusing her, rejected her and referred to her as "fat," and that he had ostentatiously begun to favor her cousins, which she found deeply hurtful, the more so in the light of her parent's divorce and her father's alcoholism. We used hypnosis at this stage to have her picture on the one hand what her grandfather did to her and on the other hand her strength in ultimately rejecting his sexual advances when she became old enough to do so.

Three months into the therapy, she reported doing better but had had a recurrence of depression and was feeling isolated and unhappy. She continued to fear intimacy, noting that relationships seemed to become more superficial rather than deeper when they became sexual and that she usually ended them feeling exploited.

Because of the recurrence of her depression at this time, which included some difficulty falling asleep and awakening once a night, although there was little energy loss or appetite suppression, she was started on fluoxetine, 20 mg a day. Her depressive symptoms improved.

At this time she also began talking about transference-related issues. She said it meant a great deal to her to feel that I cared about her. She felt like a rather small part of my life and said that it was embarrassing for her to talk about these things. She discussed how she had learned to divorce her mind from her body during the incest with her grandfather and that she repetitively acted out this means of relating in other relationships. She found it threatening and difficult to be both sexually and mentally intimate. In the therapy she found herself able to talk about sexual issues and feel cared about at the same time, something she had not experienced before. We continued to use self-hypnosis to picture episodes of abuse, focusing on one side of the screen on a clearer image of her grandfather and what he was doing to her and on the other side what she was doing to protect herself from him, either by detaching herself from what he was imposing on her or eventually by stopping the abuse even at the price of losing his preferential attention. The split-screen technique was continued in order to help her to work through feelings regarding the effects of sexual abuse by her grandfather. This involved facing the damage done on one side of the screen and experiencing the affect associated with this recognition, while giving herself credit for her efforts to protect herself. In this way she could learn to face the trauma while dissociating herself from it, seeing that it happened but that she in no way desired or deserved it.

As she did this, she talked about how difficult she felt it was to look me in the eye, fearing rejection. She expected that if she started to make herself vulnerable, she would ultimately be left. She then went on to talk about the fact that at some point she would get better and I would stop seeing her. However, she was surprised to conceptualize the separation as her leaving me rather than my leaving her. Thus, she found a more positive way of experiencing what might happen.

Four months after the therapy had begun, she reported feeling substantially better about herself. She attributed this to her working through memories involving her grandfather's sexual abuse and coming to see the abuse in terms of the damage he had done to her and that what was wrong had more to do with him than it did with her. She realized that she had initially tried to put the abuse aside, and it had wound up severely damaging her life. It had impaired her ability to form stable long-term relationships and experience any satisfactory sexual relationship with a man, and it had also resulted in her working at jobs that were far beneath her real ability. She was finding more appropriate employment, allowing herself to enjoy hobbies more than she had in the past, and heading in the direction of a more stable and deeper relationship with a man. She reported that she found the psychotherapy helpful in that she could be open with me in the therapy and yet feel accepted rather than rejected. When her true feeling about the abuse emerged with her grandfather, he rejected her and she found it very helpful that those feelings could be expressed and yet lead to a deeper sense of acceptance, rather than rejection.

She also noted that she was better able to set limits with her father, who continued to drink. She came to see him as someone who had let her down, rather than her feeling that she had let him down. She also found herself being more independent from her mother, with whom she was rather enmeshed.

She continued to have more energy, be less depressed, and enjoy more in her life. In her new relationship with a man, she let him know that she cared about him, which was difficult, but put off the usually rapid development of the sexual relationship, telling him that she wanted to be able to trust and care about him more before she allowed that to be part of the relationship. This is the opposite of how she would normally have developed a relationship, usually giving men "what they wanted" and then breaking off the relationship, in essence reducing it to sexual exploitation. She reported thinking, "Even if I lose him over this, I won't feel bad, because I feel so good that I can put the relationship on my own terms." Her sleep had improved, and she had lost some weight, which she had wanted to do. She also told her father for the first time about the molestation by her maternal grandfather. She said that at first he was quite angry at the grandfather, but he was also supportive of her. He said it helped him to understand better why she had been so depressed. She said that her mother told her that she had noticed a more genuine smile than she had seen on her face in years. She continued on fluoxetine, at 20 mg per day.

As her relationship deepened with her new boyfriend, she found herself sad as she became more intimate with him and then resenting what had been done to her by her grandfather. She reported feeling sad that her boyfriend could "not have all of her" because of the damage that had been done.

She reiterated that she found the therapy extremely helpful and she was much happier and felt better than she had in many years. She noted that she had become more shy about her sexuality, reminiscent of that innocent childlike self that she felt was a much healthier and happier part of herself than she had experienced in many years.

By the eighth month of therapy Nancy reported that she was doing quite well: feeling more secure, doing things she enjoyed, and getting positive responses from friends and family. She had sustained the longest relationship she had ever had with a boyfriend. Although she was not certain it was going to work out, she felt far less desperate about whether or not it did and she enjoyed being with him. She said that having worked through her feelings about what her grandfather did to her, she felt she was beginning to develop the way she should have more than a decade earlier. On a recent date her boyfriend said that she seemed like a "giddy 16 year old." Her reaction was, "How did you know?" She was able to detach herself more from her father's drinking as well. She said that she wanted to continue psychotherapy on a monthly basis.

Ten months after the therapy had begun, Nancy developed some symptoms of anxiety. We did a self-hypnosis exercise in which she imagined her body floating comfortably and pictured problems on an imaginary screen. She pictured loneliness on one side and things she is doing to enjoy the time she has to herself on the other. She was able to reduce the anxiety from 7 on a 10-point scale to 1 after the self-hypnosis and was instructed to continue using it.

Although much improved, Nancy remained sufficiently focused on herself and wanting to be in control. She did not adequately scan the environment and get to know people as they were. She noted that with men, she often just let herself go—"jumped in with both feet," as she described it. She had ended her relationship with her boyfriend but said she did not feel bad about it. However, she thought she still was selecting men who were not likely to help her develop a really intimate relationship. She expressed concern that when things started to get serious, men fled, but it may have had to do in part with choosing the wrong men. Nonetheless, she felt that her involvements were far more appropriate than they had been a year earlier. She talked about the transference issue of feeling that when she trusted someone, she wanted to be able to trust them completely (discussing her feelings about me and her brother). I pointed out to her that the absence of any anxiety that I might in some way mistreat her was odd, given her history of abuse. She reflected that she had an excessively high standard of what it is to love someone, feeling you should never be hurt by them and that you can trust them absolutely. This seemed to lead her into relationships with people who mistreated her. She was defining intimacy as the opposite of what her grandfather did. She lets down her guard and thinks it must be love because she can trust a person completely, and then at some point she feels hurt. We talked in therapy about her need to abandon her extremes of complete distrust and complete trust.

Nancy went on to admit that she had been seduced at the age of 21 by an uncle. She felt that this was someone she had admired and trusted. He tried to talk her into a long-term affair, which she refused. What became clear is that she had a blind spot created by her fantasy about what a real loving and trusting relationship is like. By trusting too much in the hope of an "ideal" love, she allowed men to exploit her. Alternatively, feeling mistrust seemed to her the end of a relationship rather than a necessary and self-protective part of developing a relationship. She had a relationship with a new boyfriend, which was time-limited because he was planning to leave the country in several months, but she said she felt that they were developing it gradually and more appropriately.

Toward the end of the first year of therapy, Nancy talked about three main concerns: being able to have a child, wanting to find a man with whom she could become deeply involved, and feeling disappointed by her father's continued drinking. By the end of the first year, she was doing better, enjoying her social life and able to become sexually involved without feeling sexually exploited. She felt that she had worked through the issue of the abuse by her grandfather. She was less preoccupied with it and felt it had less of a damaging effect on her relationships. She continued on the fluoxetine and discontinued regular psychotherapy.

At follow-up 3 years after the therapy began, she reported doing quite well. She continued to work but had undertaken a small business, had had two reasonably solid relationships with men, and said she felt far more comfortable being in intimate relationships, although she had not yet found the right man to marry and have children with. She felt that her life was going quite well. She felt that the fluoxetine had helped her and continued on it. Although it is not possible to completely disentangle the effects of the psychotherapy and pharmacotherapy, it is noteworthy that her improvement began in the first 3 months, prior to the use of a selective seratonin reuptake inhibitor. She reflected that the psychotherapy, especially in dealing with her grandfather's sexual abuse, was quite helpful. The changes she made in managing relationships, her sexuality, and self-image and the reduction in PTSD symptoms are attributed by her to the psychotherapy; the fluoxetine was clearly helpful with her chronic dysthymia. She felt that the abuse had still inflicted considerable damage on her life and that her being single at this point in her life was, in good measure, related to it. But, she said, she was not so much blaming him as relieving herself of a sense of personal defect.

CONCLUSION

This woman, suffering from PTSD and dysthymia, underwent a year of psychotherapy, first at weekly and then at monthly intervals, followed by

2 years of intermittent contact. In psychotherapy I used hypnosis more intensively at the beginning to help Nancy access and work through memories related to sexual abuse by her grandfather. She found the hypnosis helpful in gaining control over these memories, in part by allowing her to control their entry into her consciousness and also see the situation from a different point of view, focusing not so much on her own defect but on her grandfather's exploitativeness. She was able to tolerate and acknowledge not only the anger and disappointment at her grandfather (and implicitly at her parents for allowing this to happen) but also her ambivalence, her desire for special attention, her experience of some sensual pleasure, and her guilt about it. One of the major kinds of damage inflicted on children who are sexually abused is their limited capacity to understand external causation. They tend to blame themselves inappropriately for events over which they have little or no control. She, thus, experienced her grandfather's abuse as her trading his access to her body for special attention. The more damaged she felt by this, the more she needed the attention and the more she felt that it was an appropriate judgment on her that he ultimately rejected her. Thus, her initial adaptive response, ultimately rejecting him, led to a situation in which she felt judged and humiliated. This became a pattern of considerable influence on her subsequent ability to develop relationships, complicated by the absence of her alcoholic father, which reduced opportunities for a corrective developmental experience. She entered into a series of fleeting relationships with inappropriate men, giving them "what they wanted" and then feeling exploited. The therapy coupled with hypnosis enabled her to acknowledge and bear these feelings and work through her memories, picturing and accepting what her grandfather had done to her, the damage he had inflicted on her, and at the same time blaming him more and herself less and acknowledging her adaptive reactions to this abuse and the damage that he had done to her.

Furthermore, in the transference Nancy was able to experience feeling cared about, while admitting events about which she felt deeply ashamed. She is gradually coming to feel worthy of being cared about because the relationship in the therapy deepened rather than ended when she acknowledged her anger and disappointment at the sexual abuse. The hypnosis, in particular, helped her to focus on, and become clearer about, the damaging impact of the abuse and at the same time see how it had damaged part of her but had not contaminated all of her. It helped her to see that there was a part of her that always had and continued to reject that exploitation. Furthermore, it helped to convince her that she did not deserve what had happened to her, that she had suffered considerably, but not deservedly, as a result of the abuse. As she did this, the intrusion, avoidance, and hyperarousal symptoms receded, as did her dysthymia.

In this case the hypnosis became a focus for eliciting and working through the traumatic memories, as well as a starting point for the discussion of the issues related to Nancy's intimate relationships, the transference, her relationships with her family, and her choices regarding work and other activities in her life. In this sense the hypnosis was a facilitator of treatment, especially useful because she was highly hypnotizable and because many of her PTSD symptoms were undisciplined and uncontrolled intrusions of dissociative and hypnoticlike phenomena. The hypnosis provided a framework for eliciting, controlling, and working through the aftermath of this sexual abuse.

REFERENCES

Cardeña, E., & Spiegel, D. (1993). Dissociative reactions to the Bay Area earthquake. *American Journal of Psychiatry, 150*(3), 474–478.

Koopman, C., Classen, C., & Spiegel, D. (1994). Predictors of posttraumatic stress symptoms among Oakland/Berkeley firestorm survivors. *American Journal of Psychiatry, 151*(6), 888–894.

MacFarlane, A. C. (1986). Post traumatic morbidity of a disaster. *Journal of Nervous and Mental Disease, 174*(1), 4–14.

Marmar, C. R., Weiss, D. S., Schlenger, W. E., Fairbank, J. A., Jordan, B. K., Kulka, R. A., & Hough, R. L. (1994). Peritraumatic dissociation and posttraumatic stress in male Vietnam theater veterans. *American Journal of Psychiatry, 151*, 902–907.

Noyes, R., & Slymen, D. J. (1978–1979). The subjective response to life-threatening danger. *Omega, 9*, 313–321.

Sloan, P. (1988). Post traumatic stress in survivors of an airplane crash landing: A clinical and exploratory research intervention. *Journal of Traumatic Stress, 1*(2), 211–229.

Spiegel, D. (1994). Hypnosis. In R. E. Hales, S. C. Yudofsky, & J. A. Talbolt (Eds.), *The American Psychiatric Press textbook of psychiatry* (pp. 1115–1142). Washington, DC: American Psychiatric Press.

Spiegel, D., & Cardeña, E. (1990). New uses of hypnosis in the treatment of posttraumatic stress disorder. *Journal of Clinical Psychiatry, 51*, 10, 39–43, 44–46.

Spiegel, D., & Cardeña, E. (1991). Disintegrated experience: The dissociative disorders revisited. *Journal of Abnormal Psychology, 100*, 366–378.

Spiegel, H., & Spiegel, D. (1987). *Trance and treatment: Clinical uses of hypnosis.* Washington, DC: American Psychiatric Press. (Original work published 1978)

Tellegen, A. (1981). Practicing the two disciplines for relaxation and enlightenment: Comment on "Role of the Feedback Signal in Electromyograph Biofeedback: The Relevance of Attention," by Qualls and Sheehan. *Journal of Experimental Psychology, General, 110,* 217–226.

Tellegen, A., & Atkinson, G. (1974). Openness to absorbing and self-altering experiences ("absorption"), a trait related to hypnotic susceptibility. *Journal of Abnormal Psychology, 83,* 268–277.

6

WHEN ALL ELSE FAILS: HYPNOTIC EXPLORATION OF CHILDHOOD TRAUMA

WILLIAM H. SMITH

There is little controversy about the profound and long-lasting effects of childhood sexual abuse. The symptomatic consequences seen later in adulthood may include amnesias, physical disorders, sleep disturbance, sexual dysfunction, mood and appetite disorders, low self-esteem, self-mutilation, guilt and shame, and difficulty trusting others (Davies & Frawley, 1994). In addition, abuse victims may have a pattern in adulthood of unstable relationships and may be at significant risk for repeated victimization by others (Herman, 1992). There is also little controversy about the widespread prevalence of childhood sexual abuse. As many as one third of all women are sexually abused in some manner before they are 18 years old (Finkelhor, 1984; Russell, 1986). What has become controversial is whether children subjected to traumatic experiences can become amnestic about the trauma and later recover the memories reasonably accurately through triggering life events, a therapy process, or hypnotically enhanced recall (Briere & Conte, 1993; Herman & Schatzow, 1987; Loftus, 1993; Terr, 1994).

The recovery of repressed or dissociated memories is considered by some to play a vital role in overcoming the sequelae of early life trauma (e.g., Courtois, 1992). Others caution that memory is so vulnerable to distortion, especially memory that has been elicited in a treatment context, that enormous harm can be done when such memories falsely identify an alleged perpetrator of abuse (e.g., Loftus, 1993).

In the midst of such controversy, it is important to avoid polarization. Clinicians must heed relevant laboratory research about the nature and vulnerability of memory, and researchers must respect the plight of clinicians who daily face suffering patients and need ways of providing help. Investigations must proceed in both areas to better shape psychotherapists' understanding of this complex phenomenon. This clinical case study is offered as a contribution to the debate about whether, when, and how hypnosis may be used in exploring the possibility of unremembered childhood trauma, consistent with the recommendations of Lynn and Nash (1994) that psychotherapists "use hypnosis with caution and . . . carefully evaluate not only our clients but our clinical practice as well" (p. 205).

BACKGROUND INFORMATION

Cindy was a 35-year-old, White, married nurse whose husband was a radiologist. They had two sons, ages 6 and 10, and resided in the southwestern United States. She had stopped working outside the home after the birth of the first child and tried hard to devote herself to being a perfect wife and mother. She knew she was a compulsive person whose needs for cleanliness and order were excessive, and she tried not to make unrealistic demands for neatness on her children. She was extremely sensitive to criticism and felt that her husband's parents were disappointed in her performance as a homemaker. The marriage was generally good, though she had little enthusiasm for sexual intercourse.

For a little over a year prior to her admission to a private psychiatric hospital, she had become increasingly unhappy with her life. Her compulsive behaviors, such as washing dishes several times and remaking the beds, increased. The husband's affiliation with a new medical group had been stressful, and Cindy experienced any family problems as somehow being her fault. Some vulgar comments made by one of her husband's partners troubled her enormously, and she began to feel that her husband was somehow becoming "contaminated," less respectable, and even less clean through his association with the partner. Sexual relations became aversive, and she became withdrawn and clearly depressed. Cindy lost weight, had difficulty sleeping, and cried for no apparent reason.

The psychotherapy Cindy began felt promising at first but was difficult for her. She was not used to expressing her feelings and was reluctant to complain about her life, past or present. She was prescribed medication, but the depression worsened nonetheless. When she disclosed a suicide plan, hospitalization was arranged. She intended to crash her car into a tree, hoping for a fiery explosion that would "eradicate every shred" of her body.

DEVELOPMENTAL CONSIDERATIONS

Cindy was the youngest of two children born to a now-retired chemist and his homemaker wife. She had a brother who was 12 years older, and she always thought she was unplanned and unwanted. Adding to her feeling of insecurity was the inordinate amount of parental attention required by her brother because of his chronic physical illness. She tried hard to be perfect to satisfy her parents' high expectations. Their strict approach to child rearing was supported by their fundamentalist religion. Cindy learned to be quiet, polite, scrupulously clean, and diligent in school. Strong emotions were not to be expressed, unruly behavior was out of the question, and sexuality was never discussed.

Dating was forbidden throughout high school. Cindy's introduction to intercourse was a brutal, painful rape in her co-ed dormitory during her first year at college. She never spoke about it to anyone. Years later, she passively acquiesced to intercourse with a very gentle and considerate boy she had been dating. Unaware of contraceptive measures, she became pregnant and had an abortion. This distressing experience, too, went unspoken.

After graduation from nursing school, she met her future husband, a medical student at the hospital where they both worked, and married him after a 6-month courtship. They shared the same religion and both wanted children. Until depression incapacitated her, their lives together had been satisfying and comfortable. Their income provided a nice home and other economic advantages, such as a private school for their boys.

INPATIENT ASSESSMENT

At the time of admission, Cindy was entirely cooperative with the examination process. She was eager to get help. Her physical examination and laboratory findings were all within normal limits, although she was noted to be rather thin (116 lb at 5'4"). Her mental examination was also unremarkable, except for some vagueness in describing the traumatic sexual events. Indeed, she had not remembered the rape and the abortion for many years until she began the outpatient psychotherapy and even then had blurred the two events. She thought the rape had impregnated her and led to the abortion but on careful reflection realized that the events were 2 years apart. Cindy's range of affect was narrow; guilt for what she regarded as her many shortcomings was her most prominent emotion.

Intelligence and personality testing (Wechsler Adult Intelligence Scale-Revised [WAIS-R] and Rorschach) administered by a staff psychologist soon after her admission found her to be bright, articulate, and psychologically minded. The intensity of her emotional experience was described in the test report as "striking," sometimes requiring detachment as a defense. When emotionally stirred, her reality testing could become quite unreliable, and her perceptions became colored by distortions. Quoting the test report: "She experiences herself as depleted and deficient, as one who lacks the resources it would take to move forward in life. Her sense of inadequacy and vulnerability is pervasive, and she sees little hope for her future. Indeed, she readily stated that she is more likely than not to kill herself at some point." The report continued, "Her ability to accurately perceive and empathize with the experience of others is currently limited, and she may all too easily see others as rejecting or criticizing her, thereby confirming her negative view of herself."

Significant behavioral observations by hospital staff included that Cindy was quick to feel criticized and at such times plunged into suicidal despair, often ruminated about the past, and was intolerant of her roommate's messiness. On several occasions, the patient was noted to be so withdrawn as to be unresponsive to verbal stimuli.

CONCEPTUALIZATION OF THE PROBLEM

Cindy was clearly suffering from a serious depression, but what was its source? From a developmental perspective, she had grown up with an exaggerated sense of duty and responsibility, predisposing her to feeling that whatever she did was not good enough. What she perceived as her parents' high expectations and lack of nurturance led to her sense of inferiority and fear of criticism. Rigidity of moral beliefs fostered the intolerance she felt for any misdeeds and even slight deviations from perfection. Her lack of friends deprived her of the moderating influence of other, more lenient attitudes toward life and of the reassurance that she was likeable and normal. Thus, her upbringing had an influence on her characterological development and its predisposing influence toward depression. But what about more contemporary factors?

Cindy had subordinated her career interests to play a supportive role for her husband and children. She accepted no household help, even though the couple could have easily afforded it, and preferred to do all the cooking and cleaning herself. Expressing frustration and dissatisfaction, let alone provoking conflict in her marriage, was strongly contrary to her values. She only epxressed anger comfortably against herself. She felt any unhappiness was her fault and any lack of perfection in carrying out her responsibilities was evidence of her ultimate failure as a person.

But what of the sexual trauma? The rape in the college dorm surely consolidated her sense that sexuality was evil and dangerous. Feeling that she must have caused the assault only added to her conviction that she was basically worthless, as did the later pregnancy and abortion. Within her marriage, sexual activity became acceptable to her but seldom pleasurable. Sexual innuendo by her husband's partner in medical practice kindled strong feelings of disgust and shame, feelings that were projected onto the husband so that he seemed "contaminated."

In a preadmission questionnaire, Cindy included in her statement about her concerns to be addressed in treatment: "Not wanting to share with Ted his work, whether it be getting together with his partners, visiting the hospital and department he works in, or discussing procedures he does, especially OB/GYN (e.g., endovaginal ultrasound). I become very nauseated and want to get further away from Ted when I have these feelings. This is a big problem (for me and him) and is *very much* related to my wanting to commit suicide."

Before referring the patient for inpatient care, Cindy's psychiatrist had wondered about earlier sexual trauma in her life on the basis of some dream material she had shared and the puzzling severity of her symptoms. He discussed with her the possibility of hypnosis, but she refused any such exploration. As badly as she already felt about herself, how could she tolerate learning anything more?

TREATMENT

Weeks went by with no improvement in Cindy's condition. At the time she was being transferred to a longer-term unit, the new treatment team recalled the referring psychiatrist's suspicion of childhood sexual trauma. Because she had no memories of abuse, such a possibility had not received attention. In light of Cindy's failure to improve, the idea of hypnosis was revisited. This time she was willing. She would do anything to get help.

As a 14-session psychotherapy incorporating hypnosis began, Cindy was curious about what might be learned about her past. She had now differentiated between the two memories that had reemerged into consciousness—the college rape and the abortion. An intelligent and increasingly psychologically minded woman, she had begun to grasp what impact those experiences might have had on her subsequent fear and guilt about sexuality. She also was struck by how detached she had become during both events, removing herself from the terror of the moment and later acting as if nothing had happened. She understood how recovering other memories from the past might help her understand and gain control over her symptoms and how connecting the appropriate emotions to the memories could help her deal with the meaning of what happened. Aside from using hypnosis to help her master the traumatic experiences, Cindy might enhance her capacity for experiencing a normal range of emotion by allowing herself to have natural feelings in a context of safety.

I warned the patient and the treatment team of the possibility of memories emerging in hypnosis that are distorted or inauthentic. Specifically, I said,

> many people believe that the events of one's life are recorded somewhere in the mind like a videotape and can be elicited by hypnosis or drugs. In fact, memories are subject to distortion when they are first registered in the mind, and they may be later distorted by blurring with fantasy or imagination. Something that one feared or wished may be later "recalled" as a memory, just as a dream can seem very real. Hypnosis often stimulates more memories than a person may have before the hypnosis, but it is not true that the "new" memories must be authentic. They may be mostly true, mostly untrue, or entirely untrue. To make matters worse, memories emerging in hypnosis may feel compellingly real because of the vividness of imagery and emotion that some people achieve in hypnosis.

In addition to these influences, leading questions by the therapist or the patient's eagerness to find an explanation for her suffering might lead to "bogus" memories. Unless her memories could be verified by other sources, the truth would be questionable. Cindy and her treatment team accepted the risk because the prospect of continued despair, and even suicide, clearly outweighed it.

HYPNOTIC STRATEGIES

Cindy had learned a bit about hypnosis in nursing school, and her attitudes were generally realistic. She was aware that the purpose was to put her *more* in control of herself, not *less*, and that the therapist would serve as a coach or guide in the process. She clearly appreciated this emphasis on her not only retaining but also achieving more self control.

I neither formally tested Cindy for susceptibility nor measured hypnotic depth during the treatment work. She was an excellent subject, and almost any induction procedure was effective. Most often, induction consisted of having her sit comfortably in a reclining chair with the light in the room dimmed somewhat. Her gaze was directed upward until her eyelids began to feel heavy and her eyes tired. I instructed her to allow them to close gently, then allow a pleasant wave of relaxation to progress from head to toe, noticing as her breathing slowed and lowered to her abdomen. I suggested increasing feelings of well-being and safety. She listened as I counted from 1 to 10 and pictured the numbers in her mind, allowing each to deepen her relaxation as she entered a comfortable state of hypnosis. I instructed her to feel peacefully at ease, with her mind open and calm.

After such an induction in one of our early sessions, I asked Cindy to picture herself seated at a desk, turning the pages of a calendar back to help her recall a happy memory. Having one or more especially happy memories available to call on can serve as a relief and a stabilizing procedure when dealing with traumatic material. Interestingly, even though I suggested that she only go back a few years in her life, she went back to age 5, describing herself as alone and playing with a doll. She emphasized having on a "really nice dress" and how everything seemed "real clean." In response to questioning, she commented that she really didn't like playing with anyone else and that being alone was like an escape. This memory may provide a glimpse into some important issues in the patient's characterological development. When asked to recover another memory from that same age, she recalled a very unpleasant experience of having her mother be angry because her father was late coming home: she felt upset that her mother was angry and commented that her mother was angry a lot. She recalled her kindergarten teacher being angry at her because she couldn't tie her shoes. I asked her to move ahead in time to age 8, because the period from 8 to 14 had been of concern to her previous therapist.

We spent the remainder of this session and the next two slowly reviewing her memories from age 8 that next appeared—of Cindy entering a neighbor's house at their request when a young girl a few years older than herself was there for a visit. The girl took her into a bedroom, and the two adults later joined them. They encouraged her to keep what happened there a secret, saying that if she was a good girl she would cooperate with them. They had her take her clothes off, encouraged the girls to touch their own vaginas and each other's. The man took photographs and then fondled the girls while the woman took photographs. The patient recalled being quite frightened and puzzled throughout this experience but apparently was intimidated by their cautioning her about secrecy. They repeatedly told her that if she was a good girl she would do what they said. When she was allowed to dress herself, she had a strong urge to wash her hands.

The memory was recovered slowly, but Cindy was able to recall the details of the room and the appearance of the people quite clearly. To facilitate her recall, I used only nonleading questions and comments such as, "What happens next?" "Do you see anything else?" and "Allow the memory to proceed." She was clearly uneasy in the recollection but never seriously upset. She did experience some flashbacks and sleeplessness between sessions but apparently talked by telephone with her husband about the memories and to hospital staff members to some extent. I told her at the end of each session before terminating hypnosis that she could remember as much or as little of the memory as she was ready to, but each time she maintained full recall.

Cindy's emphasis on being neat and clean in her first early memory, and the subsequent comment about wanting to wash her hands, seemed significant to me in the formation of her obsessional tendencies, in addition to whatever biological predisposition she may have had. She related some elements of the experience to other aspects of her life, such as noting that there was a window near the bed that had sunlight streaming through and that to this day she feels uneasy in brightly lit rooms. Also, she is quite self-conscious about having her picture taken. She had once dropped out of a modeling class, never realizing why being photographed was so unpleasant to her.

I made a number of reassuring interventions during the course of the sessions regarding Cindy's sincere efforts to be a good girl. She had learned to be trusting of adults, but she had been taken advantage of. Cindy had not caused the situation herself. I indicated on several occasions that this was an entirely inappropriate and upsetting introduction to sexuality and that her fear and bewilderment were all entirely understandable. Cindy suspected that she had gone back to that same house on another occasion, so exploration of that possibility would be the focus of our next session.

After a hypnotic induction, I asked her to go back in time and begin recalling the next time she went to the neighbor's house. She reported that the next summer she was playing on her patio and the other girl in the memory appeared in the neighbor's back yard and asked her to come over. She at first refused, but a few days later when asked again she went with her, first talking to her on the patio and then going inside the house to play a game of Monopoly. No one else appeared to be home. The girl spoke of what good friends they were and how much she had missed the patient. A few years later, when Cindy was 12 or 13 years old, the girl appeared again and once again invited her inside. She recalled being hot and sweaty after running outside and needing a drink of water. When she went into the friend's kitchen, she found the older couple there and felt frightened and nauseated. She soon found herself back in the room as before, and the older couple seemed angry because she had not returned sooner. She tried to leave but her path was blocked, and the woman brandished a knife. Again they instructed her to take her clothes off and began taking pictures of both of the now naked girls. She recalled the girl's name, something that had not occurred to her during the former memory. As the girl sat astride her, the patient remarked that there was blood everywhere, presumably menstrual blood. When the patient seemed distressed and commented about it, she was told by the older woman that the knife would cause a lot more blood if she didn't cooperate. The recall was interrupted at this point because of time constraints, and Cindy was advised that she could remember as much or as little of the memory as she was ready to on awakening, but that she should not pursue the memory further until our next session. She misunderstood this instruction as a prohibition to discuss what she had already remembered. She found it hard to keep the memory to herself and had nightmares and emotional upset. In the next session, we resumed the hypnotic recall of the memory, which consisted of the older couple having the girls pose in various fashions. Cindy felt nauseated and tried to detach herself from the experience. Her concern about the blood seemed to anger the older woman, who kept asking what was wrong with her and emphasizing that if she was a good girl she would cooperate with them. When the picture taking was finished and the adults left the room, she remarked about how upset she was about the blood on the bed and described in detail the two girls cleaning themselves up. She was emphatic to the other girl that she was never coming back, and the other girl said as long as she kept the secret she wouldn't have to come back. While the patient was still hypnotized, I commented about the connection between her revulsion for blood in this memory and her subsequent revulsion for blood. I emphasized that it was not her fault because she was trying to cooperate and was actually trapped by these adults. I also commented about what an unfortunate introduction this was to sexuality and how now she would be able to sort out her various feelings about sex and guilt in relationships.

The next two sessions were spent reviewing her various heterosexual relationships and the impact of these early experiences on her. On a weekend pass, she drove with her parents to the town in which she had grown up and felt a strong wish to see the schools and homes she had previously lived in. This clearly was part of her effort to re-create a coherent childhood memory. She described not having dated until she was a senior in high school, having none of the interest in boys that her classmates did. She started dating a boy 4 years older than herself, but stopped when her mother objected. We agreed that her interest in nursing as a career might have been influenced by her wish to help others who had been hurt or mistreated as she had been. She noted what a strong feeling of concern she had about her husband's female partner and realized that she was experiencing her husband and the female physician as being like the male and female adults who had molested her. She also recalled that one of the precipitating factors to her suicidal urges was her disgust at remarks made by her husband's partner.

Cindy did not experience a dramatic degree of catharsis during the memory recall, but she felt a good bit of emotion and had enough discomfort to keep her working actively on the material between sessions. She was still reluctant to talk very much to hospital staff members but made progress in this regard and in describing her memories to her husband.

She began the next session by wondering about the strong sense of "frustration" she had been feeling, wondering if this was actually an experience of anger. She reported never expressing anger in her life and being uncomfortable when anyone else appeared to be angry. She recalled how angry the man was who raped her when she was in college. Why did sensing her own anger remind her of that? It seemed time to have her revisit that experience in hypnosis. She had gone to another room in the dormitory to join a group watching television and later found herself alone in the room with two men. As the memory unfolded in hypnosis, one of the men left the room and the other grabbed her as she tried to leave and threw her on the bed. She hit her head on the wall and felt stunned and confused. He pushed her back on the bed as she struggled to arise, and she felt paralyzed and helpless in his powerful grasp. She experienced the attacker as angry, his features distorted by the emotion. He did not respond to her pleading to stop and tore her clothes off. She felt like she wanted to die and tried to hit the wall with her hands to summon help. When he restrained her, she started to cry, but he proceeded to tear off her clothes and forcibly subjected her to intercourse. She underwent some degree of dissociation, beginning to feel as though she were not present and then to feel as though she would die. There is some gap in her memory; the next thing she remembers is his standing up and getting a towel. "There's blood everywhere—I feel sick." Throughout the recall of this memory the patient was experiencing considerable emotion but was not remarkably distressed. I reassured her that this episode was not her fault, that she had joined the group innocently, and that she indeed had tried to resist but was truly helpless in this situation. On awakening from hypnosis, she reported feeling slightly upset but feeling more sad than angry. She later reported having cried later in the day following the session. She was now feeling emotions that had been dissociated or stifled.

In the next session we reviewed how Cindy's vulnerability to guilt and criticism was connected to her guilt about her various traumas, an inclination heightened by her upbringing. We reviewed her previous strong reactions to joking remarks made by one of her husband's coworkers about a vaginal ultrasound diagnostic procedure and how she began feeling because of her past experiences that physicians are molesting and harming women. She also realized that her discomfort with her husband's female partner grew out of her equating the two of them with the older couple who took nude photographs of her. She felt she was beginning to reestablish normal boundaries between her past traumas and the reality that professionals in the health-care field may occasionally make jokes about patients but that this does not warrant equating them with rapists and child abusers.

In the next session, Cindy reported a recent trip home in which she felt fairly comfortable around her parents and her husband's parents and that she had enjoyable intercourse with her husband for the first time in many months. She was even more impressed by being able to have fun with her children and not be bothered by the disarray of the house. She saw her burgeoning capacity for pleasure as being a very positive development for her. All of her emotions were becoming more available. When we reviewed her sexual history, she related that sex had not been pleasurable for her with the young man she had dated seriously in college but was something of a duty she carried out. She only became orgasmic once married. She had become pregnant by her second boyfriend and went through an abortion without thinking much about it or discussing it with anyone. Interestingly, when she went to the clinic for the procedure, she noticed another woman who seemed distraught and thought to herself that this other woman certainly needed someone to talk to.

In the remaining few sessions I used no hypnosis. We reviewed Cindy's vulnerability to depression and how it was linked to her compulsive personality traits by having unrealistically high standards for herself. We also discussed how her highly moral and perfectionistic style had distanced her from her peers throughout her life, leaving her feeling isolated and unaccepted. When her children became old enough to be in school at least part of the day, she was unable to stave off feelings of loneliness and guilt by being a dedicated wife and mother and thus began feeling depressed. She understood that she needs to pursue sources of pleasure in life, to "lighten up" and not be so concerned, for example, about the cleanliness of the house. Being less demanding of herself may help her to be less demanding and critical of others and, therefore, make her more open to social relationships. She realized that working on the expression of anger will be a continuing need in her psychotherapy. She recalled living in fear of her mother, experiencing her as moody and unpredictable. She always wished her mother would stop being so angry at her father and felt very protective toward him. We wondered together if her disavowal of anger had something to do with not wanting to be like her mother in that respect.

Cindy brought her husband to our last session so that I might review with him the key elements of our work to help make her difficulties and her treatment course more understandable to him. They both felt very pleased with the progress she had made and seemed to have quite realistic plans for the future. They both expressed gratitude for the treatment work and expressed confidence that they would be able to work effectively with the recommendations that had evolved through the work.

FOLLOW-UP

I contacted Cindy by telephone 5 years after she returned home. Two telephone interviews were conducted to get as complete a picture as possible of her overall functioning and of her appraisal of the role of hypnosis in her treatment. She and her husband reviewed a draft of this case report and gave their consent for its publication.

No longer taking any medication, Cindy still sees her psychiatrist but not regularly. She is making up some coursework that will enable her to apply for medical school soon. Still doing the cooking and cleaning herself, she knows that will have to stop once she is a full-time student.

The couple's marriage is strong, and they enjoy life together. She no longer has difficulty visiting her husband at the hospital and no longer worries about his partners. Their sexual relationship is greatly improved. He still has to be the initiator, and she is sometimes a bit uncomfortable, but she quite often enjoys intercourse and is frequently orgasmic. Their communication is quite open about sexual matters, and Cindy is pleased that their household is providing a different climate about sexuality for the children than was true in her parental home. She is still uneasy about bright lights and being photographed but less so than before. She laughs easily and often, can be playful with the children, and is less concerned about the house being neat all the time.

HOW WAS HYPNOSIS HELPFUL?

Cindy credits the work done in hypnosis as the key factor in her improvement. "It was incredible," she said. "It allowed me to get deeper into my mind and find out what was bothering me." She still is puzzled about how she was able to develop such remarkable trust in such a short time. The use of hypnosis seemed to facilitate her ability to remember and share intimate details very quickly. She had made no effort to validate the memories of the people next door, fearing that questions would only upset her parents. In response to an oblique question she felt safe about venturing, her mother had commented that the neighbors were "extremely odd people."

In the absence of external verification, there is no way to know whether Cindy's memories are authentic or not. They seemed compellingly real to her and to me, but from a scientific standpoint, "seeming" real is not confirmation. The patient's remarkable improvement is also not actually a validation of the memories. It may be that memories that are entirely fictitious could still provide a plausible and satisfying rationale for Cindy's symptoms and thereby serve as therapeutic leverage for recovery.

CONCLUSION

There is no reason to believe that traumatic experiences underlie every form of characterological disturbance or that all depressions are linked to mistreatment by others. For Cindy, what was known about her upbringing and the contemporary pressures in her life could have adequately explained both her compulsive behavior and her depression. Her depression, however, was triggered by sexual remarks, was made worse by recalling adult sexual trauma, and persisted in the face of what should have been adequate treatment. Although not exclusive *causes* of her difficulties, Cindy's sexual traumas became interwoven with other aspects of her development. Thus, emotionally potent early experiences strengthened her negative attitudes about herself, her guilt and shame about sexuality, and her tendency to stifle her feelings. Recognizing the significant connection between traumatic events in her childhood that had been repressed or dissociated, and both the early and adult traumas and the contemporary triggering events, made Cindy's symptom picture comprehensible. Abreaction and mastery of the various traumas allowed a synthesis or integration of what had been dissociated and fragmentary. She now has a coherent narrative of her life, recognizes the links between her past and her present, and enjoys richer access to her emotional life.

Would Cindy's treatment course have been different without the use of hypnosis? All that is certain is that treatment was not proving successful until hypnosis was introduced. Would she have improved anyway, without the use of hypnosis? Perhaps, but the compelling experience of what unfolded in the treatment and its very favorable outcome suggests that at best her treatment would have taken a much longer time and may not have been as helpful.

Why Did Hypnosis Help?

Hypnosis in itself is not a treatment. It can produce alterations in the subjective experience of the patient along several lines that provide opportunities for treatment interventions. For Cindy, the hypnotic experience facilitated a rapidly developed positive relationship with the therapist. I was experienced as attentive, benign, creating a situation of comfort and safety for her, and respecting her need for control. Even in the initial sessions, something of a "corrective emotional experience" was occurring. In contrast to others who had forced her to do their will without regard for her feelings, I was clearly devoted to helping her accomplish her goals, respecting her wishes and feelings. I was sensitive to her level of discomfort, never urging her to continue with recall to the point of distress.

The opportunity hypnosis affords for relaxing the barriers in the mind against unpleasant memories is, in part, based on an alteration in consciousness and on the trusting relationship with the therapist. Cindy was not just *remembering* things, she was *remembering with* a trusted other whose comforting presence would counter the terrible aloneness and helplessness that trauma evokes. In hypnosis, painful emotion can be limited: slowed, muted, and stopped, when necessary. Patients can recover emotions that are dissociated or stifled at the time of the trauma, thereby integrating the experience with the continuity of one's life. What happened no longer seems unreal, nor poorly understood, and the person is no longer detached or absent as if it all happened to someone else.

As the therapist helps the person recall and now "own" his or her experience, a coherent narrative can be formed. By helping Cindy put into words what happened next door and what happened years later in the dormitory, another sort of mastery was accomplished. Not only did she tolerate the emotions in hypnotic recall, but she also became the narrator of her experience. Now in the reliving, she is the active describer rather than the passive victim. Without making leading statements that could shape or distort the memory, the therapist can help in ordering the elements of what happened. The experience can, in a sense, be analyzed and explained in terms of sequence and causality. What was a confusing jumble now makes sense.

The therapist also has the opportunity to correct distorted thinking that may have arisen during the trauma. Cindy had been confused by the woman next door telling her that if she was a good girl she would keep their secret. That seemed to mean that telling her parents would make her a bad girl, something she feared already. She needed to hear from the therapist that it was good, not bad, that she was telling now and furthermore, that enforcing the secrecy in this way was only a corrupt adult's way of intimidating and controlling a child. In recalling the dormitory rape, Cindy could now accept reassurance that she had not caused the attack. Not only did the memory itself make her innocence clear but the therapist's opinion also now seems to carry persuasive weight. Worry about therapists' ability to exploit their patients' heightened suggestibility and to influence them in a manipulative way is ill-founded in a respectful intervention where reassurances and explanations are provided that are perfectly consistent with the patient's conscious wishes and treatment goals.

Transference and Countertransference Issues

As noted earlier, hypnosis tends to promote positive transference. Cindy quickly felt both understood and helped in the hypnotherapeutic relationship. She maintained a sense of safety and gratitude throughout the treatment work and afterwards. What about negative transference? Isn't a therapist likely to "inherit" feelings "left over" from the mistreatment the patient had earlier received? It stands to reason that potent bad experiences from the past should emerge in the course of treatment, especially if the therapist adopts a stance of relative anonymity and thereby "invites" projections or displacements of feelings about past relationships. Reliving traumatic events in hypnosis, however, seems to awaken and focus the negative emotions where they belong: toward the actual abuser. Thus, the therapist doesn't have to become the object of projections that could then be traced to their original sources. The source has already been identified and the appropriate feelings expressed during the recall.

At times, patients can be encouraged to vividly imagine speaking up to or even punishing their abuser in fantasy, a measure that can promote resolution and integration of the traumatic past. But negative transferences sometimes do occur; the therapist is experienced as abusive, rejecting, or controlling. These distortions can usually be dealt with through interpretation. They are normal reactions to the previous trauma and usually are mollified by the affirming, empowering effects of the caring treatment relationship.

Countertransference reactions are seldom problematic with cooperative and appreciative patients who both want and deserve help. One possible problem might be an overprotective stance by the therapist that could promote dependency or passivity on the part of the patient. This was not true with Cindy. She approached her treatment very much as a partner: cooperative, but not submissive. I respected her strengths. Another possible problem might be voyeuristic curiosity about the details of the patient's sexual experiences. Indeed, in reviewing the prospect of relieving her molestation in trance, another patient asked, "How do I know you won't enjoy it?" On the contrary, the author's experience has uniformly been of attunement with the plight of the victim, feeling empathic concern about her fear and pain. Identifying with the abuser and feeling some sort of erotic stimulation in the sessions would signal a problem for a therapist to take to a consultant or supervisor.

Cautions and Contraindications

Hypnotic interviewing carries the risk of eliciting memories that are more fiction than fact. Therapists are increasingly aware that the retrieval of memories is always, in part, a reconstruction and is vulnerable to distortion by the motives for remembering, the context of remembering, and the shaping influence of an interviewer. Although memories don't have to be entirely and literally true to carry some sort of valuable meaning about a person's experience, it is hard for the remembering person not to take the details seriously. Thus, a person may recall being molested by a sibling at age 8 when in fact it was a babysitter when the person was 6. In the distorted memory, the sibling could have been substituted for the actual abuser because of threats made about disclosure, or memories of actual or wished-for closeness with the sibling might have become blurred with the memory of abuse. For clinical purposes, the fact of some sort of childhood abuse may be all that is important. For a patient who is tempted to confront (or even prosecute) the sibling, however, the validity of the memory takes on vital importance. Accusations of abuse based on hypnotically enhanced memories that could be distorted or even totally false can have tragic consequences.

Exploration of childhood trauma, then, must be undertaken with considerable caution. The clinical circumstances must warrant the risks. Anyone curious about whether they may have suffered childhood trauma should pursue their concern with a therapist who has no investment in supporting the idea that trauma must have occurred. Patients who have persistent, intractable symptoms that defy diagnostic understanding and treatment efforts by competent clinicians, however, may benefit from hypnotic exploration. Such a patient should understand the risk of memory distortion and the inadvisability of acting on what they remember outside of the treatment context (e.g., legal proceedings). Such patients should also be advised that recalling traumatic events from childhood will not automatically—or even easily—resolve their difficulties. In some instances, it may make no difference at all; in others, only a little. For some patients, though, hypnosis enables therapists to significantly alter an unproductive treatment course and help patients make solid and lasting change.

Unfortunately, not every patient who might benefit from the sort of hypnotic treatment described here is a good candidate. Age regression and other forms of hypnotic exploration can be destabilizing, especially if trauma is uncovered. Despite the therapist's efforts to pace the recall and modulate the emotional reactions, facing memories that were held out of consciousness for good reason can be upsetting and even disorganizing. Worsening of symptoms instead of improvement may follow, unless the patient's personality resources are equal to the challenge. Vulnerabilities to uncontrolled ego regression must be taken seriously and precariously organized patients treated supportively until they can undertake expressive work. Some may never be able to engage in such treatment, just as some physically ill patients cannot tolerate the surgery that might otherwise be helpful.

For Cindy the strength of her underlying personality structure was reassuring despite the severity of her symptoms. Although sometimes retreating into states of detachment that resembled her mental escape from unbearable experiences earlier in her life, she had never been psychotic. Indeed, she had completed postgraduate education, had functioned well in a demanding work environment, and had maintained a generally good adjustment until her mid-30s. She was intelligent and free of paranoid leanings that might have interfered with the trusting relationship that was pivotal in the treatment relationship.

From a research perspective, how can the principles and techniques presented here be further evaluated and refined? Some issues touched on here are part of large and important domains of scientific knowledge such as the pathogenesis of childhood trauma in adult psychopathology and the vulnerability of memory to distortion. Research is well under way in those areas and will no doubt have an impact on how the role of hypnosis is understood. More narrowly, therapists can think of a few variables that are both worthy of attention and possible to approach systematically. Patient variables to be studied might include hypnotizability, symptom picture, and characterological features. What sort of person, with what sort of problems is most likely to improve with this approach? A therapist variable might be the gender of the therapist. Is an opposite-sex patient–therapist pairing more productive than a same-sex pairing, or not? What about the experience level of the therapist, the familiarity of the therapist with dealing with trauma, and the therapist's guiding theory? What treatment variables might be studied? Could some form of biofeedback be compared with hypnosis? What about the approach to abreaction? Should full and even painful degrees of emotion be encouraged, or can mastery occur with feelings sharply limited? Could a therapist experienced in this sort of treatment get similar results without the formal induction of hypnosis?

Until these questions can be answered, clinical experience and judgment—transmitted through case studies such as this one—will have to form the basis of therapists' work with patients. From a historical standpoint, hypnosis has been linked with the treatment of trauma-based disorders for over 100 years. What began with Freud and Janet has been steadily refined through trial and error and anecdotal data. This potent clinical tool has stood the test of time and begs for more systematic study and wider use in bringing help and relief to patients.

REFERENCES

Briere, J., & Conte, J. (1993). Self-reported amnesia for abuse in adults molested as children. *Journal of Traumatic Stress, 6*, 21–31.

Courtois, C. A. (1992). The memory retrieval process in incest survivor therapy. *Journal of Child Sexual Abuse, 1*(1), 15–31.

Davies, J. M., and Frawley, M. G. (1994). *Treating the adult survivor of childhood sexual abuse: A psychoanalytic perspective.* New York: Basic Books.

Finkelhor, D. (1984). *Child sexual abuse: New theory and research.* New York: Free Press.

Herman, J. L. (1992). *Trauma and recovery.* New York: Basic Books.

Herman, J. L., & Schatzow, E. (1987). Recovery and verification of memories of childhood sexual trauma. *Psychoanalytic Psychology, 4*, 1–14.

Loftus, E. F. (1993). The reality of repressed memories. *American Psychologist, 48*, 518–537.

Lynn, S. J., and Nash, M. R. (1994). Truth in memory: Ramifications for psychotherapy and hypnotherapy. *American Journal of Clinical Hypnosis, 36,* 194–208.

Russell, D. E. H. (1986). *The secret trauma: Incest in the lives of girls and women.* New York: Basic Books.

Terr, L. (1994). *Unchained memories: True stories of traumatic memories, lost and found.* New York: Basic Books.

7

HYPNOTIC STRATEGIES FOR SOMATOFORM DISORDERS

JOHN F. CHAVES

Patients who present with chronic unexplained physical symptoms pose a diagnostic and therapeutic challenge for health professionals. Commonly, these patients undergo extensive medical workups that fail to identify any organic pathology sufficient to explain their presenting complaints (Barsky & Klerman, 1983; Smith, 1985). Either specific pathophysiological processes underlying their symptoms are not demonstrable or the disabling effects of any observed pathology are far greater than expected. The need to practice defensive medicine (Tancredi & Barondess, 1978) can lead to comprehensive workups for these patients that are expensive, invasive, and unrevealing. Moreover, these workups can place patients at significant risk for iatrogenic illness (Quill, 1985; Roberts, 1994).

As routine pathophysiologic explanations are ruled out, psychological constructs may begin to be invoked to conceptualize the clinical findings. Contemporary differential diagnosis with these patients normally leads to consideration of factitious disorders and malingering, as well as several related somatoform disorders, including somatization disorder, conversion disorder, pain disorder, hypochondriasis, or more rarely, body dysmorphic disorder. The somatoform disorders are grouped together because they all require the exclusion of serious medical conditions rather than because of any assumptions about a shared etiology. This approach is consistent with the general diagnostic strategy in medicine of ruling out rare, but possible organic causes of illness, rather than ruling in the most probable causes, especially when those are nonorganic. Of course, diagnosis solely by exclusion is fraught with difficulties. Sometimes this strategy leads to incorrect diagnosis of somatoform disorders with later discovery of occult organic pathology (Fishbein & Goldberg, 1989; Lazare, 1981).

Adding to the complexity of the situation is recent evidence that it may be important to identify and to treat subclinical manifestations of somatoform disorders (Smith, 1994; Wickramasekera, 1993). The emphasis on early identification has accelerated because these patients tend to be remarkably intensive users of medical services, to have a major disability, and to display a progressive course that can persist for years (Smith, 1994).

Historically, the topics of hypnosis and suggestibility have been closely intertwined with the study of hysterical conversion reactions (Ellenberger, 1970). Serious questions have arisen regarding the comparative use of social-psychological and medical models to account for these manifestations of psychopathology (Goffman, 1961; Scheff, 1966; Szasz, 1961). Nevertheless, hypnosis has continued to be used as a treatment modality for the somatoform disorders. In fact, at least one contemporary model proposes that hypnotizability itself may predispose some patients to these disorders (Wickramasekera, 1993, 1994).

Clinicians who wish to use hypnosis in the treatment of these disorders face a core of common issues. These include the patients' disease conviction, their reluctance to accept interventions that are plainly psychological, secondary gain considerations, and an impoverished awareness of their emotional life, as indexed by such phenomena as alexithymia. This kind of altered awareness displayed by somatoform patients has led Kihlstrom (1994) to conclude that the syndromes listed under this disorder actually should be classified as dissociative disorders.

Psychogenic conceptualization may not be readily embraced by somatoform patients who, typically, remain convinced that they are suffering from an organic disease that ought to be treatable by the normal array of medical and surgical interventions. They may not see hypnotic interventions as a part of this array. Thus, the clinician who seeks to use hypnotic procedures in treatment often faces the additional hurdle of lack of initial patient acceptance. Accordingly, proper preparation of these patients for hypnotic interventions is critical to their successful treatment (Chaves, 1979, 1985).

This case involves a patient with a history of episodic low-back pain who eventually displayed a rare conversion disorder, camptocormia (Lazare & Klerman, 1970). Issues pertaining to the hypnotic management of somatoform pain disorders, including phantom limb pain, have been discussed elsewhere (Chaves, 1985, 1993, 1994). Here we turn to some of the additional special considerations relevant to the hypnotic treatment of patients with conversion disorders.

BACKGROUND INFORMATION

Demographics and Presenting Problem

E. K. was a 42-year-old, married White woman who presented with a chief complaint of an impaired gait and posture. In our initial telephone contact, she stated that she had been diagnosed as having a conversion disorder, camptocormia, and was seeking hypnosis as a treatment modality at the suggestion of her psychologist. She had been in psychotherapy for several months, and although she found it beneficial in many ways, she was not seeing any improvement in her gait.

At our first appointment, she presented an unusual appearance. Her gait disturbance involved walking with a bent posture, reminiscent of that of a speed skater. The anterior flexion of her back varied between about 20° and 70°, although frequently her back would be virtually parallel to the floor while she was attempting to stand erect or walk forward. When she attempted to stand straight she would briefly stand erect, waver momentarily, and then quickly resume her bent posture.

An interesting aspect of her presentation was that she could walk backwards in an erect position without difficulty. Her seated posture appeared relatively normal. She also reported that she could lie flat without discomfort. Her above-average height was masked by her stooped posture. She was stocky and complained of having gained about 30 lb since the onset of her disorder, approximately one and a half years previously.

Although conversion disorders are generally more commonly diagnosed among women than men, camptocormia is rarely seen in women (Kosbab, 1961; Lazare & Klerman, 1970; Rockwood & Eilbert, 1969; Rosen & Frymoyer, 1985). Most previous cases were reported among soldiers during the first and second world wars (Fetterman, 1937; Hall, 1919; Hamlin, 1943; Hurst, 1918; Massa & Slater, 1989; Miller & Forber, 1990; Saliba, 1919; Sandler, 1945; Sutro & Hulbert, 1946; Walker & Leeds, 1928).

Family History

E. K. was a sixth-grade teacher in a rural community and lived at home with her 43-year-old husband, who was also an elementary school teacher, and three male children, ages 15, 12, and 10. Her father was a 69-year-old retired railroad worker. Her mother, age 66, was a retired factory garment worker. Both were said to be in good health. Her father was described as introverted, short-tempered, and moody. He would "clam up" if he got into an argument with his wife. He was also seen as being very critical of E. K., who felt that she could never do anything right as far as he was concerned. Her mother was described as needing to be in command and being extroverted. When her mother did not get her way, she pouted and "put you on a guilt trip." E. K. stated that "I never thought I was thin enough, pretty enough, dressy enough or good enough although she [her mother] never said it in words."

Her father worked nights and slept during the days. He became quite angry when he would be awakened by the children. The parents fought a lot and never seemed satisfied with each other. Problems were never discussed. Nevertheless, E. K. said she "felt safe" at home and stated that "there was never any violence." She acknowledged, however, that her father would discipline her by hitting her on the head, whereas her mother would use a fly swatter.

Sex was never discussed at home, although her father once confided to her that her mother had a problem with sex that could be fixed, but she refused to be treated for it. No further specifics were provided for her. She learned about sex in junior high. During adolescence, a friend's father attempted to fondle her breasts. That experience was described as very distressing, although she did not disclose the event to anyone at the time. There was some premarital petting, about which she reported much guilt. After marriage, sex was described as good initially, but with a lot of anxiety about being overheard by the children, or by others when they were visiting family. In recent years, sex was characterized as unenjoyable.

Her parents lived nearby and were seen as having been helpful through the course of the patient's hospitalizations and medical care. Her father had driven her to medical appointments, while her mother had prepared food for the family, which the patient acknowledged had been a "tremendous help."

The patient had a married 39-year-old brother who was said to be her mother's favorite. When growing up he was seen as always getting what he wanted from the parents. In turn, his son was now seen as the favorite grandchild.

The patient's husband was described as helpful, considerate, and caring but also as having a critical attitude and hard time accepting people who did not live up to his expectations. They had been married for 20 years and had known each other for 2 years prior to marriage. She described herself as very satisfied with the marriage and having a good relationship with her in-laws, although she acknowledged that when she got married her mother-in-law "lit candles at the Catholic Church and prayed for our divorce."

Until age 12, the patient spent a lot of time visiting her maternal grandparents' farm. Then her grandmother was killed in an automobile accident in which her upper torso was crushed. Her grandfather sustained a crushed hip in the accident and endured a long recovery. Subsequently, he married an aide at the hospital. Following that marriage there was an abrupt deterioration in the relationship with his children and grandchildren. They remained estranged until the time of his death from cancer 15 years later.

History of the Problem

E. K.'s presenting complaint was first manifested on the morning of November 18, 1991. At that time she found that when she got out of bed she was bent forward, with her thighs and knees drawn together. She was unable to walk in an upright position. She stated that she was not in any discomfort when she was lying down or sitting. Pain was notable when she walked or stood in one place. When she was standing, her muscles would start "shaking and jerking." Fatigue quickly ensued, and she had to sit down.

At the time her symptoms developed, E. K. said she was experiencing extraordinary stress at work. She was teaching a sixth-grade class, consisting of 34 students. "Lots of these kids were dirty, nasty, and vulgar," behaviors for which they suffered few if any consequences, she said. She observed a lot of aggressive behaviors, including one student choking another with a string from a pair of sweatpants. She reported feeling very distressed by the sexual comments and innuendos that she encountered on a regular basis. Her distress was greatly exacerbated by the fact that administrators at the school seemed unwilling to be supportive of her effort to control these behaviors. Further discussion related her stress in this situation to feelings of anxiety she reported whenever people are "out of control." Her concerns about emotional volatility and acting out included such circumstances as when people are inebriated, very angry, or sexually aroused.

Prior Treatment and Assessment

Following emergence of her symptoms, the patient was evaluated by a local physician. X-rays of the lumbar spine showed narrowing at L-5/S-1. A computerized axial tomography (CAT) scan showed bulging discs at multiple levels. A magnetic resonance imaging (MRI) showed degenerative disc disease at L-3 through L-5 with osteophytes and mild stenosis. An electromyographic (EMG) examination was negative. The tests concluded that she might have L-4/5 and S-1 radiculopathies associated with lumbar spondylosis and lateral recess syndrome. She was started on Lodine, Skelaxin, Pamelor, and Lorcet Plus and then underwent physical therapy. After 4 months of therapy, she was finally able to stand erect, but not without pelvic and truncal thrusting. If she stood and relaxed, her trunk would pull over into a camptocormic type of position. In that position she was able to walk normally, but her back and thighs would gradually tire. There was no problem with weakness or atrophy, although she did develop occasional cramping in her feet.

An initial neurological evaluation indicated she might have viral myelitis. An MRI of the thoracic and lumbar spine revealed no additional abnormalities. Valium, Naprosyn, Baclofen, and Prozac were added to her array of medications, without benefit. She also reported head discomfort when exposed to drafts. This was accompanied by the sensation that there was fluid in her ears and tinnitus that occurred at night. She also developed a dizzy sensation described as "waviness." She had a history of dysgeusia and oral blisters and irritation of the mouth. At night she reported a 2-inch numb strip that ran on either side of her nose associated with a "drawing" sensation in her mouth and tongue. She also had a writing tremor in her right hand. Her fingers occasionally felt sensitive to touch.

Her past medical history was notable for hyperthyroidism, diagnosed in 1984. Her status was postthyroidectomy and she took .1 mg Synthroid daily. She also had stable interstitial cystitis, about which she did not complain. She reported a long history of intermittent back pain that began around 1970 while she was employed by a packing company. She sought no treatment for this but did have discomfort that lasted for several weeks. In 1979 she hyperextended her back while lifting one of her children and developed severe pain from the waist down to the sacral region, but with no radiation to her lower extremities. She was treated with bed rest and chiropractic manipulation with dramatic improvement occuring over a 2-week period. Between 1979 and 1991 she experienced activity-induced low-back pain that responded to chiropractic manipulation. In 1986 and again in 1988 there were exacerbations of her back pain associated with activity. Throughout this time her symptoms were localized in her back, with no radiation to the lower extremities.

A psychological evaluation was conducted in September 1992 by her previous psychologist. She was administered a test battery including the WAIS-R, Wagner's Hand Test, Rorschach, Minnesota Multiphasic Personality Inventory-2 (MMPI-2), Bender Gestalt, Rotter's Incomplete Sentences Blank (ISB), and Buck's House-Tree-Person Technique (HTP).

On the WAIS-R, the patient earned a Verbal IQ of 120, a Performance IQ of 98, and a Full Scale IQ of 110. Her MMPI profile was within normal limits. The projective test results were interpreted as suggesting that the patient was anxious and distrustful of other people. She was often unsure as to how she would "measure-up." She acknowledged many significant problems regarding her sexuality, including fluctuating desire, variable enjoyment, and discomfort with her own body. She interacted with others largely on a superficial basis and feared intimacy. Although there was no evidence of a thought disorder, she appeared to have a limited capacity to be objective and adopt other points of view. On the basis of this evaluation she was diagnosed as having a conversion disorder (Diagnostic and Statistical Manual of Mental Disorders, 3rd ed., rev. [DSM III-R] American Psychiatric Association, 1987; Axis I: 300.11) with a recommendation that organic brain syndrome be ruled out. A subsequent MRI brain scan was within normal limits.

Current Assessment

E. K. stated that she thought her problem was due to stress she experienced in connection with her sixth graders' engaging in sexual jokes and pranks that were very difficult for her to handle. One boy, 2 years older than the other pupils, was especially difficult for her. She cited examples of male students (two thirds of her class) asking female students to "suck their dick" or being told to "go eat their mother." She also described children comparing the size of their penises to balloons. The patient initially expressed concern that only a "Christian psychologist" could really understand her level of distress about these events, but she made no further inquiry regarding my religious beliefs. Exacerbating the problem was, in her view, a total failure of the school administrators to understand or support her in managing this class.

When asked to describe what she experienced phenomenologically during these periods of intense stress, she related having intense feeling localized in a box-shaped zone that extended from around her breasts to her mouth. In discussing these stressful events she would frequently bring her right hand to a protective position at the base of her throat. Exploration of symptom phenomenology frequently provides useful insights about the presenting complaints and provides an approach to the development of hypnotic suggestions.

The significance of this zone was explored with her. Three themes were uncovered (a) Her grandmother, to whom she was very close, was killed in an automobile accident by hitting a dashboard and sustaining crushing injuries to that area; (b) she described an incident in which a girl friend's father attempted to fondle her breasts when she was a teenager; and (c) she acknowledged that after 5 years of marriage, she began to alter her posture so as to minimize the protrusion of her breasts. This was concurrent with a diminished interest in sex and anger at her husband for insisting on sex when she did not wish it. Resigned compliance, accompanied by unacknowledged rage, was her characteristic response to his advances during these periods. Another theme identified during the initial session was an intense fear of others being out of control. This included children in the classroom, people who were inebriated, and people who were angry.

After her initial manifestation of camptocormic posture, she stayed home for few weeks and reported that she started to improve. This improvement ended abruptly when a fellow teacher came to visit her a few weeks later and related the ongoing problems with the children at school. She provided a vivid description of the effect of this discussion on her "distress zone." Only later was it clear that she was angry at her colleague for "dumping" these issues back on her and for reactivating the stress she had been experiencing in the classroom. A full resumption of her camp-tocormic posture ensued, accompanied by the revival of intense disquieting feelings in her "distress zone." During the initial session, there was some brief discussion about assertive strategies that she might use in several of these stressful situations. Following the initial session, she reported dramatically renewed sexual interest in her husband and found herself taking the initiative with him for the first time in many years.

Further discussions regarding strategies for identifying and negotiating with her husband about her needs, as well as explicit suggestions about the importance of her needs, were part of the first several visits with E. K. In addition, her attitudes, expectations, and beliefs about hypnosis were elicited. She appeared optimistic about the use of hypnosis in her case and very eager to begin treatment.

CONCEPTUALIZATION OF THE PROBLEM

E. K. appeared to be very angry but with a limited capacity to recognize the intensity of her anger and an impoverished repertoire of skills to deal with it. This pattern of unexpressed anger and hostility has been reported in other camptocormic patients (Carter, 1972; Sandler, 1945). She felt imposed on by virtually everyone: family members, students, administrators, and other teachers who she felt would "dump" their school-related troubles in her lap without regard for her needs. She had enormous difficulty being assertive. Her physical symptoms could be understood as providing a focus that deflected attention from her emotional issues and providing her with a role as victim that permitted her to punish those people at whom she was angry. In the later phases of treatment, as she began to be able to walk erect, she would find herself pulled back into a camptocormic posture by merely encountering an administrator in the halls at school or by becoming engaged in discussion with one of several teachers who would tell her about their problems managing children in the classroom. She realized that these people would feel very uncomfortable about her obvious symptoms, and in the case of the administrators, there was eventually a hope expressed that they would feel guilty for their role in causing the problem.

The symptoms also provided immediate secondary gain in extricating her from the stresses of the classroom. She had been out of work for one and a half years when I first saw her. Her symptoms also provided an opportunity for her to remain in therapy to deal with a wider variety of issues for which she had previously not been able to seek help. Indeed, she was quite emphatic on starting therapy that she was aware that she would continue to need help after remission of her symptoms. Fears of abandonment were voiced at several points when she feared that her uneven progress might lead to termination.

TREATMENT

Rationale for the Use of Hypnosis

E. K. expressed a lot of confidence in the psychologist who had initially proposed hypnosis as a treatment. Although she had not shown any improvement in her gait while being treated, she recognized that she was benefiting in other ways by being in therapy and expressed the desire to continue receiving psychotherapeutic help after recovering from her back problems. Her attitude toward hypnosis, thus, was quite positive. Her previous therapist had suggested to her that her symptoms could be understood as the outcome of unconscious conflict. She appeared ready, at that point, to accept this formulation of the dynamics of her problems. Hypnosis was characterized as a uniquely effective approach to the identification and resolution of these conflicts.

Hypnotic interventions can be fit, conceptually, within a wide variety of psychotherapeutic approaches (Brown & Chaves, 1980; Kirsch, 1994). In this case, it was used as a platform for the delivery of a variety of cognitive–behavioral interventions, including assertion training, cognitive restructuring, stress management, and anger identification and management. In addition, because treatment with hypnosis was viewed so favorably by the patient, administration of the hypnosis treatment was made contingent on dealing with other therapeutic issues, especially those related to secondary gain. This presented the added possibility of enhancing the efficacy of the hypnotic intervention through the mechanism of cognitive dissonance. The implications of E. K.'s decision about whether or not to return to school, regardless of whether her symptoms had abated or not, and the implications of her decision whether or not to pursue litigation were explored fully in an effort to "clear the pathway" for the effective use of hypnosis. These discussions led to a decision for her to return to her teaching position regardless of her symptoms at the time. Strategies for dealing with whatever symptoms she might have at the time she resumed teaching were discussed.

Why Was Hypnosis Used Rather Than Other Treatments?

A wide variety of treatment approaches have been used in dealing with conversion disorders. Hurst (1918) first successfully used hypnosis in a case of camptocormia. The particular advantage of hypnosis in this case related to E. K.'s positive attitude toward the modality and the foundation for its use that had been established by her previous therapist. Combining hypnotic interventions with appropriate cognitive–behavioral and insight-oriented approaches seemed most appropriate in dealing with the range of concerns exhibited in this case. Moreover, the use of hypnosis was also consistent with the patient's understanding of the etiology and dynamics of her condition. The higher levels of suggestibility expected in these patients also support the assumption that the addition of hypnosis to the normal range of cognitive–behavioral approaches would potentiate the overall efficacy of therapy (Kirsch, Montgomery, & Sapirstein, 1995).

Description of Treatment

The use of hypnosis was deliberately delayed in therapy with E. K. This provided an opportunity to explore fully the wide range of problems presented by the patient and to come to a better understanding of how the symptoms fit into the larger scheme of things. In addition, it provided an opportunity to allow rapport to develop and to begin working on some issues related to secondary gain. Furthermore, delay also provided an opportunity to help further explore and shape the patient's expectations regarding the course of treatment, including helping her to anticipate problems in her recovery and helping her to mobilize her resources in dealing with the inevitable backsliding that would be expected during treatment.

This period also provided an opportunity for the patient to become angry at me about several minor issues related to scheduling; this enabled me to observe and analyze her characteristic responses to these situations and to develop alternatives that led to more desirable outcomes for her. Modeling the recognition of anger with its appropriate management and the development of assertive response alternatives seemed particularly helpful.

Her background as a teacher provided the useful metaphor of the "learning curve" and the recognition that, as her own experiences had taught her, learning often progresses in an erratic fashion and one must emphasize the learning opportunities provided by each mistake and setback. The following is a sample generic script for the initial induction procedure, followed by some of the principal variations of the therapeutically relevant suggestions that were the primary focus of the hypnotic phase of her treatment. Several considerations were relevant in the decision about the approach to take during the induction procedure:

1. The induction procedure needs to be preceded by a careful elicitation of patient expectations regarding what hypnosis is expected to be like and what consequences are expected. Specific expectations must be dealt with by either adapting

to the patient's expectation or educating the patient. Thus, patients who believe that hypnotic inductions require shiny objects may be readily accommodated by the well-equipped practitioner. Alternatively, patients who expect to experience spontaneous amnesia are likely to be disappointed because of its rarity. As a consequence, they may decide that they had not been hypnotized and, thus, could not be expected to experience therapeutic gains. Accordingly, educating the patient is the best alternative. Issues pertaining to the management of patient expectations and the essential elements of patient preparation have been dealt with elsewhere (Chaves, 1979, 1985, 1989, 1994). In this case, E. K. did not reveal any specific expectation of the nature of the induction procedure but did verbalize some concerns about loss of control. As a result, additional information was provided regarding the power of the patient to accept or reject suggestions and to terminate the procedure at any time and for any reason. Furthermore, suggestions were administered in a somewhat indirect and passively worded fashion to minimize evocation of her concerns about control issues.

2. I considered relaxation training itself a meaningful therapeutic goal for E. K. Accordingly, during the first induction procedure attempted with her, I emphasized relaxation and did not directly address issues that appeared to have immediate relevance to her symptoms.

3. I attempted no formal assessment of her hypnotizability, although I incorporated a couple of comparatively easy motoric suggestions into the induction protocol to provide a crude assessment of her objective response to suggestions and to provide her with what many subjects describe as a compelling subjective experience of differential heaviness of the two arms. I administered these suggestions with appropriate goal-directed fantasies (Spanos, 1971, 1986) to encourage the experience of involuntariness that, for many patients, is the hallmark of hypnotic responding and helps, in turn, to facilitate responses to other suggestions. The issue of whether or not to assess hypnotizability formally in this context is controversial. Those who view hypnotizability as a trait are inclined to recommend formal assessment (e.g. Nadon & Laurence, 1994). Those who view hypnosis as a learnable and modifiable skill, alternatively, are more likely to avoid a formal assessment of hypnotizability because of concern for the adverse therapeutic impact of possible failures to respond to difficult suggestions (Kirsch, 1990, 1994). The use of a small

number of easy suggestions permits patients to learn what they have to do to respond to hypnotic suggestions without creating a high risk of failure and the development of negative expectations. Outlined below is a generic induction procedure, typical of that used with E. K., as well as several variations of the types of therapeutic suggestions that followed the induction protocol.

Sample procedure:

As we begin today . . . I'd like you to just let your eyes comfortably close . . . and as they do . . . notice how you can begin to be aware of how your body is fully supported by the chair. Notice the support under your head . . . under your neck, back . . . legs . . . and feet . . . and as you feel the support, notice how you can let all your muscles relax . . . letting the chair do all of the work of supporting your body . . . just letting go . . . think of the chair as if it were a gigantic sponge, absorbing every last bit of tension from your body . . . the tension just seems to flow from your body into the chair . . . leaving you to enjoy the deepening feelings of comfort that result . . . notice how with each breath, you find yourself becoming more and more relaxed . . . more and more comfortable . . . more and more at ease . . . and as you become more relaxed physically . . . you may notice your body just becoming limp and relaxed . . . just like a wet dishrag . . . completely limp . . . very comfortable . . . and as your comfort increases . . . notice your mind slowing down as well . . . think about time expanding . . . as if there were more time between each second . . . more time for you to relax. Now to help you relax more mentally, as well as physically, I'd like to ask you to imagine yourself standing at the top of a staircase, in an old house . . . the stairs and the landing on which you are standing are covered with a thick carpeting that feels soft and luxurious under your feet. Make it any color you like . . . perhaps something soothing and relaxing . . . there is a heavy wooden railing on one side of the stairs . . . it is made of a sturdy wood . . . the kind of railing that kids would love to slide down . . . very solid and secure. Hold on to that railing with one hand and, as you may have already guessed, in a moment as I count from 20 down to 1, go down the steps . . . one at a time and . . . notice as you do how much more deeply relaxed you become as you go down. Let's begin with number 20 . . . notice lifting your foot and then letting it move, almost in slow motion to the next step . . . number 19 . . . feeling your foot sink deeply into the carpet . . . 18 . . . time continuing to slow down . . . this is your special time . . . 17 . . . deeper . . . 16 . . . so wonderfully relaxed . . . 15 . . . after a while . . . 14 . . . it almost begins to seem . . . 13 . . . as though you're floating down the stairs . . . 12 is so very relaxing . . . but 11 is even more so . . . 10 so comfortable . . . 9 . . . so deeply hypnotized that . . . 8 . . . you enjoy being relaxed so very much . . . 7 . . . and as you approach the bottom of the stairs . . . 6 . . . you become aware of a door . . . and begin to anticipate . . . 5 . . . that I will ask you to . . . 4 . . . open the door . . . 3 . . . and step through it . . . 2 . . . and . . . 1 . . . just so relaxed at the bottom as you reach out with your hand and reach for the door knob and open the door to find a beautiful garden on a delightful spring day . . . there are tall trees . . . flowers . . . the sun is bright but not too warm . . . it is comfortably warm and there is that peaceful serenity that comes at those times when you are at the beginning of a long vacation . . . when you know your work is done . . . all of the cares and worries are behind you . . . that wonderful feeling of freedom from responsibilities . . . as you look around you notice that between two of the larger trees there is a large sturdy hammock. Go over and climb into the hammock and notice as you do, how you immediately become aware of the hammock providing full support for your body and notice the sides of the hammock curling around your body, almost like a cradle . . . soon you notice the hammock beginning to sway gently, first to one side then the other . . . feeling a gentle breeze as the air flows over your face, first from one side and then the other as the hammock goes back and forth . . . back and forth . . . and you begin drifting even deeper . . . a feeling that might remind you of those very relaxing times between sleeping and wakefulness . . . drifting in time and space . . . making it hard to know whether you're really awake or really asleep . . . but it really doesn't matter . . . all that matters is that deep feeling of relaxation . . . it might surprise you to know that even now your mind is continuing to open up to the ideas, thoughts, and feelings I describe and so it might be interesting even now to see that you can begin to experience things in a different way . . . I'd like to illustrate that to you by asking you to hold your arms out in the air, straight in front of you . . . that's right . . . now imagine that you are holding something very heavy in your left hand, a bucket filled with something very heavy . . . I'm not sure what it is . . . it might be sand, or water, or rocks, but right away you notice yourself gripping the handle of the bucket firmly as it seems to become heavier . . . and heavier, and heavier. Meanwhile, your right hand and arm feel wonderfully light and buoyant . . . as if helium-filled balloons were attached to your right wrist and fingers, pulling it up higher and higher . . . meanwhile notice how heavy that left arm has become . . . notice how the heaviness has begun to move up your arm, through your wrist, and forearm . . . past your elbows . . . I wouldn't be surprised if the heaviness had already reached up to your shoulder. Your whole left arm begins to feel as if it's made of lead and notice . . . as it gets heavier . . . how it begins to move down to your lap and soon . . . the heaviness becomes so great that the harder you try to hold the left arm up the heavier it becomes . . . and as your left arm moves down to your lap . . . when it touches your lap . . . let the arm relax and fall into a comfortable position . . . and the heaviness will disappear . . . good . . . now notice that the helium-filled balloons that were holding your right arm up are beginning to leak and as they do and become smaller and smaller your right arm also begins to move down into a comfortable position in your lap and as that happens you can just feel yourself going deeper and deeper . . . now with both arms at your side . . . resting comfortably, notice how they both feel perfectly normal, as before . . . now back in the hammock, going back and forth . . . back and forth . . . your mind becoming more and more open to the ideas, thoughts, and feelings I describe . . . first becoming aware of a growing feeling of personal strength within you . . . every day becoming stronger and more resilient . . . perhaps even surprising yourself, and you become aware that some of the little things that might have bothered you in the past no longer seem as troubling and, that, increasingly you are able to see things in proper perspective . . . it is so wonderful to have been able to clear the pathway ahead, so you know what you want. Each and every day you will see yourself feeling more committed to those goals and more and more pleased and comforted with your choices . . . because you know that they are the right ones for you . . . and each time you hear these words you'll notice a deeper and more profound sense of calmness . . . and, as a consequence, each day you will bring a deep serenity to your life that will be wonderful for you to appreciate . . . the serenity growing just like the flowers in the garden that surrounds you. Now, of course . . . if you wished to enjoy these deep relaxing feelings for a few more moments . . . that would be fine . . . but there always does come a time when we want to turn to other pleasures in life, so in a moment, as I count from 1 to 3, notice yourself feeling more alert, aware, and oriented and . . . when I get to 3, just let your eyes comfortably open when you wish . . . and it might surprise you how long those comfortable relaxed feelings continue as you resume your activities for the rest of the day . . . just feel the energy, slowly returning to your body . . . 1 . . . feeling very good . . . 2 . . . more and more energy returning to your body . . . 3 becoming fully alert and comfortably relaxed.

Variation One: Images of Walking Erect, Muscular Balance, and Stress Reduction

And so feel yourself walking through the woods . . . enjoying the freedom from responsibility . . . feeling the twigs cracking under your feet . . . touch the bark of one tree . . . then the next . . . seeing them standing tall and erect and feeling yourself walking tall and erect through the woods and feeling wonderful . . . letting go of all of the tension . . . enjoying the smell of pine . . . feeling the sense of freedom

. . . so very, very comfortable that as you walk you feel free . . . so much a part of nature . . . as you continue to go deeper . . . and in the course of walking along, you come across a stream . . . sit yourself next to it . . . noticing leaves floating on the water . . . being carried away . . . so much a part of nature . . . dipping your hand into the water . . . cool . . . relaxed and at times like this being so much aware of the things that are truly important to you . . . that you treasure . . . your health and well-being . . . your body is so precious . . . can heal . . . grow . . . it serves us for so many years . . . but we know that our body demands to be treated with dignity and respect . . . to guard against overdoing . . . it will be interesting to stay within your limits and yet to balance your goals to achieve a positive outcome . . . and as you think of your muscles coming together in harmonious balance . . . harmony and balance . . . it's not tension we seek to avoid . . . but rather a balance we seek . . . have a clear picture of yourself standing tall and erect and signal me with your left hand when you have the image clearly in mind and feeling yourself merging with that image . . . so aware of the balance and harmony that represents . . . strong tall . . . aware of that tingling feeling . . . controlling that feeling . . . and whenever you wish you can have that image . . . tall . . . erect . . . and confident.

Variation Two: Perfectionism, Affective Awareness and Expression, and the Learning Curve

And as you walk along the beach you may become aware of the beautiful sandy beach and know there is no "perfect" way for the sand to be laid out on the beach . . . there are an infinite number of ways for the sand to lie there, one just as beautiful as the next . . . and so you find yourself coming to a greater appreciation for what is . . . and noticing how you can let it be . . . you've suffered long enough . . . it's time to let that go . . . and becoming aware of your feeling . . . knowing your feelings are important . . . you deserve to be treated with respect and dignity . . . you deserve to choose how to communicate your feelings to others . . . in a way that respects both your rights . . . and theirs . . . and as you walk along the beach . . . and you reflect on being a teacher and how change occurs . . . you know learning requires patience . . . and it requires motivation and dedication . . . and that learning always proceeds unevenly . . . unpredictably . . . learning is never perfect . . . we accept that because that is the nature of human beings and as you relearn those skills . . . of standing . . . and walking erect . . . that you used to take for granted . . . but as you enjoy the progress you experience each and every day . . . you will notice your confidence growing stronger and stronger . . . feeling those muscles necessary for your proper walking growing stronger . . . enjoying the newfound freedom to express yourself.

Variation Three: Protecting the Distress Zone and Premise of Assertion

> And now as you feel your "distress zone" becoming stronger and stronger, each and every day . . . feeling almost as though you were protected by a kind of invisible shield so that the things that once bothered you are seen in proper perspective . . . and so you know how you feel and that you begin to make conscious decisions about how to deal with the circumstances in which you find yourself . . . always knowing deeply and firmly, and without reservation . . . that you are ALWAYS entitled to be treated with dignity and respect and that YOUR NEEDS COUNT and that you can find the right pathway to get your needs met in a way that harms you neither mentally nor physically.

I used other variations to reinforce the main cognitive–behavioral themes that guided E. K.'s treatment. She conscientiously used the audiotapes that I made for her. These appeared to be very helpful in facilitating the cognitive restructuring that seemed essential in working with E. K.

Outcomes

E. K. returned to teaching while still experiencing her camptocormic symptoms. After experiencing symptomatic fluctuations that were inevitably correlated with circumstances likely to evoke her anger, she began to add assertive elements to her repertoire, both with her family and with the school administrators. She found herself quite surprised and pleased when her assertiveness failed to result in catastrophes or in her loss of control, the prospect of which was very frightening to her.

Some dimensions of her gains were quantified. These included time and distance measures in which she was walking or standing erect, so that evidence of progress, which she conscientiously charted, was available to point to when she encountered difficulty. As she began walking erect, she first started walking with her feet at somewhat of an angle to her forward path. However, this slowly improved in a process of successive approximation. The monitoring of her progress as she walked into the office from the waiting room became a regular and important part of each session and made the linkage between her gait and posture and her emotional life painfully obvious.

She continues to be seen biweekly with her gait now dramatically improved and with mounting evidence of her ability to better recognize anger and frustration and to seek adaptive ways of dealing with the circumstances and people who give rise to these feelings. She is able to stand and walk erect for most of the time she is at school and home. She still sees herself as "having a ways to go" to achieve all that she would like and anticipates the possibility that she may choose to become more assertive with her parents, something she would have seen as impossible until recently.

CONCLUSION

Somatoform symptoms can be conceptualized as a form of social communication (Szasz, 1961; Barsky & Klerman, 1983). They represent the elements of a story that patients tell themselves and others that express important needs that seem to be unmet in any other way (Sarbin, 1986). Psychotherapy with these patients can be understood as an effort to help them acquire the skill to recognize their needs and express them in new and more effective ways.

It has been proposed that somatic therapeutic approaches, such as biofeedback, with the somatoform patient provide a "Trojan horse" that enables the clinician to administer needed psychotherapeutic interventions wrapped in a somatic disguise (Wickramasekera, 1989). The notion is that the disguise makes palatable interventions that, for most of these patients, have little face validity.

Hypnosis itself can also be viewed as a Trojan horse of a different color. It also provides a platform for the administration of a wide variety of traditional psychotherapeutic interventions within a context in which positive expectations can be identified or shaped (Kirsch, 1994). From the clinician's perspective, hypnosis offers the benefit of theoretical neutrality. It has been integrated effectively with all of the major theoretical orientations from the cognitive–behavioral to the psychodynamic (Brown & Chaves, 1980). Moreover, its use is particularly consonant with the notion of brief therapy, which is becoming more important in today's managed-care environment (Talmon, 1990). Of course there are cautions here. Although there is mounting evidence that adding hypnosis to traditional psychotherapeutic interventions enhances treatment success (Kirsch, Montgomery, & Sapirstein, 1995), it is not clear whether or not there is a time saving as well. That important question requires further exploration.

Similarly, the matter of the suitability of hypnosis is a concern. Not all patients are good hypnotic subjects, although somatoform patients, as a group, are probably more responsive than most when suitably prepared. Hypnotizability has traditionally been thought of as a relatively stable trait (Nadon & Laurence, 1994). Moreover, it has also been assumed that patients must possess sufficient hypnotic ability to benefit from this approach (Levitt, 1993).

Alternatively, data collected in recent years support the notion that hypnotizability is more accurately viewed as a skill than a trait (Bertrand, 1989; Spanos, 1986). Exposing motivated patients to an appropriate training protocol might be expected to augment their ability to use hypnosis as a treatment modality. In any case, it is by no means clear that high levels of hypnotizability are necessary to obtain clinical gains (Chaves, 1989). My impression is that while totally unresponsive patients can probably be more effectively treated with other modalities, once some minimal level of hypnotic responsivity has been achieved, hypnotic procedures can be beneficially used on patients who have positive expectations of its success. Moreover, once that threshold level of hypnotic responsivity is reached, the correlation between formal measures of hypnotizability and clinical outcome is negligible. Thus, from a clinical standpoint, one needs to determine only that the threshold level of responsivity has been exceeded. These, of course, are merely hypotheses that require systematic empirical validation.

The clinical implications of a cognitive–behavioral perspective on hypnosis are only beginning to be appreciated (Chaves, 1994; Spanos & Chaves, 1989). Freedom from a theoretical commitment to the hypnotic trance state can provide an opportunity to redirect attention to those critical aspects of the hypnotic protocol that can maximally enhance treatment outcomes. If hypnotic procedures enhance the efficacy of other psychotherapeutic interventions as the findings of Kirsch and his colleagues suggest (Kirsch, Montgomery, & Sapirstein, 1995), skill in using these techniques should become an integral part of training in psychotherapy. In addition, further research pertaining to expectation effects, preparation for hypnotic interventions, the development of skills training programs for clinical patients to augment responsivity, and additional research on cognitive strategies to facilitate responses to suggestion will be critical to the further explication of the clinical implications of the cognitive–behavioral perspective toward hypnosis.

REFERENCES

American Psychiatric Association. (1987). *Diagnostic and statistical manual of mental disorders* (3rd ed., rev.). Washington, DC: Author.

Barsky, A. J., & Klerman, G. L. (1983). Overview: Hypochondriasis, bodily complaints, and somatic styles. *American Journal of Psychiatry, 140,* 273–283.

Bertrand, L. D. (1989). The assessment and modification of hypnotic susceptibility. In N. P. Spanos & J. F. Chaves (Eds.), *Hypnosis: The cognitive-behavioral perspective* (pp. 18–31). Buffalo, NY: Prometheus Books.

Brown, J. M., & Chaves, J. F. (1980). Hypnosis in the treatment of sexual dysfunction. *Journal of Sex and Marital Therapy, 6,* 63–74.

Carter, T. (1972). Camptocormia: Review and case report. *Bulletin of the Menninger Clinic, 36,* 555–561.

Chaves, J. F. (1979). *Tactics and strategies in clinical hypnosis* (Cassette). San Francisco: Proseminar Inc.

Chaves, J. F. (1985). Hypnosis in the management of phantom limb pain. In T. Dowd & J. Healy (Eds.), *Case studies in hypnotherapy*. New York: Guilford Press.

Chaves, J. F. (1989). Hypnotic control of clinical pain. In N. P. Spanos & J. F. Chaves (Eds.), *Hypnosis: The cognitive-behavioral perspective* (pp. 242–272). Buffalo, NY: Prometheus Books.

Chaves, J. F. (1993). Hypnosis in pain management. In J. W. Rhue, S. J. Lynn, & I. Kirsch (Eds.), *Handbook of clinical hypnosis* (pp. 511–532). Washington, DC: American Psychological Association.

Chaves, J. F. (1994). Recent advances in the application of hypnosis to pain management. *American Journal of Clinical Hypnosis, 37,* 117–129.

Ellenberger, H. F. (1970). *The discovery of the unconscious: The history and evolution of dynamic psychiatry*. New York: Basic Books.

Fetterman, J. L. (1937). Back disorders of psychic origin. *Ohio State Medical Journal, 33,* 777–781.

Fishbein, D. A., & Goldberg, M. (1989). Camptocormia and perceived pain. *Psychosomatics, 30,* 357.

Goffman, E. (1961). *Asylums*. New York: Anchor Books.

Hall, G. W. (1919). Camptocormia (bentback). *Journal of the American Medical Association, 72,* 547–548.

Hamlin, P. G. (1943). Camptocormia: Hysterical bent back of soldiers. Report of two cases. *Military Surgeon, 92,* 295–300.

Hurst, A. F. (1918). The bent back of soldiers. *British Medical Journal, 2,* 621–623.

Kihlstrom, J. F. (1994). One hundred years of hysteria. In S. Lynn & J. W. Rhue (Eds.), *Dissociation: Clinical and theoretical perspectives* (pp. 365–394). New York: Guilford Press.

Kirsch, I. (1990). *Changing expectations: A key to effective psychotherapy*. Pacific Grove, CA: Brooks/Cole.

Kirsch, I. (1994). Clinical hypnosis as a nondeceptive placebo: Empirically derived techniques. *American Journal of Clinical Hypnosis, 37,* 95–106.

Kirsch, I., Montgomery, G., & Sapirstein, G. (1995). Hypnosis as an adjunct to cognitive-behavioral psychotherapy: A meta-analysis. *Journal of Consulting and Clinical Psychology, 63,* 214–220.

Kosbab, F. P. (1961). Camptocormia: A rare case in the female. *American Journal of Psychiatry, 117,* 839–840.

Lazare, A. (1981). Conversion symptoms. *New England Journal of Medicine, 305,* 745–748.

Lazare, A., & Klerman, G. L. (1970). Camptocormia in a female: A five-year study. *British Journal of Medical Psychology, 43,* 265–270.

Levitt, E. E. (1993). Hypnosis in the treatment of obesity. In J. W. Rhue, S. J. Lynn, & I. Kirsch (Eds.), *Handbook of clinical hypnosis* (pp. 511–532). Washington, DC: American Psychological Association.

Massa, E., & Slater, C. B. (1989). Camptocormia and depression: A case report. *Military Medicine, 154*, 352–355.

Miller, R. W., & Forbes, J. F. (1990). Camptocormia. *Military Medicine, 155*, 561–565.

Nadon, R., & Laurence, J.-R. (1994). Idiographic approaches to hypnosis research (or how therapeutic practice can inform science). *American Journal of Clinical Hypnosis, 37*, 85–94.

Quill, T.E. (1985). Somatization disorder: One of medicine's blind spots. *Journal of the American Medical Association, 254*, 3075–3079.

Roberts, S. J. (1994). Somatization in primary care. The common presentation of psychosocial problems through physical complaints. *Nurse Practitioner, 19*, 47, 50–56.

Rockwood, C. A., & Eilbert, R. E. (1969). Camptocormia. *Journal of Bone and Joint Surgery, 51A*, 553–56.

Rosen, J. C., & Frymoyer, J. W. (1985). A review of camptocormia and an unusual case in the female. *Spine, 10*, 325–327.

Saliba, J. (1919). Antalgic spinal distortion. *Journal of the American Medical Association, 72*, 549–550.

Sandler, S. A. (1945). Camptocormia: A functional condition of the back in neurotic soldiers. *War Medicine, 8*, 36–45.

Sarbin, T. R. (1986). *Narrative psychology: The storied nature of human conduct.* New York: Praeger.

Scheff, T. J. (1966). *Being mentally ill: A sociological analysis.* Chicago: Aldine.

Smith, G. R., Jr. (1994). The course of somatization and its effects on utilization of health care resources. *Psychosomatics, 35*, 263–267.

Smith, R. C. (1985). A clinical approach to the somatizing patient. *Journal of Family Practice, 21*, 294–301.

Spanos, N. P. (1971). Goal-directed fantasy and the performance of hypnotic test suggestions. *Psychiatry, 34*, 86–96.

Spanos, N. P. (1986). Hypnosis and the modification of hypnotic susceptibility. In P. L. N. Naish (Ed.), *What is hypnosis?* (pp. 85–120). Philadelphia: Open University Press.

Spanos, N. P., & Chaves, J. F. (1989). Future prospects for the cognitive-behavioral perspective. In N. P. Spanos & J. F. Chaves (Eds.), *Hypnosis: The cognitive-behavioral perspective* (pp. 437–446). Buffalo, NY: Prometheus.

Sutro, C. J., & Hulbert, B. (1946). Hysterical flexion deformity of the vertebral column-camptocormia. *Bulletin of the United States Army Medical Department, 5*, 570–574.

Szasz, T. (1961). *The myth of mental illness.* New York: Dell.

Talmon, M. (1990). *Single session therapy: Maximizing the effect of the first (and often only) therapeutic encounter.* San Francisco: Jossey-Bass.

Tancredi, L. R., & Barondess, J. A. (1978). The problem of defensive medicine. *Science, 200,* 879–882.

Walker, G. F., & Leeds, M. D. (1928). A note on camptocormia. *Lancet, 21,* 808–809.

Wickramasekera, I. (1989). Enabling the somatizing patient to exit the somatic closet: A high-risk model. *Psychotherapy, 26,* 530–544.

Wickramasekera, I. (1993). Assessment and treatment of somatizing disorders: The high risk model of threat perception. In J. Rhue, S. J. Lynn, & I. Kirsch (Eds.), *Handbook of clinical hypnosis* (pp. 587–621). Washington, DC: American Psychological Association.

Wickramasekera, I. (1994). Psychophysiological and clinical implications of the coincidence of high hypnotic ability and high neuroticism during threat perception in somatization disorder. *American Journal of Clinical Hypnosis, 37,* 22–33.

Wickramasekera, I. (1995). Somatization: Concepts, data and predictions from the high risk model of threat perception. *Journal of Nervous and Mental Disease, 183,* 15–23.

8

EMOTIONAL SELF-REGULATION THERAPY FOR TREATING PRIMARY DYSMENORRHEA AND PREMENSTRUAL DISTRESS

SALVADOR AMIGÓ and ANTONIO CAPAFONS

Dysmenorrhea (painful menstruation) is a very common problem, with serious personal, social, and economic ramifications. Estimates of its prevalence vary in the range of 35% to 95% as a function of sample characteristics, assessment instruments, and the definition of the term (Larroy, 1993). The most common estimates are between 50% and 70%, with young women showing the higher rates. Despite differences in estimated rates, one fact is acknowledged by every researcher in the field: In all cultures and in every social class there are dysmenorrheic women. Moreover, they suffer considerably, not only from the pain but also from other aversive symptoms. During a few intense days, the quality of life of the dysmenorrheic woman is severely compromised by a variety of symptoms: pain in the legs, back, abdomen, and other body parts; negative affect prior to menstruation (e.g., irritability, dysphoric feelings, and loss of interest); gastrointestinal alterations (e.g., diarrhea, constipation, and nausea); and other disabling idiosyncratic symptoms.

In the United States alone, as many as 150 million work hours are lost each year because of dysmenorrhea (Larroy, 1993), with some authors (Sobcyzk, 1980) estimating that dysmenorrheic women miss at least two days of work per month. Although some have argued (Friederichs, 1983) that this statistic may underestimate the magnitude of the problem, there is general agreement that dysmenorrhea decreases work performance during the menstrual period. It is also worth noting that dysmenorrhea is one of the most frequent causes of labor absenteeism in Spain. Botella (1978), for example, reports that dysmenorrheic women lose between one-half and five work days per month.

Although several pharmacological and surgical treatments have been tried for dysmenorrhea, all of them have shortcomings. Surgery is especially problematic because it is not only invasive but also ineffective. Ovulation inhibitors have been widely used, but their range of application is limited. They cannot be used with patients who want to become pregnant, their use is contraindicated in other patients, and they have the potential to produce negative side effects. Prostaglandin inhibitors also have iatrogenic side effects and may need to be prescribed in combination with analgesic drugs (Larroy, 1993).

Psychological interventions seem to be especially indicated for dysmenorrhea because they can be applied to nearly everyone and do not provoke negative side effects. Moreover, they are easily learned and are more cost-effective than physical interventions. Several different psychological strategies have been used for treating dysmenorrheic patients (Denney and Gerrard, 1991; Larroy, 1993). Among these strategies are hypnosis, relaxation, biofeedback, information, and stress-inoculation training. Although methodological problems make it difficult to establish the effectiveness of psychological treatments, relaxation training and stress-inoculation training seem to be the most promising approaches.

Hypnosis has been used for relaxation (Dorcus & Kirkner, 1948; Leckie, 1964) and with accompanying suggestions that menstruation is a natural process and will no longer be painful (Kroger & Freed, 1943; Leckie, 1964). Hypnoanalysis has been used when prior direct suggestions have failed to reduce discomfort (Leckie). Unfortunately, despite these encouraging early reports of the use of hypnotherapy in ameliorating dysmenorrheic symptoms, dysmenorrhea has become a forgotten problem in the hypnosis literature. This is somewhat surprising, insofar as dysmenorrhea has a topographic similarity to pain, which is one of the most extensively studied topics in the field of hypnosis. Because dysmenorrheic patients suffer pain every month, they can be considered chronic pain patients.

Misleading conceptions of hypnosis and the lack of rigorous outcome data indicating its effectiveness have made many professionals reluctant to use hypnosis in treating dysmenorrhea. Similarly, some patients are leery of hypnosis, and it is not always possible to assuage their fears by giving them corrective information. Emotional self-regulation therapy is a set of treatments developed by Amigó (Amigó 1992, 1995; also see Capafons & Amigó, 1995) as an alternative to conventional hypnosis. It is especially useful for patients with fearful or otherwise negative attitudes toward hypnosis.

Self-regulation therapy is based on the use of sensory recall exercises, through which clients learn to respond actively to suggestions. Suggestions are given without a trance induction and without having the client close his or her eyes or adopt a passive attitude. Also, unlike conventional hypnosis, there is no loss of initiative or "subsidence of the planning function" (see Hilgard, 1986, p. 164) during self-regulation therapy. As a result, there is no inhibition of fluent, spontaneous, self-initiated speech and behavior. During emotional self-regulation therapy, the client can speak with the therapist as usual, while maintaining a high level of responsiveness to suggestions. Because there is no inhibition of initiative, the patient is able to play an active role in choosing and improving strategies and suggestions proposed by the therapist.

Outcome studies have demonstrated that self-regulation therapy is an effective treatment for smoking cessation and obesity (Capafons, 1993; Capafons & Amigó, 1995; Capafons & Amigó, 1995). In a pilot study, Sanchez and Moix (1993) reported the successful treatment of two dysmenorrheic patients through emotional self-regulation therapy, the most common form of self-regulation therapy. This work, as well as the personal, economic, and social repercussions of dysmenorrhea, encouraged us to apply emotional self-regulation therapy to a patient, Anna, who sought psychological help for dysmenorrhea.

BACKGROUND INFORMATION

Anna was a 22-year-old, single undergraduate student majoring in nursing. In the diagnostic interview, she reported that she experienced several distressing symptoms during menstruation: swelling and hypersensitivity in her breast, irritability, crying, and an intense pain in her lower back and abdomen. Her menstrual cycles were irregular, with an approximate duration of 30 days. The average duration of her menstruation was 6 days. Pain and discomfort appeared during the first 2 days, fading slowly as menstruation progressed. She could tell when her menstruation was starting because of a disagreeable taste in her mouth prior to her period. Both her mother and her sister were also dysmenorrheic.

Anna had been in treatment for dysmenorrhea for 3 years before seeking self-regulation therapy. Her initial therapist was a physician who prescribed contraceptive pills. Anna used them for about 3 months, during which time she experienced some symptomatic relief. Nevertheless, she decided to stop this treatment because of medication-related side effects (specifically breast swelling). Her physician then prescribed antangil 500, an analgesic and anti-inflammatory drug, which Anna used during the first days of her menstruation. Although it was effective in reducing pain, Anna was very interested in exploring psychological treatment for residual discomfort.

At the end of the diagnostic interview, Anna was given two assessment instruments to be completed during her next menstruation: the Menstrual Symptom Questionnaire (MSQ; Chesney and Tasto, 1975) and the Inventory of Primary Dysmenorrhea Symptoms (IPDS; Larroy, Vallejo, & Labrador, 1988). The MSQ is a 24-item scale, on which the frequency of various dysmenorrheic symptoms is assessed. As recommended by Stephenson, Denney, and Aberger (1983), the scale was changed to a 6-point intensity of symptom scale (0 = no intensity; 5 = high intensity). The Inventory of Primary Dysmenorrhea Symptoms (IPDS; Larroy, Vallejo, & Labrador, 1988) contains a list of symptoms to be rated by the patient on an 11-point scale (0 = no intensity; 10 = severe, disabling intensity) three times per day (covering the periods of 7 a.m. to 2 p.m., 2 p.m. to 8 p.m., and 8 p.m. to 7 a.m.). The results of periodic assessments during and after treatment will be examined in the case discussion that follows.

TREATMENT

Choice of Treatment

Anna knew that the therapist (the first author) worked with suggestive techniques, including hypnosis. She was particularly interested in being treated with self-regulation therapy, as she had been told by a friend that it was effective for many problems. Anna hoped to develop control of her menstrual pain and to learn psychological techniques for reducing her menstrual discomfort. In the initial diagnostic session, when Anna received the questionnaires, the therapist informed her about the different techniques he used in his clinical practice. Anna was told that hypnosis could be applied as well as self-regulation therapy. The latter technique, however, would allow her to keep her eyes open and to move around without the constraints produced by suggestions for heaviness or drowsiness.

The therapist suggested that self-regulation therapy might be more advantageous than traditional hypnosis, which does not emphasize a flexible, individualized approach to generating and using optimally effective suggestions for pain relief. According to Hilgard and Hilgard (1975), substantial levels of pain reduction occur only in a very small percentage of highly suggestible subjects. Moreover, there is a wide variety of analgesic suggestions, and the effectiveness of a particular suggestion can vary considerably from subject to subject. Usually, it is necessary to test different suggestions, until the most effective one for a particular patient is found. The same appears to be true of other sensory suggestions (e.g., suggested warmth leading to an increase in peripheral temperature), which are very useful in the treatment of dysmenorrhea. In short, emotional self-regulation therapy, which emphasizes flexibility and active patient involvement, has clear advantages over standard hypnotic techniques with respect to choosing and using the most effective analgesic and sensory suggestions.

The Therapeutic Rationale

Anna returned for the first treatment session 1 week after the beginning of her menstrual period. At the beginning of the session, her responses to the assessment instruments were analyzed. Her MSQ score was 57, with the highest scores being for lower abdominal pain and swelling, breast sensitivity and pain, lower back pain, and premenstrual tension and nervousness. Her average daily IPDS scores during the first 3 days of menstruation are shown in Table 1. As can be seen, the most severe symptoms occurred on the second day of menstruation.

After reviewing Anna's self-monitoring records, the therapeutic intervention was initiated. The therapist began by explaining the concept of sensory recall as follows:

> Self-regulation therapy is mainly based on the training and use of sensory recall. Sensory recall is a brain mechanism that allows us to reexperience feelings and emotions associated with significant past events. So, if we listen to a particular song that was associated with the end of a love relationship, we may reexperience sadness and depression, very similar, if not equal, to those we experienced in the actual situation, even though it happened long ago. It is possible, also, to reexperience emotions and sensations when we look at pictures of an exciting trip we made several years ago to the Sahara Desert. When

TABLE 1
Mean Scores of Baseline Dysmenorrhea Symptoms

Symptom	Menstruation Day		
	1	2	3
Spasms	2.00	6.30	0.00
Swelling	2.00	5.60	0.60
Back pain	2.30	6.30	0.00
Irritability and depression	2.30	6.60	4.30
General discomfort	1.60	5.30	0.80
Digestive symptoms	0.00	2.60	0.00

Note. Anna's scores on the 11-point scale of the Inventory of Primary Dysmenorrhea Symptoms (Larroy, Vallego, & Labrador, 1988). Spasms = spasms and contractions in the abdomen and inner side of the thighs; Swelling = Swelling and tenderness in breast and low abdomen; Back pain = lower back pain or spasms; Irritability and depression = irritability, depression, fatigue, and lack of motivation; General discomfort = headaches and weakness; Digestive alterations = nausea, vomiting, diarrhea, and so on.

observing these pictures, we can feel, to some degree, the enjoyment of the trip, or we may feel the hot sensation of the sun burning our skin, or perhaps the fear of getting lost.

So you can see that sensory recall allows to us to experience emotion and sensations from the past, in a very automatic, involuntary, and intense way. If we could use this mechanism voluntarily, we would benefit a lot from it. For example, we could reproduce the relaxed feelings of a peaceful and calm day or the happiness of achieving a success. Maybe we could reproduce the anesthetic sensation produced by a Novocain injection during a dental procedure.

As you will soon see, we can use mental exercises in sensory recall to stimulate the cortex of the brain, after which we can use direct suggestions to reexperience any sensation of emotion stored in our memory. Self-regulation therapy enables us to manage and master sensory recall. Thus it will be very useful for ameliorating your problem. Now, we will do several exercises created for stimulating, developing, and controlling the sensory recall process, and for profiting from it therapeutically.

Emotional self-regulation therapy, which is one of a number of self-regulation therapy procedures, was the chosen alternative for Anna. It has three phases, which are described in the following sections.

Phase One: Acquisition

After reviewing the therapeutic rationale, the therapist told Anna that treatment success depends on several factors:

1. Motivation. The patient should be motivated and interested in collaborating with the therapist to master the sensory recall exercises essential to the treatment of her primary dysmenorrhea.
2. Attitude. The patient should neither "force" her responses to the sensory exercises nor become impatient for their appearance. The correct attitude to adopt is "to let things happen," while confidently awaiting the response to come. It is not helpful to try too hard or to be anxious about the outcome.
3. Interferences. Because it is very important that the patient collaborate with the therapist and that she develop a favorable attitude toward the exercises, she should reject any interfering thoughts, such as "these exercises are stupid" or "it won't work."
4. Learning. The client is told that self-regulation therapy is a learning process. In other words, performance improves with practice. Following this line of thinking, a failure should not discourage the patient because she can check for possible mis-

takes and learn how to use suggestions in a more effective way. Responding will improve with practice.

5. Individual differences. The therapist explains that not all people respond in the same way to suggestions. As in nearly every therapeutic procedure, some people benefit more than others. Moreover, some sensory recall exercises work better than others for the same person, and some sensations may be easier to experience than others. For example, sensations of warmth may be easier to experience than anesthesia in the thumb. Thus, the patient should not become worried if she cannot experience some of the suggested sensations, as she and the therapist can choose those sensations that work best for her.

After this explanation of the factors that are essential for the effective use of self-regulation therapy, the therapist initiated sensory recall exercises. The exercises were based on four items of the emotional self-regulation scale (Amigó, 1992): hand numbness, arm heaviness, smell, and taste.

First, the therapist asked Anna to introduce her right hand into a receptacle filled with cold water (about 4° Celsius, 39.2° Fahrenheit). She submerged her hand in the water and reported all the sensations she experienced. Anna said that her palm was cool, her fingers tingled, and she had sensations of numbness, as if her hand were made of cardboard. Finger stiffness was also reported. Anna was asked to make a note of each of these reactions so that she could later reproduce them without the help of the physical stimulus (cold water).

Once Anna observed her reactions, she took her hand out of the receptacle, letting it dry while the therapist explained the other parts of the exercise. The next task was for her to reintroduce her hand into the receptacle, and when sensations appeared, mentally associate them with a cue to facilitate reproduction of the sensations. The therapist suggested several possibilities: The cue could be imagining putting her hand into a freezer or thinking of the words "cold" or "stiffness"; perhaps associating the image of the freezer with the words, repeating them several serial times; or telling herself something like "later, when I try to reproduce sensations, I will think of my cold hand, numb and stiff, and then the sensations will happen easily."

Anna chose an image of an ice cube in her hand. She put her hand back into the receptacle and held it in the cool water. At the same time she imagined holding the ice cube. Once she had established an association of the image of the ice cube with the sensations she was experiencing, she took her hand out of the water and dried it. When the sensations disappeared, she was able to reproduce the sensations without the aid of the stimulus.

First, the therapist asked her to select a cue for stopping the sensation. This cue could be counting to 3, imagining the hand becoming warmer, or saying "stop." Anna chose the word *stop*. Then, the therapist took the receptacle off of the table and asked Anna to put her hand into the same position she had before, as if the receptacle were still there. In this position, Anna was instructed to think of an ice cube in her hand and await the reactions, but without forcing them—just let them happen. Anna began to report a tickling sensation, numbness, and stiffness. She could not reproduce coldness. The therapist told her that it was not necessary to reproduce all of the sensations for the exercise to be considered successful. After Anna was informed that depending on the person, some sensations are more easily reproduced than others, she said the word *stop* and was able to curtail the reproduced sensations. The therapist reinforced her for reproducing sensations on the first trial and encouraged her to perform the three remaining sensory recall exercises on the emotional self-regulation scale.

The second item of the scale teaches the patient to reproduce a sensation of heaviness, together with arm tension and lowering, instigated first by placing a large book or similarly heavy object on the person's hand. The third item uses an ashtray with ashes to reproduce an olfactory sensation. In the fourth item, the patient reproduces taste sensations instigated by lemon juice. Anna accomplished all of these exercises by following the same sequence of procedures described for the first exercise (iced water). Then, the therapist started the second phase.

Phase Two: Stimulus Generalization

In this phase the goal is to develop the patient's sense of mastery. One or two exercises of the first phase are repeated, without use of the physical stimulus. The patient does this until she is able to reproduce reactions and her brain "gets more activated," thus facilitating the use of direct suggestions. This is achieved at the end of the second phase.

In Anna's case, the therapist chose the hand stiffness and ash smell exercises because these were the sensations produced most successfully during phase one. Using the ice cube image, Anna was asked to reproduce stiffness and numbness in her hand. When she succeeded, the therapist explained that these sensations could be reproduced if associated to other objects or activities. The idea is for the patient to practice eliciting the response several times, using a different cue each time. Anna was told that she could associate the sensations she was experiencing with grasping the knob of the office door. This association could be made through any of a number of "strategies" suggested by the therapist. For instance, Anna could repeat verbally "stiff hand–doorknob"; she could successively pair images of the stiff hand with images of the doorknob; she could tell herself "later, when I grasp the doorknob, I will notice all sensations I am feeling now"; or she could imagine herself going to the door, touching the doorknob and reproducing sensations.

Anna chose the imagined association between stiff hand and doorknob. When she believed that the association had been established, she ended the sensations by telling herself "stop." A few seconds later, the therapist asked Anna to grasp the doorknob. She went to the door; took the doorknob; and, trusting the appearance of the response, she awaited it. Indeed, only a few seconds later, she reported noticing finger itching and hand stiffness. This last sensation was evident when the therapist separated the hand from the doorknob. The hand was stiff and her fingers remained curved, as if they were really grasping the knob. This was an especially surprising experience for Anna.

After Anna stopped the response, she did a similar exercise using the ash smell. When she reported the ash smell sensation and noticed her nose stinging, the therapist suggested that she could associate those responses with a book that was on the table. Thus, by smelling the book, she could reproduce the ash smell and stinging sensation. The therapist told her that she could use the same strategy she had used in the hand exercise, associating an image of the book with the sensations she had described. She succeeded again: After smelling the book for a few seconds, she reported clear sensations of nose sting and ash smell. This was a very surprising experience for Anna.

Next, both exercises were repeated with different cue objects, for example, touching a ballpoint pen, a lighter, and a book and smelling a pencil, a sheet, and a watch. The procedure in all cases was the same: to associate repeatedly the reactions with an image of the object, as was done in the first exercise. With each new exercise, the therapist suggested increased control and mastery. When an exercise was initiated, the therapist told Anna: "Each time you try, you can make the association between sensations and objects more quickly and easily. The time needed to do so is shorter each time, and you will need fewer trials to make the association. The sensations are clearer and you can reproduce them more quickly. This is due to repetition of the association, which stimulates the brain, as if you were doing a mental exercise. This practice produces faster and easier associations. Soon your brain will be able to reproduce the sensations automatically in response to direct suggestion alone, without you having to imagine anything."

The patient continued doing exercises, each time more quickly and with stronger feelings of effectiveness and mastery. When all exercises were completed, the therapist told Anna that as a result of her practice and training, they could use direct suggestion alone for producing responses. She would now be able to reproduce nearly every response without using cognitive strategies. To achieve hand rigidity, for example, it was sufficient to offer a suggestion such as: "When you touch the side of the table, your hand will become stiff." With a few trials, Anna was able to verify for herself that direct suggestion from the therapist was sufficient to produce the expected outcome, without first establishing mental associations.

Phase Three: Response Generalization

This phase is started by the therapist telling the client:

Now you have verified that all of the responses you practiced in the exercises can be produced by suggestion alone. The repetition of these exercises has activated the cortex of your brain. It has increased your responsiveness to suggestion and made it easier to reproduce sensations you have not experienced here in the therapy room. This implies that a new suggestion (for example, warmth in the hand) will initiate a process in which your brain will activate the proper associative centers for producing this sensation clearly and automatically. We will test it, with several new suggestions, while you preserve the same positive collaborative attitude of "letting things happen" that you have developed in the previous exercises.

Next, the therapist suggested a number of sensations and emotions such as those described by Amigó (1992). In Anna's case, happy feelings and selective amnesia were chosen. Both suggestions were very effective for Anna. When the therapist suggested that she feel happy, her face brightened, she smiled, and began to laugh. She felt very joyful and happy. For the amnesia suggestion, the therapist told Anna that she would be able to forget the number 4 when she counted from 1 to 5. To do so, she needed to rely only on the belief that it will happen, eliminating any distracting interference. Anna counted to 5 without the 4. Then, after the therapist canceled the suggestion she counted to 5, naming the 4. Anna expressed surprise that she had experienced a "mental vacuum" between the numbers 3 and 5.

These exercises proved to Anna that she could respond to novel suggestions without needing to associate them with actual stimuli or to practice generating them. The therapist told her that in the next session, one week later, she would learn how to manage therapeutic suggestions for the treatment of primary dysmenorrhea. Finally, a rapid reinduction cue was established to avoid having to repeat the whole training procedure. This was comparable to the use of posthypnotic suggestion to produce rapid induction of hypnosis in later sessions. Anna, advised by the therapist, chose hand stiffness as the reinduction cue. Another session was then scheduled for the following week.

The Second Therapy Session

In this session, the therapist showed Anna several ways of using suggestion therapeutically. The first step was to establish therapeutic goals based on ameliorating dysmenorrhea symptoms noted during the assessment session. The first goal was to reduce the psychological tension, anxiety, and irritability that usually appeared in the days before menstruation and continued into the menstrual period. A second very important goal was to reduce the pain associated with Anna's period. Anna suffered from intense and intermittent pain in the lower abdomen, lower back, and inner sides of the thighs. Breast pain and sensitivity were another very uncomfortable symptom. She was very motivated to learn to control the pain psychologically so that she might reduce or even eliminate the need for analgesic medication. Finally, Anna wished to alleviate the more general feelings of discomfort that she experienced in her lower abdomen and back.

Once therapeutic goals were established, the therapist gave Anna the reinduction cue created in the last session, by suggesting that her hand was becoming stiff and numb. After only a few seconds, she began to feel tingling, stiffness, and numbness, indicating that she was receptive to suggestion. Nevertheless, because this was the first time that the cue was used, the therapist repeated this "reinduction" procedure several times, by suggesting hand stiffness when Anna touched various objects. These exercises took about 5 minutes. Next, the therapist told Anna that she was as highly receptive to suggestions as she had been at the end of the last session.

The first therapeutic suggestions were given to reduce psychological tension. The therapist suggested that Anna would become very gay and happy. After a few seconds, her face blushed a little, she smiled openly, and she reported feeling gay and happy. Then the therapist suggested that each time she thinks of the word *happiness*, she will quickly and easily experience the sensations of the very good mood she felt at that moment. Moreover, each time she looks at her watch for at least a minute, the happiness and good mood will reappear. These cues would allow her to reproduce a good mood under nearly any circumstance, including the days or hours before her period.

Relaxation suggestions often improve general mood. Therefore, the therapist suggested that Anna could relax quickly and completely by thinking the word *float*, by imagining herself floating on the water of the ocean on a peaceful spring afternoon, or by imagining traveling weightlessly to the moon (Spiegel & Spiegel, 1978). This strategy is based on the rationale that when the human body floats, the muscular system relaxes completely. Anna preferred to close her eyes and sit comfortably in an armchair, while awaiting the effects of the relaxation suggestion. When she thought of the word *float*, she noticed that her whole body relaxed completely and her breathing became more slow and peaceful. Next, the therapist suggested that she feel the relaxation with eyes open, when seated in an uncomfortable position, and even when standing. Within a few minutes, Anna learned to relax quickly and easily.

The next therapeutic goal was pain control. The therapist emphasized the efficacy of self-regulation therapy for this goal because it allowed the therapist and patient to collaborate actively in searching for the most effective suggestions for ameliorating pain. Pain management is a complex task because there is great interindividual variability in responses to various general analgesia suggestions. Thus, the therapist presented a wide range of pain-management suggestions to Anna. She choose the pain-thermometer and distraction suggestions as most likely to be effective and sustain her interest.

The pain-thermometer technique was presented as follows: Anna assessed her pain on an 11-point scale (from 0 = no pain, to 10 = intense and disabling pain), while imagining it on a mercury thermometer. Her task was to slowly lower the mercury level until it reached 0, while simultaneously reducing her pain. To distract herself from the pain, Anna imagined a very pleasant scene, in which she was sailing her brother's boat with relatives and friends. While she was absorbed in the image, the pain disappeared.

The effects of these suggestions were tested during the session, using a variation of the sub-maximum-effort tourniquet technique (Smith, Egbert, Markowitz, Mosteller, & Peecher, 1966). This consists of inflating a blood-pressure cuff on the subject's arm until it reaches 240 mm/hg. Then the subject closes the fist tightly for 20 seconds, followed by 20 seconds of relaxation, for 10 trials. At the end of the 10 trials, a pain report is requested. Using this as a pain stimulus, Anna was able to verify that the most effective and interesting suggestion for her was the pain thermometer. Distraction was not very effective: Anna was able to reduce her pain by only 2 points (from 8 to 6) on each of two trials. The therapist, therefore, suggested she change to the thermometer method. This produced better results. On the first trial, she reduced her pain to 4 and, on the second trial, reduced her pain to 0.

Finally, the therapist suggested that Anna experience warm sensations in her right hand. At first, she could only achieve a light sensation of warmth. Then the therapist asked her to generate additional images. Anna imagined her hand coming near a stove. It provoked a stronger sensation of warmth than the previous direct suggestion. Nevertheless, it was very difficult to transmit this sensation to her abdomen. Anna put her warmed hand on her lower abdomen, but she did not feel the sensation in this area of her body. The therapist did not continue with this suggestion because the session had become too long (1 hour and a half). Instead, the therapist suggested that she would learn to transfer the warmth sensation to the lower abdomen in the next session the following week (before her next menstruation).

The Third Therapy Session

Because of an illness, Anna's third session was rescheduled for the week following her period. In the meantime, the therapist recommended that she use self-suggestions of general well-being and relaxation and the analgesia and warmth suggestions. To assess the efficacy of suggestions, Anna was also asked to complete the MSQ questionnaire and to rate her symptoms on the IPDS.

During the next session, Anna reported that the most effective suggestion was relaxation when thinking of the word *float* with closed eyes. Analgesic instructions were moderately effective because she was able to reduce her medication to 50% less than her usual dose during the first days of her menstruation. Anna's score on the MSQ was 43 (compared with the score of 57 that was recorded following her pervious menstruation). Mean symptom scores during the first three days of her menstruation are shown in Table 2. On the whole, the MSQ and self-record scores were somewhat lower during this menstruation than at base line.

After reviewing her scores, the therapist proposed that Anna practice the therapeutic suggestions, especially the warmth suggestion. She began by activating the cue for the reinduction of receptiveness, while the therapist suggested feelings of stiffness and numbness in her right hand. She repeated the exercise twice, while receiving suggestions of increasing receptiveness and capacity for responding to suggestion. Then she practiced the mood change suggestion. The therapist proposed that she begin using it in the hours prior to her next period. Later, the therapist suggested

TABLE 2
Mean Scores of Dysmenorrhea Symptoms After Two Therapeutic
Sessions

Symptom	Menstruation Day		
	1	2	3
Spasms	1.00	2.00	0.00
Swelling	1.60	5.00	1.60
Back pain	2.00	4.30	0.60
Irritability and depression	2.00	4.30	3.60
General discomfort	2.00	4.30	2.00
Digestive symptoms	0.00	0.60	0.00

Note. See Table 1 for description of symptoms.

relaxation, with particular emphasis on the painful and problematic perineal muscles. Next, Anna applied the pain-induction and the thermometer suggestions. Anna easily lowered her pain to 0 on both trials.

Finally, Anna attempted to achieve a sensation of warmth in her lower abdominal and lumbar zone. Although she could warm her hand, she could not transfer this sensation to other locations. The therapist then proposed another kind of suggestion, based on giving a color to cold and warm sensations: blue for cold, and red for heat. Anna imagined that her lower abdomen was colored blue and frozen, but that it was slowly becoming red, warm, and comfortable. Anna reported a very pleasant warm sensation when imagining red, but it was weak and faded quickly. The therapist then proposed another suggestion: She was to briefly but vigorously rub her lower abdomen with her hand, until she produced a warm sensation. To facilitate sensory recall, Anna was instructed to remember the warm sensation so as to be able to reproduce it later. Anna was able to reproduce a slight sensation of warmth, similar to that achieved by rubbing her abdomen, but it was not very intense. The therapist considered abandoning this suggestion, but Anna suggested that she combine both exercises: sensory recall and the visualization of a red color in her low abdomen. Anna reported that this new strategy was very effective, and she performed it two or three times until the session was finished.

Anna's idea of combining suggestions emphasizes several important aspects of self-regulation therapy: the active collaboration of the patient in the therapeutic process, the possibility of learning to creatively develop and apply new suggestions, and the importance of practice and training for improving the response to therapeutic suggestions.

Fourth and Fifth Therapy Sessions

Before her next menstruation, Anna received two more therapeutic sessions, one per week. In these two sessions, the therapeutic work consisted of repeating and perfecting the responses that were practiced in previous sessions. During these sessions, Anna mastered all of the strategies she practiced. She was able to relax deeply in any position by merely thinking of the word *float* with open or closed eyes, although she could relax better with closed eyes. She also could improve her mood by looking at her watch for a minute. If she simultaneously remembered pleasant experiences from the past, her positive mood lasted for a longer time.

The effectiveness of the pain-thermometer suggestion obviated the use of other analgesia suggestions. Anna was able to reduce her pain to 0 each time she used that suggestion. Response to the warmth suggestion improved greatly when she visualized a red color that expanded from the center of her lower abdomen to the full girth of her waist. Anna was able to voluntarily produce warmth through this image, regardless of her body position and whether her eyes were open or closed.

During these two sessions, Anna imagined that her menstruation was beginning, practiced using the strategies she had learned and gained confidence in their effectiveness, and monitored how the symptoms were reduced, eliminated, or controlled. The therapist encouraged Anna to use all of the strategies she learned from the first moment she noticed symptoms of her next period. The disagreeable taste Anna experienced several hours before her menstruation served as the cue for applying therapeutic strategies, especially the change in her mood, the relaxation of her lower abdomen, and the feeling of warmth. The therapist scheduled an appointment for 1 week after her period and asked her to bring in completed questionnaires at that time.

Termination and Follow-Up

At the beginning of the termination session, Anna reported that her menstrual discomfort had been much lower than during her two previous periods. The abdominal swelling had felt considerably less intense, and she had used medication only on the first day of her period. She also reported that she had made use of a hot-water bottle that she generally used during her periods as a stimulus for sensory recall exercises to improve her ability to reproduce the sensation of warmth. Anna's score on the MSQ had gone down to 25. As shown in Table 3, the average IPDS scores for the first 3 days of her menstruation were considerably lower than during the two prior menstrual periods.

In this session, difficulties in the application of the techniques during her last menstruation were discussed, and exercises chosen because of their effectiveness in previous sessions were practiced. Also, Anna was encour-

TABLE 3
Mean Scores of Dysmenorrhea Symptoms at the Post-treatment

Symptom	Menstruation Day		
	1	2	3
Spasms	0.00	2.60	0.60
Swelling	2.00	2.00	0.00
Back pain	0.00	0.60	0.60
Irritability and depression	0.60	3.60	1.60
General discomfort	0.60	3.60	1.60
Digestive symptoms	0.00	0.00	0.00

Note. See Table 1 for description of symptoms.

aged to develop her creative ability for developing new suggestions and to use those that proved effective. Finally, Anna was asked to complete the questionnaires during her next three periods.

Anna recorded symptoms only during the last of her three subsequent periods. As can be seen in Table 4, her mean scores indicate that her therapeutic gains were stable. Scores on the first day are slightly higher than those at posttreatment, becoming lower on the third day. Anna reported that she no longer used any medication for ameliorating her symptoms.

CONCLUSION

This case study demonstrates the advantages of using suggestion in place of physical interventions for dysmenorrhea. Suggestive therapies are cost-effective; they can be conducted on a timely basis; and they are well-tolerated and even experienced as pleasant, with no iatrogenic effects. In this case, suggestions were used within the framework of self-regulation therapy that encouraged immediate feedback from the patient, within an atmosphere of collaboration and mutual effort. In addition the patient adopts an active creative attitude toward treatment, avoiding the traditional "passive" role of the "hypnotized" participant.

The most salient principle of self-regulation therapy is flexibility. Self-regulation therapy can be adapted to each patient's preferences, needs, and styles. Because patients provide the therapist with immediate feedback regarding the effectiveness of a particular suggestion or metaphor, the therapist is able to modify strategies to maximize treatment gains. The flexibility of this method makes failure impossible. Because the procedures involve trial-and-error learning and experimentation, an ineffective suggestion does not imply that the patient or the therapist is incompetent.

TABLE 4
Mean Scores of Dysmenorrhea Symptoms at Follow-up (Three Months)

Symptom	Menstruation Day		
	1	2	3
Spasms	1.30	2.60	0.00
Swelling	1.30	2.00	0.00
Back pain	0.30	1.30	0.30
Irritability and depression	0.60	2.30	1.00
General discomfort	1.00	1.60	0.00
Digestive symptoms	0.00	0.30	0.00

Note. See Table 1 for description of symptoms.

On the contrary, both patient and therapist acquire useful knowledge: that a particular sensory recall strategy is not effective and that an alternative intervention must be explored. This is to be expected, on occasion, because each patient may have different experiences of the same stimulus or bring different skills and abilities to treatment. Thus, the principles of flexibility and making failure impossible are linked to the collaborative therapeutic alliance and the patient's active participation in the treatment process.

Through flexibility and trial-and-error learning, self-regulation therapy promotes a sense of hopefulness. It teaches patients that they can do many more things than they initially thought were possible, and that the new skills they acquire can alleviate their problems. As Frank (1985) has pointed out, patients improve when they believe that the therapeutic ritual and rationale are convergent and when both are perceived as a source of future well-being.

It is important that patients receive a scientific explanation of the therapeutic process and that they view themselves as the primary agent of change. The therapist is only a collaborator, an expert in research and scientific methods who helps the patient to discover optimal ways of accessing and using relevant skills and abilities. Emotional self-regulation therapy provides patients with experimentally derived and empirically tested techniques. It is not useful, however, for every problem and every patient. Moreover, it is not a technique that should be used by every therapist. Self-regulation therapy should be used only by therapists with considerable experience in hypnosis, who can readily generate appropriate suggestions and metaphors, inspiring in the patient a sense of mastery.

The effectiveness of self-regulation therapy for obesity and nicotine addiction has been demonstrated in controlled research (Capafons, 1993; Capafons & Amigó, 1995). Similar research is needed to establish the efficacy of the treatment described here for dysmenorrhea. Among the questions that should be addressed are the role of active and creative patient attitudes, the kind of patients that benefit from this approach, the persistence of treatment gains (including the effectiveness of support sessions for long-term maintenance), and the effectiveness of self-regulation therapy compared with traditional hypnosis, placebo, and wait-list control groups.

REFERENCES

Amigó, S. (1992). Manual de terapia de auto-regulación [Self-regulation therapy manual]. Valencia, Spain: Promolibro.

Amigó, S. (1995). Self-regulation therapy and the voluntary reproduction of stimulant effects of ephedrine: Possible therapeutic applications. *Contemporary Hypnosis, 11*, 108–120.

Botella, J. (1978). Tratado de ginecología [Gynecological treatment]. Barcelona, Spain: Editorial Cientifico-Técnica.

Capafons, A. (1993). Terapia de auto-regulación e investigación empírica [Self-regulation therapy and empirical investigation]. In A. Capafons & S. Amigó (Eds.), *Hipnosis, Terapia de Auto-Regulación e Intervención Comportamental*. Valencia, Spain: Promolibro.

Capafons, A. & Amigó, S. (1995). Emotional self-regulation therapy for smoking reduction: Description and initial data. *International Journal of Clinical and Experimental Hypnosis, 53,* 7–19.

Chesney, M., & Tasto, D. (1975). The development of MSQ. *Behaviour Research and Therapy, 13,* 237–253.

Denney, D. R., & Gerrard, M. (1991). Tratamientos conductuales de la dismenorrea primaria [Behavioral treatments for primary dysmenorrhea]. In J. Gil Roales-Nieto & T. A. Ayllon (Eds.), *Medicina Conductual I. Intervenciones conductuales en problemas médicos y de salud.* [Behavioral medicine 1. Behavioral interventions for medical problems and health]. Granada: Universidad de Granada.

Dorcus, R. M., & Kirkner, F. J. (1948). The use of hypnosis in the suppression of untractible pain. *Journal of Abnormal Social Psychology, 43,* 237–239.

Frank, J. (1985). Therapeutic components shared by all psychotherapies. In M. Mahoney & A. Freeman (Eds.), *Cognition and Psychotherapy.* New York: Plenum Press.

Friederichs, M. A. (1983). Dysmenorrhea. *Women and Health, 8,* 91–106

Kroger, W. S., & Freed, S. C. (1943). The psychosomatic treatment of functional dysmenorrhea by hypnosis. *American Journal of Obstetrics & Gynecology, 46,* 817–822.

Hilgard, E. R. (1986) *Divided consciousness: Multiple controls in human thought and action* (expanded ed). New York: Wiley.

Hilgard, E. R., & Hilgard, J. R. (1975). *Hypnosis in the relief of pain.* Los Altos, CA: Kaufman.

Larroy, C. (1993). Menstruación: Trastornos y tratamiento [Menstruation: Disorders and treatment]. Madrid, Spain: Edudema.

Larroy, C., Vallejo, M., & Labrador, F. (1988). Evaluación de tres tratamientos conductuales para la dismenorrea funcional [Evaluation of three behavioral treatments for functional dysmenorrhea]. *Cuadernos de Medicina Psicosomática y Sexología, 6,* 33–34.

Leckie, F. H. (1964). Hypnotherapy in gynecological disorders. *International Journal of Clinical and Experimental Hypnosis, 12,* 121–146.

Sanchez A., & Moix, J. (1993). Aplicación de la auto-regulación en dismenorrea [Application of self-regulation therapy to dysmenorrhea]. In A. Capafons & S. Amigó (Eds.), *Hipnosis, terapia de auto-regulación e intervención comportamental. Valencia, Spain: Promolibro.*

Smith, G. M., Egbert, M., Markowitz, M., Mosteller, S., & Peecher, H. K. (1966). An experimental pain method sensitive to morphine in man: Submaxim effort tourniquet technique. *Journal of Pharmacological Experimental Therapy, 145,* 324–332.

Sobcyzk, R. (1980). A case control survey and dysmenorrhea. *Journal of Family Practice, 7,* 285–290.

Spiegel, H. & Spiegel, D. (1978). *Trance and treatment. Clinical use of hypnosis.* Washington, DC: American Psychiatric Press.

Stephenson, L., Denney, E., & Aberger, D. (1983). Factor structure of the Menstrual Sympton Questionnaire: Relationship to oral contraceptives, neuroticism and life stress. *Behavior Research and Therapy, 21,* 129–135.

Warrington, C., Cox, D. & Evans, W. (1988). Dysmenorrhea. In E. A. Blechman & K. D. Brownell (Eds.), Handbook of behaviour medicine for women. Oxford, England: Pergamon Press.

9

HYPNOSIS WITH A BORDERLINE PATIENT

JOAN MURRAY-JOBSIS

The case presented in this chapter is that of a patient with a diagnosis of borderline personality disorder (BPD). The material and techniques described may sometimes be used in an abbreviated form with psychotic patients. However, hypnotic techniques with psychotic patients will frequently require individualized variations according to the needs of the patient.

The essential feature of BPD is a pervasive pattern of instability affecting three areas of functioning: self-image, interpersonal relationships, and mood. Identity disturbance is typically present with confusion over self-image, sexual orientation, and chronic feelings of emptiness. Interpersonal relations are typically intense and unstable with shifts between over-idealization and over-devaluation of significant others. In addition, affect is typically unstable. Marked mood shifts may occur from depression, to irritability and anger, to anxiety (American Psychiatric Association, 1994).

Special problems in treating patients diagnosed with BPD include recurrent suicidal threats and behavior, self-mutilation, manipulative behavior, and explosive acting out of anger. As a result of these behavior patterns, patients with BPD present a very difficult challenge for the therapist. In dealing with such patients, treatment will generally involve long-term psy-

---

Murray-Jobsis has previously published under the names Scagnelli and Scagnelli-Jobsis.

chotherapy. The therapist will need to be able to maintain a caring, supportive relationship against a background environment of stormy chaos and crises created by the patient. In addition, the therapist must be able to establish and maintain a framework of clearly set limits that permit patients to eventually understand and accept their separate identity and responsibility for themselves and, at the same time, prevent them from destructively manipulating the therapy relationship.

Medication to alleviate depression, anxiety, and excessive anger may frequently be part of the treatment program for patients diagnosed with BPD. Hypnosis can be integrated into the treatment of such patients if the patient is accepting of hypnosis and if the therapist is comfortable with the traditional (nonhypnotic) management of therapy with these patients.

BACKGROUND INFORMATION

Jane was 44 years old when she first came to see me in therapy. She remained in therapy with me for almost 3 years. She had never been married or significantly involved in a relationship. She had been certified as a registered nurse but worked in a clerical-nursing capacity to avoid the stresses and demands of clinical nursing.

Before entering therapy with me, Jane had been in treatment with several different therapists over a period of many years, during which she had been diagnosed as having BPD. She had been hospitalized several times in the past for depression and suicidal tendencies. She also had a history of self-mutilation, mostly cutting and burning herself. Thus, she had much self-destructive potential. In addition, Jane displayed the classic borderline symptom of splitting the world into "all good" and "all bad" segments. She also exhibited the borderline therapy pattern of switching back and forth from a dependent, needy, idealizing relationship with the therapist to an angry, hostile, rejecting relationship.

Her first psychiatric contact was initiated in her late teens when she was medically discharged from the military for emotional instability. She was later referred for a second brief therapy contact when she was discharged from a Catholic convent and discouraged from continuing her novitiate. Jane's next therapy contact was self-initiated and was perceived by her as supportive and positive. However, this therapy was terminated when Jane chose to move out of the state. Jane's most recent therapy before coming to see me was the longest and most bonded of her prior therapies, lasting for approximately four and a half years. This previous therapy relationship had initially been very positive and nurturing but had ended very destructively. The therapy had broken down, apparently from the stress of Jane's borderline behaviors—her anger, her dependency needs, her regressive behavior, and her inability to improve. In any event, the prior therapist had abruptly refused to continue seeing Jane, and Jane had drifted for several months in confusion and despair, without any real therapy support.

As one might expect given these circumstances, when Jane ultimately came to see me she was in great distress. She was clearly very depressed and desperate for a safe dependency relationship but also extremely distrustful and angry at the prospect of another possible relationship where she could be rejected again.

At our initial meeting, we discussed therapy limits and guidelines. I assured Jane that if we began working together, I would not leave her and I would be as consistent and reliable as possible about our appointment times. However, I also told her that I would be away on trips from time to time, which might be difficult for her to handle. I suggested the possibility that she might also be angry at me from time to time and that that was all right. I stated that if she were able to stay with the therapy relationship and not abandon it, I believed she could resolve her conflicts and learn how to live a happier life. I explained my limits on phone calls: I would accept after-hours phone calls for very brief support or for emergency hospitalization. I also explained that I would hospitalize her if she told me that she felt suicidal and felt she could not control her impulses and behavior. I suggested that she should only say she was suicidal if she really meant it because I would take her seriously. In addition, I also stated that if she did become suicidal and out of control, I would want her to tell me so directly rather than to hope that I could "read" her feelings and rather than act out suicidal gestures.

In my experience, presenting the guidelines and limits of therapy early in the relationship and as clearly as possible is useful when working with a BPD patient. Although such explicit statement of limits may seem harsh, it is ultimately kinder to the patient than confusion over limits. It also offers patients a fair choice about therapy and the therapist before they are too dependent to be able to exercise choice. In addition, a clear statement of limits forces therapists to clarify for themselves the therapy limits that they can live with over an extended period of time without resentment and without abandoning the patient. This helps both patient and therapist recognize that the therapist is a helper, not a savior, and that the therapist can meet some of the patient's needs but not all of his or her needs.

Jane's history was one of severe childhood neglect and abuse. Her earliest memories of her father were of his explosive anger and threatening behavior. Nevertheless, Jane felt some positive attachment to her harsh father. She recalled that when she was 5 and her father left the family, she had felt terribly frightened and abandoned. Jane's mother attempted to maintain a home for herself and her six children by living for a while with an abusive, alcoholic man. Jane remembered this man as extremely threatening and terrifying.

Eventually her mother put Jane and two of her sisters in a children's home. A brother was sent to live with relatives, but her mother kept the oldest daughter and the baby living with her. Her mother promised to come back and get Jane and the other children, but she never did. Thus, Jane felt not only abandoned by her mother and father but also betrayed and distrustful. The children's home where Jane lived for the next 4 years was run by an abusive headmistress. The children were frequently beaten, and Jane was singled out for extra abuse by the headmistress, who disliked her stubbornness and refusal to cry.

When Jane was 10 years old, her father returned and "rescued" her and her sisters from the home. He brought the three sisters into his new family with his second wife and their baby. However, her father was still overly controlling and physically abusive, beating and terrifying the sisters. In addition, beginning at the time Jane was 12 years old and lasting until she reached her late teens, her father sexually molested and humiliated her. He had sexual intercourse with her, ridiculed her sexual body parts, forced her to assume humiliating positions, and told her that she "belonged to him" and that he "could do whatever he wanted" with her. He kept her isolated from others, terrorized her, and kept her dependent on him.

Jane was mostly too frightened by her father to fight back and too isolated and intimidated to seek help. At one point when Jane did express anger at her father in a rare moment of assertion, her father became enraged and started choking her, apparently trying to kill her. The family intervened and managed to stop the attack. Some months later during another verbal fight, Jane grabbed a butcher knife to protect herself and threatened to kill her father if he ever touched her again. Within a year, Jane enlisted in the military to escape her home life. Given her dysfunctional family and her abused childhood, Jane's ability to handle the demands of military life was limited, and she was discharged for psychiatric illness within a few months. She then made a brief, unsuccessful attempt to enter the Catholic sisterhood. Eventually, she succeeded in obtaining her registered nurse certification and was able to maintain an economically independent but emotionally limited lifestyle.

When Jane came into therapy with me she was working as a medical reviewer of hospital charts for insurance certification. She was economically self-sufficient but was totally isolated in her social and emotional life. Outside of therapy and work, there were no other human contacts, and Jane mostly spent her nonworking time sleeping, walking, or watching TV alone. Jane remained in therapy with me for almost 3 years, coming in for sessions two times a week. Hypnosis was integrated into the general psychotherapy work when needed and appropriate, about 20% of the total therapy time. Hypnosis was used more frequently in the earlier stages of therapy when renurturing work was used to reduce Jane's agitation and to stabilize the therapy relationship.

CONCEPTUALIZATION OF THE PROBLEM

It was clear from Jane's history that she had a childhood filled with both neglect and physical and sexual abuse. Jane also carried a long established diagnosis of BPD. I basically agreed with this primary diagnosis. Jane exhibited the general neediness, the desire for symbiotic dependency, and the conflicting need for distance that are characteristic of BPD. She expressed great anxiety and anger at any perceived loss of connectedness. But she was also anxious and ambivalent about possible closeness and connectedness. Behaviorally, Jane could be very cooperative and idealizing of me at one moment and then very angry and accusing at the next moment. She needed both closeness and distance with equal intensity and was in constant conflict. It was clear that Jane needed to work through the borderline issues of separation and individuation and the issue of autonomy within closeness.

However, it was also apparent that Jane had experienced a deficit in nurturance. Although she had received enough early nurturance to permit her to accomplish the early developmental tasks of identifying a separate sense of herself and of connecting with others, her sense of connectedness was weak and her sense of self was largely negative. Her nurturance had apparently been mixed with enough neglect and abuse so that her sense of self contained little esteem or worth. Thus, Jane needed positive renurturing to establish a positive sense of self; a capacity for self-love and self-esteem; and a deeper, positive capacity for connectedness.

In addition, Jane had some features of a dissociative disorder, possibly due, in part, to her experience of severe and prolonged abuse. She spoke of several "people" inside her head. She referred to these "people" as "they" or "it." She never developed more specific names or personalities for these "people" in her head. Also, she never exhibited repression or dissociation of the original sexual-assaultive experiences. She had apparently always remembered these experiences but had locked them emotionally apart and never dealt with them. Thus, while she did not appear to be a true dissociative identity disorder patient, Jane did exhibit symptoms of a less-specific dissociative disorder. In addition to referring to "people" in her head, Jane also reported apparent dissociative experiences in her adult life where she was amnesiac for periods of time. Specifically, she had little memory of the 3 months of her life following the abrupt termination of her previous therapy relationship. Furthermore, these dissociated 3 months appear to have been punctuated with much self-destructive behavior.

Therefore, in addition to treatment for her borderline problems, Jane needed help dealing with her past sexual abuse. She needed to work through the corrective cognitions, to handle the affect without becoming overwhelmed, and to find her own sense of adult power. As a result of these multiple layers of childhood developmental and abuse problems, there were several levels of therapy work to be done with Jane.

TREATMENT

When Jane began her therapy with me, she was in a dependent, needy state and tended to view me in those early weeks as all good (once the residual distrust from her prior therapy had been overcome). Recognizing this early positive transference as transitory, I focused the initial stage of therapy on renurturing with hypnotic imagery to reduce her general agitation and to foster a more long-range and more grounded bonding.

The techniques of renurturing with hypnotic imagery, of creating positive healing scripts, and of providing restitution for the patient's missing positive developmental environment of the past are therapy techniques that I have developed over the past 20 years of clinical work with patients with diagnoses of personality disorders, dissociative disorders, and psychotic disorders (Murray-Jobsis, 1984, 1985, 1986, 1989, 1991, 1992, 1993). I also developed a theoretical model of hypnosis as adaptive regression and transference as a framework for understanding and explaining the capacity of patients with personality disorders and psychoses for working with hypnosis (Scagnelli-Jobsis, 1982, Murray-Jobsis,1988).

In hypnotic renurturing, using the technique of age regression, the patients imagine themselves "back there" as infants or little children. The therapist then creates an imaginary series of nurturing experiences with the patient. In essence, the therapist creates an imaginary healing script and a restitution for the patient's missing nurturing environmental history. Both the patient and therapist know that the real life experiences of the patient were most likely different from the imaginary renurturing. They know that they are creating new experiences in imagery that will not change the past but may help make the present and future better.

Given the focus on renurturing in Jane's early therapy, hypnosis became the treatment technique of choice because of the flexibility in renurturing that can be achieved with hypnosis. The renurturing techniques developed in hypnotic therapy work are facilitated by the conditions of the hypnotic experience. Because of the use of imagery, the increased access to feelings, and the temporary, partial suspension of critical judgment during hypnosis, both the patient and the therapist are able to play out in imagery the parent and child roles that can promote a renurturing healing process.

In addition to facilitating patient–therapist bonding, renurturing with a patient with a borderline disorder is designed to make up for missing, essential developmental experiences in the patient's life. In the theoretical developmental model presented in the chapter on "The Borderline and the

Psychotic Patient" (Murray-Jobsis, 1993) in the *Handbook of Clinical Hypnosis*, the original nurturing experiences were seen as essential for the original bonding of the infant and his or her future bonding and relational capacity. In addition, the original nurturing experiences provide the foundation for a positive sense of self. Therefore, a technique of renurturing that allows patients to fill in the missing experiences of nurturing can be seen as extremely important to the therapy of a patient with a borderline disorder. Thus, the use of hypnotic renurturing messages in the early stages of Jane's therapy was designed to help reduce her agitation and to promote a positive transference and a more lasting bonding than her initial borderline attachment. In addition, the renurturing experiences were designed to create a "redoing" of Jane's history as "it should have been." Thus, the renurturing sessions also provided Jane with a positive set of relationship experiences that had not existed in her real life, similar to Erickson's work in "The February Man" (Erickson & Rossi, 1979). These hypnotically created positive experiences then provided the foundation for Jane's later building a positive self-image and a positive capacity for relationship.

Several months of repetition were invested in this early renurturing work. In addition, audio tapes were made of several of our renurturing sessions, so that Jane could keep them and replay them as often as she wished. Jane reported that she used the tapes daily. She felt that they reduced her agitation and anxiety and that they further helped her decrease and eventually cease her self-mutilating behavior.

Following the initial renurturing work, Jane's hypnotherapy work focused on the creation of images and messages for individuation and for a developmental progression from symbiotic infancy to a more autonomous sense of child-self. This focus on individuation and separation was initiated with the specific goal of helping Jane address a specific deficit in her developmental history because BPD presumes a deficient or a pathological environment in the childhood separation–individuation process. Again, hypnosis was considered to be the treatment of choice because hypnotic imagery is an ideal vehicle for presenting and rehearsing a corrective process of separation and individuation against a background of bonding and connectedness.

These first two stages of therapy lasted many months. The first stage essentially addressed the primary issue of creating a positive bonding and a capacity for a positive self-image. The second stage of therapy focused on developing a positive capacity for separation and the development of autonomy. This autonomy was founded on a healthy curiosity, discovery, and mastery rather than on the borderline pathological feeling state of abandonment with its resulting anxiety, anger, and despair.

Following these first stages of therapy and this fundamental work of renurturing, bonding, and individuation, Jane began to move spontaneously into more difficult and conflicted areas with hypnosis. She began to deal with her physical and sexual abuse history. Again hypnosis provided an ideal therapy technique. Hypnotic techniques promoted the accessing of abuse memories in imagery. Although Jane already had recall of most of her past abuse memories, hypnosis facilitated imaging and accessing the feelings associated with these memories.[1] At the same time, hypnosis facilitated Jane's capacity for distance and for containment of affect to help protect her from becoming overwhelmed by her revivified memories. In addition, hypnotic imagery provided a technique for redoing and reshaping past abuse experiences to promote healing and empowerment.

At this stage in therapy, Jane began to use her hypnosis sessions to access feelings and to talk about events that had been impossible for her in the past. Although her abuse memories had been previously available to Jane, they had never been expressed or shared with another person. Instead, Jane had kept these memories and experiences locked inside. A tremendous sense of worthlessness and feelings of shame and isolation had kept the memories under tight censorship through the years. However, hypnosis provided an environment that allowed for the temporary and safe lifting of this censorship, thus permitting Jane to share her memories for the first time and to discharge pent-up feelings associated with the memories. This expression and sharing of memories and feelings also allowed Jane to receive her first messages of acceptance as a good person in spite of her "bad experiences." I gave Jane assurances of her goodness and acceptance. I also gave her reinterpretations of her experiences. I helped her understand that "the child" was good and that it was the adults who had been destructive and inadequate.

In summary, the initial work of therapy dealt with issues of renurturing, bonding, and individuation and with resolving the central borderline conflict over dependency and separation, with its concomitant rage, despair, and anxiety. Once these primary borderline issues had been addressed, Jane was then freed up to work on her other issues. Subsequent therapy

---

[1]In general, the child and adult memory research confirms reliable memory reports starting with ages 3 and 4 years (Pillemer & White, 1989). A few studies report capacity for accurate memory in children as young as 2 years (Eisenberg, 1985; Nelson & Ross, 1980). A study by Guenther and Frey (1990) relating specifically to repressed memories suggests that "repressors remember as much about victimization experiences as do nonrepressors but are more likely to fill in memory details . . . with positive reconstructions to reduce the overall negative quality associated with victimization." (p. 257).

Recent studies on validity of hypnotically enhanced recall suggest that there is "no evidence for hypermnesia and that hypnotized subjects can make errors and confabulate." (Watkins, 1989, p. 80). Research by Nash, Drake, Wiley, and Khaba (1986) reported that hypnotically enhanced memories may not be an exact replay of historical events and may produce confabulation that may contaminate later waking memories. Beahrs (1988) further noted that "hypnosis had the potential to alter cognition, perception and recall" (p. 18). However, both Watkins and Beahrs emphasize that nonhypnotic as well as hypnotic memory can be distorted by suggestion and affect and that hypnotic memory needs to be evaluated on the same basis as nonhypnotic memory for its individual case validity.

then dealt with resolving the issues of physical and sexual abuse. In this second stage of therapy, hypnosis was used to promote access to past feelings, to promote catharsis, and to provide and convey acceptance. In addition, hypnosis was helpful in promoting insight and in correcting cognitions and interpretations of past experience. Hypnosis also provided an excellent environment for redoing past experiences in a corrective and healing manner.

Renurturing

Initial hypnosis work with Jane focused on early renurturing. I used an induction method of relaxation messages and general ego-building messages for competency, mastery, and self-acceptance. I used the following ego-building messages:

> Now that we have come to a comfortable place of relaxation, we can begin to explore and understand ourselves more fully—coming to understand and accept both our strengths and our limitations. Allowing ourselves to develop our strengths to the fullest potential, without fears or apologies—without worrying whether others are pleased or displeased by our strengths—but knowing that each of us has the right to become our own best self. But at the same time acknowledging and allowing for our imperfections and limitations. Learning to discriminate those limitations that can be changed or improved with growth and learning and other limits that may be an inevitable part of the human condition. Improving those things that we can change or improve and letting go of things that are beyond our power to control or change. But coming to accept our total selves—with strengths and limits—giving ourselves the freedom to take the necessary risks and to risk the necessary "missteps" involved in growth and learning. And then everything becomes easier, and we begin to engage in the adventure and the challenge and the excitement of living and growing and evolving into our own best self.

Following these ego-building messages, I developed age regression by suggesting that Jane travel back in time "to middle and early childhood." We then created images of the therapist and adult Jane as a composite "mother" taking the child Jane out of the children's home and creating a new home for her and her sisters. This new home was warm and sunny and loving. In this imagery the child Jane and "mother" rocked together in a rocking chair, read stories together, sang songs, and talked of feelings. Jane was tucked safely and lovingly into bed at the end of each day in this imaginary home.

As Jane became more comfortable with the renurturing of her child self, we began to travel back in hypnosis into some of her "earliest times of existence," the early days of infancy. We then began renurturing the infant Jane by re-creating an infancy and a sense of self "as it should have been and could have been if we [adult Jane and I] could have been there to be the 'mother' to little Jane." In hypnosis I created the following nurturing images:

> "Mother" would be holding the infant in warm, strong arms, smiling down on her. The infant Jane would feel the warmth and protection of the encircling arms. In the smiling face, the infant could perceive a sense of self as whole and well, loved and loving, warm and secure. The infant would hear the soothing sounds and feel the soothing touch of "mother." The infant could feel the rhythm of the rocking and hear the rhythm of the heartbeat, constant and steady. The infant could feel the rise and fall of the breast in harmony with the rhythm of the breathing. The infant could taste the warm, sweet milk and feel the feelings of fullness and satisfaction.

Then, as a result of this imagery and sensory input, the infant Jane could begin to identify a sense of physical self with positive sensory feelings and a sense of emotional self as "whole and safe and loved." This sense of self would be identified "within a framework of connectedness and bondedness."

Separation and Individuation

Later therapy work focused on establishing the groundwork for a positive building of separation and autonomy. Jane was regressed, in hypnosis, to her early months of existence. Then after positive renurturing, Jane and I created the following images:

> The infant Jane reaching out for toys, grasping and letting go; and the infant developing a beginning awareness of her physical boundaries, of self as separate from "other." "Mother" coming and going but always returning, and the infant perceiving the beginnings of separateness. The infant holding the image and the feeling of "mother" within her, even in moments of separation. The awareness of a bondedness and a connectedness even in moments of separateness.

Later, we imagined the child creeping across the floor and moving away from "mother" toward some newly discovered toy. The infant would look back and know that she could always return to "mother," but she would be fascinated with the world she was beginning to discover "out there." Still later, the growing child would move even further out into the world of discovery, play, and mastery. However, the child would know that she could always return and that even when "mother" could not be seen, "mother" was still there, always constant. Thus, we began to build, with hypnotic images, a sense of constancy, connectedness, and support between infant and "mother." We built a capacity within the infant Jane for holding the image of "mother" and a capacity for holding a sense of connectedness within her memory and eventually holding it within her emotional self.

This early renurturing and individuation work was designed to help Jane work through: (a) her initial positive bonding with a nurturing caretaker; (b) her beginning sense of a positive self-image based on this bonding and nurturance; (c) a beginning awareness of physical separateness (loss of symbiosis) in a safe, protective environment; (d) a later emotional awareness of separateness within an environment of connectedness and support; (e) an ability to internalize the image and feeling of the nurturing "mother" and the connectedness; and (f) a positive view of separateness and autonomy based on exploration and mastery (rather than abandonment and anxiety) and allowing for positive independent growth.

These early renurturing and individuation sessions were designed to correct developmental failures in Jane's past and to redo a corrective developmental process. During this early phase of therapy, Jane was at times agitated. At times she would pace around the office during therapy sessions, moving from chair to chair. At other times, she would curl up in a fetal position behind a chair and refuse to talk. Between sessions she was intermittently self-destructive, cutting or burning her arms. At times she was suicidal and required brief hospitalizations of 3 to 5 days to regain control.

The renurturing work rapidly reduced much of Jane's agitation and self-mutilating behavior. Her angry withdrawals from communication and her suicidal impulses, however, took longer to work through and to subside. However, in spite of her need to withdraw, Jane would always return to communicating and to her commitment to the therapy work.

Jane and I gradually worked out a cooperative plan for dealing with her suicidal feelings and impulses. She agreed to tell me clearly and directly when she felt she needed a brief hospital stay because of suicidal impulses. This direct communication replaced her previous tendency to act out suicidal impulses with threats or abortive acts or gestures. I always responded to Jane's verbal messages of "being out of control of suicidal impulses" with support for hospitalization so that she did not need to escalate her messages. In addition, we had a positive relationship with the medical doctor in charge of Jane's in-patient care so that brief hospital stays could be arranged. Jane was allowed out of the hospital on passes for therapy visits and for work as soon as she was able to handle these freedoms. In general, Jane used these temporary brief hospitalizations for protection from her suicidal impulses constructively, and she gradually worked out of the need for such protection. Jane clearly understood that hospital stays were for her protection but that the solution to her long-term problems lay in therapy and not in the dependency of hospital care.

Reshaping Abuse Memories

As Jane became stronger in her sense of self-worth and autonomy through our renurturing and individuation work, she gradually expanded her hypnotic work. She began to recall and reexperience traumatic past events in her therapy sessions. Hypnosis assisted this recall of past experiences and also facilitated a cathartic reconnection with the feelings associated with these past experiences. In dealing with these past traumatic experiences, Jane and I used hypnosis for reinterpreting and correcting cognitions about these experiences and for redoing them.

One of the first of these past experiences that Jane recalled in hypnosis was her experience in the children's home with the sadistic headmistress. Jane recalled her loneliness, desperation, and pain. She recalled feeling deserted and deceived by her mother and her prayers to be rescued.

In response to these painful memories, Jane and I created a positive, healing alternative set of images as a form of redoing. We again created an image in hypnosis of the adult Jane and me as a composite "mother" to little Jane. We then redid some of the past experience of the children's home with a positive, alternative script. In hypnosis I created images of

> "mother" taking little Jane and her sisters from the children's home and creating a new home that was warm and sunny and loving. We would snuggle together in a rocking chair and read stories. We would bake cookies and take walks together. We would tuck little Jane into bed at night and kiss her goodnight. If little Jane became frightened in the middle of the night, we would hear her. We would go to her and comfort her and calm her fears.

Later in therapy Jane recalled the first sexual assault by her father. In this hypnosis session, I had suggested that Jane go back in time and explore some of the feelings that were currently difficult for her, perhaps the feeling "of not being listened to." This feeling "of not being listened to" had been expressed by Jane in the past. She had stated that she was afraid that she was "going to be buried" and that "no one would hear her."

In hypnosis Jane remembered herself lying on the black tile floor of her childhood home where her father first sexually assaulted her. Her father had sent everyone away to the store, so that she was alone in the house with him. She recalled him feeling her body, taking her clothes off, and then having sex with her. He told her that she belonged to him and that he was allowed to touch her. But he also told her that she must never tell anyone about this. Jane remembered then feeling very frightened. She had a difficult time staying with the hypnotic imagery at this point, and she recalled that she had started to "go away" back when this assault had originally happened (a possible dissociation of feelings, although not of the memory of these events).

In hypnosis, Jane saw herself lying on the floor and looking up and seeing trees outside the window, and she felt like she "was being buried." We also learned that, in real life, Jane had not been listened to. Jane had been too afraid to tell anyone directly about her father's assaults. However, she reported that she gave indirect messages about the sexual abuse to her stepmother, which were ignored. In addition, her teachers at school ignored the cuts and bruises on her face and body when she went to school after abuse by her father.

Once again as a form of redoing and healing, we created images in hypnosis of a positive alternative scenario to her real life history of abuse and neglect. We again created the familiar image of adult Jane and the therapist as "mother." Then we as "mother" protected and soothed the child Jane after the first assault by her father. We did not ignore her indirect messages; we noticed her physical and emotional hurt; we asked questions; and we listened. We soothed the hurt child, and we protected her. We told the father that he must stop his hurtful behavior or be sent away, that he must never again hurt our beautiful daughter. "Mother" then remained attentive and protective so that Jane could feel safe and loved in her home and grow strong.

This hypnotic redoing—the creation of a healing script with positive, alternative images, rather than the remembered real images of a destructive past history—is of course clearly understood by the patient as imaginary. Nevertheless, patients who have been abused appear to be able to use such redoing and alternative scripts for healing and growth.

When Jane realerted from hypnosis at the end of this session, she said that she felt better than she had before in spite of the difficult material. She then said that she was afraid that, with my going away on vacation in the summer, she would lose herself again. She stated that she thought she had "disappeared" the previous summer with her previous therapist and that is what caused that therapy relationship to end so disastrously. Jane's only memory of the previous summer was that she walked for miles and hours on end. She apparently had withdrawn from communication and from her therapy into a dissociated state that had contributed to the disruption of the previous therapy.

I reassured Jane that I would not leave her even if she repeated her behavior of last summer but that she did not have to "lose herself" again. I reminded her that we had already been working on building coping techniques for her to use when I was away and that we would continue to work together on these skills. We had developed transitional objects: a stuffed teddy bear and several knick-knacks from my office. We also had developed corrective cognitions for Jane to use in my absences. These corrective cognitions emphasized that Jane was no longer a helpless little girl and that she could care for herself as a strong adult. In addition, we had established a relationship with a substitute therapist and had fostered additional supportive friendships in Jane's life. I further reminded Jane that, "even though I go away, I always return and we are always connected even when we are apart." I told her that we would work together to help her "not lose herself." She then replied, "but it is so sad to have you away." And I agreed,

> Yes, it is sad. It is sad to be away from anyone we care about. But life generally demands that we have some times of being apart, because it is almost impossible to be always together. We know that it is sad, but we need to be able to handle that sadness because it is part of living.

Jane was able to accept this message and continue to work through the difficulty of separations.

At the end of this hypnotic session Jane also raised her earlier stated fear of "not being heard or listened to." This was the feeling that Jane had expressed earlier in therapy and that we had used to initiate and focus this hypnotic regression and exploration. I reassured Jane that "I would always listen." I told her that I would always try to hear and understand. I asked her to please keep trying to help me understand. Jane agreed.

Some months later in therapy, this question of listening and understanding again arose. Jane had been distant, angry, and distrustful for approximately 5 weeks. She had refused hypnosis during that time and had communicated little. However, she suddenly emerged from this distant state and specifically requested hypnotic renurturing. She especially asked me to replay a scene that I had created for her in the past where "mother" would come at night to calm a frightened "little Jane."

During this hypnotic session Jane shed a few quiet tears. At the end of the session after her return to the waking state, Jane spoke of her hurt, loneliness, and fear at night both as a little girl and also now in her current life. She then referred to the "other people" within her not trusting me. She complained that I did not understand her "people" and her messages well enough. Perhaps Jane was angry that I could not and did not meet all her needs (i.e., that she could not call me in the middle of the night and get me to come and calm her and her adult fears and loneliness in her current real life). Perhaps she chose to see me as not understanding rather than to acknowledge that I could not, or would not, meet all of her needs. Or perhaps I truly did not fully understand some important parts or feelings of Jane. It is also possible that Jane's "other people" represented alters within her (and an additional diagnosis of dissociative identity disorder). However, attempts to elicit alters produced nothing more specific than her vague references to "other people." Nevertheless, in spite of her dissatisfaction with my imperfect "mothering," Jane left her angry, withdrawn behavior of the past several weeks behind and renewed her communication and commitment to work in therapy.

Gradually, with the help of hypnosis, Jane reviewed many of the traumatic events of her early life that she had remembered but not resolved emotionally. She recounted the memory of her father choking her in a rage because she had called him a "bastard." She felt that she survived only because the family intervened and that he would have killed her. She remembered later in her teens wanting to kill her father, but fearing that if she tried and failed, he would kill her. She remembered overhearing her father and her stepmother talking about the appearance of her genitals in a derogatory way; and she remembered her fear, shame, and confusion at her first menstruation and trying to hide the blood. In each of these cases, Jane would experience some cathartic release and relief. We would then reinterpret these past events in the light of Jane's adult intellect and promote corrective understandings and cognitions. Wherever possible and appropriate, we would redo these past events in hypnosis with a healing positive script.

As therapy progressed through the borderline and then the sexual and physical abuse issues, Jane's trust in herself and in me built, and she began to use hypnosis for more uncovering kinds of work. She began to recall and report dreams in therapy and then to explore the dreams with hypnosis. This uncovering work led Jane to eventually reaccess repressed and dissociated feeling experiences. She remembered the pain when her former therapy had ended badly. She recalled the months of compulsive walking, anorexia, and self-mutilation that had marked the end of that therapy. She said the pain was why she had "forgotten" that period of her life.

At another point in therapy Jane remembered being age 6 and trying to get some attention from her mother by pretending to be sick. But her mother was too weary from work and the burdens of single parenting to do anything but go to sleep. She later remembered the terror she felt as a child of 5 at losing her father when he was suddenly gone from the family. Then for the first time, Jane made a connection between the fear she felt at losing her father and the fear she felt when I would go away on trips. Apparently, in spite of her father's angry and abusive behavior, Jane had perceived her father as a protector. His departure had been experienced as a major loss and seemed to provide some of the precedent for her subsequent separation anxiety. In addition, his departure had, in fact, led to a series of subsequent abuses by others in Jane's life. (A vicious irony for Jane was her father's return to her life as an apparent "rescuer" who then turned out to be another abuser.)

As a result of her insight into the connection between the loss of her father at age 5 and her perceived loss of me when I traveled, Jane was more able to view our current separations in a more realistic adult light and with less of the fear and despair of the 5-year-old child of the past. Thus hypnosis was used for uncovering and insight as therapy progressed.

Transference and Countertransference

Transference was a major issue with Jane, as it is with any BPD patient. As expected, Jane's transference and her concomitant behavior in therapy went through rapid and extreme swings. At times she would be excessively positive about me and the therapy relationship. Then with sudden and sometimes unexplained shifts in behavior, she would be excessively angry and distrustful of me as well as uncommunicative and uncooperative in therapy. Working through these intense swings in the transference is an essential part of therapy with a borderline patient. Examples of working with these transference issues have been presented in the discussion of the treatment above.

In general, it is important for the therapist to refrain from responding too positively to the patient's idealization phase of the transference. The therapist needs to avoid falling into the illusion that he or she can be a savior for the patient. Sometimes it is wise for the therapist to use this idealization phase of the patient's transference to remind the patient of therapist limits and of future potential dissatisfaction and anger by the patient.

It is also equally important for the therapist to refrain from responding too negatively to the patient's angry phase of the transference. Instead the therapist needs to remain generally accepting of the patient, while waiting for the anger to pass. This is perhaps the most difficult aspect of work with the borderline patient. In addition to restraint on the part of the therapist, it also requires the therapist to trust that the patient will be strongly enough committed to the therapy relationship to maintain the relationship throughout the anger.

Outcome

Jane maintained sufficient commitment to sustain the therapy relationship throughout the emotional storms of her borderline feelings. She gradually worked through her anger, her anxiety, and her sense of loss. She absorbed the pain of her abused and neglected childhood and was able to put it in the past. She became able to look at her life in the present more realistically and to begin to focus her energy on taking better care of herself in the present.

Jane eventually decided to return to her own home state and to reconnect with the sisters who were still alive in her family. By this time her mother had died of natural causes, and her brother and older sister had committed suicide. She felt little connection with the baby of the family who she never really knew but still felt close to the two sisters who had been in the children's home with her. Jane's father was still alive at this time. She had confronted him in a letter and in person before she had entered therapy with me. However, her father had never said he was sorry. He simply said he "couldn't help it."

Jane studied to be able to pass an exam to renew her certification for clinical nursing in preparation for returning to her home state. Sometimes we used therapy to help her with her skill building for this exam and to build her sense of confidence. Currently, Jane is practicing nursing in her home state. She has reestablished relations with her two sisters and many nieces, nephews, grandnieces, and grandnephews. She still writes to me a couple of times a year and states that things are going well for her. She is living on her own. She has made no significant romantic or sexual relationship and apparently is not seeking such a relationship.

CONCLUSION

The case work with Jane demonstrates how hypnosis and renurturing techniques can help a patient fill in developmental deficits in achieving bonding, in developing a sense of self-worth, and in accomplishing successful separation and individuation. This case further shows how the use of hypnosis can facilitate a patient's working through an abuse history. Hypnosis can help an abused patient by: (a) facilitating an abreaction and a resolution of feelings, (b) providing a reinterpretation of the abuse experience with appropriate corrective cognitions, (c) providing an environment for redoing and the creation of positive healing images and scripts, and (d) promoting the identification and accessing of adult patient power.

In addition, Jane's therapy illustrates the several levels of disturbance and symptomatology that a patient may exhibit. In Jane's case, she experienced early developmental deficits in the areas of bonding and in separation and individuation. These early deficits gave rise to disturbance and symptomatology surrounding the formation of a positive sense of self, her capacity for bonding, and her ability to tolerate positive separation and development toward autonomy. In Jane's case, these early developmental deficits led to a BPD and its accompanying symptomatology. However, in addition to the BPD, Jane also had a history of severe physical and sexual abuse that led to a dissociative disorder with much of the accompanying symptomatology of dissociative experiences and splitting. Thus, both the therapy and the hypnotic intervention had to be adapted to Jane's different levels of emotional functioning and to her varying symptoms and developmental disruptions. Jane's case demonstrates the versatility of hypnosis in working with many different levels of development and many different degrees and aspects of dysfunction.

This case further illustrates the capacity of severely disturbed patients for using hypnosis and the usefulness of hypnosis in psychotherapy work with severely disturbed patients. In particular, when interventions such as creative renurturing or the creation of alternative healing scripts are required, it would be difficult, and perhaps impossible, to do such work without the use of hypnosis.

In working with this therapy case, I learned great patience. Jane spent weeks in silence curled up behind a chair during one period of this therapy. That particular time of therapy required great patience, trust, and inner calm from me. I could not know with any certainty whether Jane would stay in therapy and return to communication and commitment or whether she would withdraw totally and abandon therapy. Still, it was imperative for me to remain open to the therapy relationship and to not close off my part of the relationship to protect my feelings. Essentially, it was imperative for me to remain patient and supportive without being intrusive. During this extended period of withdrawal, I sometimes talked to the silent Jane and sometimes I remained silent with her. However, I always let her know that I was there for her and that I expected and awaited her return.

The case of Jane raises some interesting questions. One question concerns the use of renurturing imagery techniques to replace a history of deprivation. A corollary question concerns the use of corrective healing scripts to modify the hurtful impact of past abuse experiences. The creation of imaginary restitution through renurturing and healing scripts for neglect and abuse clearly helped Jane work through the feelings connected with her painful past experiences. In addition, these techniques have helped many other patients with whom I have worked in the past. A similar technique of creating imaginary positive hypnotic events was also used by Erickson and is described in "The February Man" (Erickson & Rossi, 1979). In spite of this positive clinical experience, however, it is difficult to explain just how this process of restitution or redoing helps the patient heal. It seems to soothe the patient and to fill in some of the old hurts. It also seems to teach the patient new ways to think and feel. Nevertheless, it is difficult to explain just why and how these techniques work.

Another question that Jane's case raises is the question of how she was able to hold on to the therapy relationship in spite of her intense feelings of anger, pain, anxiety, and distrust. Many patients do manage to hold on and not abandon the therapy relationship, and they eventually work through their intensely difficult conflicts and feelings about the therapist and about life in general. However some patients are unable to "stay the course" of therapy. They seem to become immersed in their anger at the therapist's inability to meet *all* their needs and to become overwhelmed by their anxiety and distrust of the closeness that therapy produces. Thus, some patients abandon therapy and fail to find the resolution of feelings that could make their lives workable. It would be interesting to explore what differences among patients or therapists help patients sustain their therapy connection and work through their difficult transference feelings and the difficult feelings from their past.

REFERENCES

American Psychiatric Association. (1994). *Diagnostic and Statistical Manual of Mental Disorders* (4th ed.). Washington, DC: Author.

Beahrs, J. O. (1986). Hypnosis cannot be fully nor reliably excluded from the courtroom. *American Journal of Clinical Hypnosis, 31,* 18–27.

Eisenberg, A. R. (1985). Learning to describe past experiences in conversation. *Discourse Processes, 8,* 177–204.

Erickson, M. H., & Rossi, E. L. (1979). *Hypnotherapy: An exploratory casebook.* New York: Irvington.

Guenther, R. K., & Frey, C. (1990). Recollecting events associated with victimization. *Psychological Reports, 67,* 207–217.

Murray-Jobsis, J. (1984). Hypnosis with severely disturbed patients. In W. C. Wester & A. H. Smith (Eds.), *Clinical hypnosis: A Multidisciplinary approach.* Philadelphia: Lippincott.

Murray-Jobsis, J. (1985). Exploring the schizophrenic experience with the use of hypnosis. *American Journal of Clinical Hypnosis, 28*(1), 34–42.

Murray-Jobsis, J. (1986). Hypnosis with the borderline patient. In E. T. Dowd & J. M. Healy (Eds.), *Case studies in hypnotherapy* (pp. 254–273). New York: Guilford Press.

Murray-Jobsis, J. (1988). Hypnosis as a function of adaptive regression and of transference: An integrated theoretical model. *American Journal of Clinical Hypnosis, 30*(4), 241–247.

Murray-Jobsis, J. (1989). Clinical case studies utilizing hypnosis with borderline and psychotic patients. *Hypnos, 16*(1), 8–12.

Murray-Jobsis, J. (1991, April). Hypnosis with a borderline and a psychotic patient: Two clinical case studies. Paper presented at ASCH scientific meeting, St. Louis MO.

Murray-Jobsis, J. (1992, August). Hypnotherapy with severely disturbed patients: Presentation of case studies. In Bongartz (Ed.), *Hypnosis: 175 years after Mesmer: Recent developments in theory and application. Proceedings of the fifth European Congress of Hypnosis in Psychotherapy and Psychosomatic Medicine* (pp. 301–307), Konstanz, Germany.

Murray-Jobsis, J. (1993). The borderline patient and the psychotic patient. In J. W. Rhue, S. J. Lynn, & I. Kirsh (Eds.), *Handbook of clinical hypnosis.* Washington, DC: American Psychological Association.

Nash, M. R., Drake, S. D., Wiley, S., Khalsa, S., & Lynn, S. J. (1986). Accuracy of recall by hypnotically age-regressed students. *Journal of Abnormal Psychology, 95*(3), 298–300.

Nelson, K., & Ross, G. (1980). The generalities and specifics of long-term memory in infants and young children. In M. Perlmutter (Ed.), *Children's memory: New directions for child development* (pp. 87–101). San Francisco: Jossey-Bass.

Pillemer, D. B., & White, S. H. (1989). Childhood events recalled by children and adults. *Advances in Child Development and Behavior, 21*, 297–340.

Scagnelli, J. (1975). Therapy with eight schizophrenic and borderline patients: Summary of a therapy approach that employs a semi-symbiotic bond between patient and therapist. *Journal of Clinical Psychology, 31*(3), 519–525.

Scagnelli-Jobsis, J. (1982). Hypnosis with psychotic patients: A review of the literature and presentation of a theoretical framework. *American Journal of Clinical Hypnosis, 25*(1), 33–45.

Watkins, J. G. (1989). Hypnotic hypermnesia and forensic hypnosis: a cross-examination. *American Journal of Clinical Hypnosis, 32*(2), 71–83.

10

THE TREATMENT OF A CASE OF DISSOCIATIVE IDENTITY DISORDER

RICHARD HOREVITZ

Dissociative identity disorder (DID) remains a controversial diagnosis.[1] Many workers in the field are convinced that it is a fiction (McHugh, 1992; Mersky, 1992), a rare but vastly over-diagnosed condition (Frankel, 1993; Orne & Bates, 1992), an epiphenomenon of other conditions such as borderline personality (Kernberg, 1975) or somatization disorder (North, Ryall, Ricci, & Wetzel, 1993), or part of a complex social–psychological process of irrationality and contagion akin to the periodic outbreaks of witchcraft scare that have marked Western history since the Middle Ages (Spanos & Burgess, 1994; Spanos, Weekes, & Bertrand, 1985). Other workers in the field are equally convinced that DID is a valid diagnosis, in the same sense that any psychiatric diagnosis is valid (Horevitz, 1994;

---

[1]In the recent revision of the *Diagnostic and Statistical Manual of Mental Disorders* (DSM-IV; American Psychiatric Association, 1994), multiple personality disorder has been renamed dissociative identity disorder. This change is of great significance because it eliminates the conceptual confusion inherent in the idea of multiple personalities. It is much more readily apparent that subjective experience, together with behavioral correlates, is what is at issue. Multiple identities is not nearly so difficult a concept to understand. While there may be more to DID than subjective identity experience, dissociative symptoms, failures in affective and cognitive integration, and distinctive behavioral correlates, the nomenclature no longer appears to presuppose it. Despite the value of the change, it will probably be quite some time before its usage becomes common. Thus, it was tempting to continue to refer to the case as one of multiple personality disorder for the sake of familiarity. I have resisted the temptation. However, I have retained the convention of speaking of the separate identities as "alters" for lack of a more suitable term.

Kluft, 1991; Kluft, Steinberg, & Spitzer, 1988; Putnam, 1991; Steinberg, Rounsaville, Cicchetti, 1990). This claim is based on a variety of evidential sources including clinical observation, patients' responses to reliable and valid structured interviews, population studies, response to treatment, and commonalities of reported patient history. Although many issues remain alive and contentious, it appears that the acceptance of the diagnosis and the application of a rational treatment protocol leads not only to positive outcomes (Chu, 1988, 1991; Horevitz & Loewenstein, 1994; Kluft, 1988, 1993; Putman, 1989) but also to dramatically reduced need for treatment and significant cost savings (Fraser & Raine, 1992; Ross & Dua, 1993).

DID is currently understood to be a traumatically induced developmental disorder of childhood seen most often in adult patients (Horevitz, 1994; Kluft, 1993). Although clinical portraits of DID have emphasized a "splitting" or fragmentation of the self in the face of either overwhelming trauma or unacceptable psychological contents, a more contemporary understanding is that this disorder represents a *failure of the normal integrative processes* necessary to foster adequate development (e.g., Putnam, 1989, 1992). Under the pressure of a disruptive family life, states of traumatic terror and confusion, failures in the provision of adequate child rearing, and no doubt many other unknown factors, the complex behavioral states with which humans come equipped are neither integrated nor modulated in ways that make for smooth state transitions with continuity of memory and awareness (Putnam, 1992). The natural tendency to develop a sense of identity is associated with continuity of behavior and voluntary control of inner states. To the degree that a person cannot voluntarily modulate or master a behavioral state, there is a tendency to experience fluctuations or even discontinuities of identity.

DID is marked by such severe discontinuity of identity that the cognitive and affective linkages that bridge ordinary "separate identities" are not in place. Instead, there is agnosia among identity states; amnesia for actions, thoughts, and feelings among identity states; and real (or imagined) failures of information transfer among identity states (e.g., skill leanings). The discontinuity among identities is so great that the patient experiences each identity state in terms of a distinct personal identity (Kluft, 1991). This separateness is often characterized by the use of different names or appellations for the separate identities. In many individuals, these separate identity states are largely limited to inner experience, with only rare behavioral appearances of seemingly distinct identities. Other individuals experience *living* (e.g., acting, choosing, experiencing, interacting, role playing, having preferences, and developing attitudes and beliefs) in different identity states. When this occurs, there can be a compelling sense of the reality of separate identities, even to the point of maintaining a near delusion (over-valued idea) of differences in age, gender, body type, sexual orientation, and so forth.

The reasons for this sort of presentation are not clear but may have to do with deliberate manipulation of these identity states by others, such as therapists. It also seems likely that other processes, such as the use of fantasy and imagination, also play a role in the degree of separateness and the secondary characteristics of alter identities (e.g., gender, age, personal style, self-image, and visual self-image; Young, 1988). Clearly, the presentation of dissociative symptoms is affected by a variety of factors, as will be exemplified by the case of Foster, described below.

BACKGROUND INFORMATION

Foster was the second son of a modestly successful family and had grown up in Southern California. His father was a manager in a financial institution, and his mother was a homemaker. His older brother was only 13 months older. At the time he was first seen in treatment, Foster was 57 years old and functioning as a successful executive in a major manufacturing company where he directed engineering and scientific product research. He was married with three children, one of whom was married at the time he was first seen. His other two children were living at home. Foster's wife was an educator.

Foster was referred for treatment by his former therapist whom he had seen for less than a year when she suffered a major medical illness necessitating the closing of her practice. He initially sought treatment at his wife's insistence because of his increasing drinking problems; occasional episodes of impulsive, uncontrolled behavior; anger; emotional constriction; and a dangerous lifestyle (e.g., drunk driving or drinking and becoming involved with prostitutes.). His emotional constriction was evident in a lack of warmth expressed toward his children (although evidently not his wife) and his near absence of social relationships and friendships. His anger was displayed toward his sons, particularly the middle child who had both learning and emotional difficulties. At the point Foster entered treatment, his son was already in substance abuse and dual diagnosis treatment. On the positive side, Foster managed much of his anger through physical activity. He worked out daily at the health club and spent much of his free time doing large-scale carpentry projects around the home. By this process he had become immensely strong, with an almost ursine bearing.

Foster had a good, if somewhat dependent, relationship with his wife. They communicated openly, and he clearly loved her a great deal. However, he would often rely on his wife as a buffer between himself, his children, and the outside world.

Foster had had no treatment prior to his work with the referring therapist. He formed a good treatment alliance with this therapist and showed rapid signs of progress in terms of reduced drinking and diminished self-endangering behavior. One night, when he returned home from a therapy session, he reported that he heard a very clear inner voice tell him that he had been abused by his mother. He began to experience very intense shaking and grief-filled crying that frightened both Foster and his wife. They called his therapist and arranged an emergency session for the following day.

Subsequent to that session, his therapist introduced him to hypnosis, hypnotic age regression, and the use of ideomotor signaling for communicating during hypnosis. According to Foster, during this period he recovered various memories of abuse by his mother, grandmother, and a few of his mother's female friends, partly within what he described as an all-female satanic ritual cult. The alleged "cult" abuse occurred between the ages of 8 and 15. The abuse reportedly stopped when a severely bruised Foster was discovered by his father, who then struck his wife and threatened her with divorce and jail. Foster also reported "hearing about" isolated earlier episodes of physical and sexual abuse by his grandmother and mother dating from age 5.

The therapist apparently accepted the satanic ritual abuse memories as literal, historically accurate events and made no attempt to corroborate Foster's reports. It was difficult to ascertain whether the therapist used leading questions to elicit the memories of cultic involvement, and it was equally difficult to ascertain whether suggestive procedures were involved in the elicitation of 12 alter identities that the therapist uncovered during this period in treatment. (Concerns about generating false memories and certain caveats about memory retrieval will be expressed later in the discussion of the case.)

At any rate, the procedures Foster's referring therapist used elicited alter identities that included several young children ("Young Foster"); several identities identified only by age (8–13); "The Man from Mars," who hurled memories into outerspace; an "Angry One"; "Lover," who sought out prostitutes; "Killer" (even angrier than the Angry One); and "Destroyer," who was actually the only alter identity that Foster was clearly aware of throughout his adult life. Foster described Destroyer as an identity change he underwent at about the age of 23 in the middle of a suicide attempt. The Destroyer apparently blocked the attempt and provided the emotional wherewithal for Foster to decide to live.

Foster also reported that when he met his wife, he was far too enraged and frightened of women to become involved with her. Nonetheless, he found himself courting her and watched a part of himself emerge that engaged in courtship and asked her to marry him. He experienced this at the time in a depersonalized state in which he felt outside of himself and observed behaviors unfold that he could not voluntarily control, although he reportedly tried to do so. These two experiences of identity alteration, although not in active awareness when he entered treatment, were readily recognized by him during treatment. The other alter identities that emerged, mostly in the context of hypnosis, surprised and shocked him. He reported no prior memory of their existence.

As these alter identities emerged in treatment, the angry identities appeared several times in his wife's presence. He also became increasingly aware of the pull of the "Lover" as he was able to exert some control over his behavior. He experienced this as an internal voice urging him to drink and seek out prostitutes. Although it was humiliating, painful, and frightening, Foster eventually came to accept the DID diagnosis.

Foster's acceptance was, in fact, a thin façade. Throughout treatment, he had many doubts about the accuracy of his memories and whether elements of his past and his alter identities were delusional constructs. In many respects his training as an empirical scientist assisted him during treatment. He was able to maintain a healthy skepticism that did not impair his ability to go forward in therapy. His no-nonsense managerial style allowed him to persevere in treatment with few digressions or complications. Once he was convinced that the course of treatment was viable, he was motivated to use his many personal resources to achieve a successful outcome.

At the time I began working with Foster, I believed it made sense to treat him as a DID patient. I was, however, concerned with the *safety* of treating such a powerful bear of a man who clearly would have to deal with powerful, angry emotions during the course of his treatment. As I reviewed his history and treatment with him, I decided we could work together. Today, I would not start such a case without a thorough assessment.[2] (Posttreatment assessment results will be presented later in this chapter.)

---

[2]Today my usual assessment consists of a series of structured diagnostic interviews, a psychological test battery, self-report measures, a measure of hypnotizability, and a memory screening. The structured diagnostic interviews I use routinely include the Structured Clinical Diagnostic Interview for *DSM III-R* (Spitzer, Williams, Gibbon, & First, 1990); the Structured Clinical Diagnostic Interview for *DSM-IV* Dissociative Disorders (Steinberg, 1993); the Dissociative Disorders Interview Schedule (Ross, Heber, Norton, & Anderson, 1989); the Clinician Administered PTSD Rating Scale (Blake et al., 1990); and sections of the SADS-LA (Spitzer, Endicott et al., 1985) that review syndromes not covered in the SCID. Routine psychological assessment includes the Rorschach Inkblot Test (Rorschach, 1921), the Thematic Apperception Test (Murray, 1938), the MMPI-2 (Butcher, Graham, Dahlstrom, Tellegen, & Kaemmer, 1989), the MCMI-II (Millon, 1987), and the Wechsler Memory Scale-Revised (Wechsler, 1987). Self report measures include the Dissociative Experiences Scale (Bernstein & Putnam, 1986), the Inventory of Childhood Memories and Imaginings (Wilson & Barber, 1983), the Fear of Negative Evaluations Scale, the Personal Philosophy Inventory (Persinger, 1982), the Beck Inventories (e.g., Beck, Ward, Mendelson, Mock, & Erbaugh, 1961; Depression, Hopelessness, Anxiety, and Suicidality), Bett's Mental Imagery Questionnaire, and others as needed.

CONCEPTUALIZATION OF THE PROBLEM

Foster's treatment began with the understanding that his dissociative symptoms and history of incestuous maternal trauma required attention. Of course, it is certainly possible that his therapist made errors in her assessment and treatment of Foster. However, Foster had a great deal of trust in her, reported that he felt much improved after even a brief course of treatment, and accepted the *idea* that he was experiencing dissociation and had a traumatic history. Nevertheless, he exhibited very little mastery of his emotions: He continued to rely on his ability to suppress, deny, and avoid feelings or situations that provoked him and on intense physical activity to attenuate his turbulent emotions. With the elimination of drinking and occasional sexual pleasure-seeking outside the marriage, Foster's ability to control his anger was slipping. By the time he entered treatment with me, alter identities were occasionally appearing and *demanding* control in certain situations.

The effects of Foster's DID were pervasive and costly. His disorder compromised his marriage and family life, limited his social contacts to the workplace, disrupted and dampened his emotional life, and resulted in avoidance of situations (he avoided church, TV with its violent programs, crowds, and social gatherings) that triggered dissociative symptoms. However, in comparison with many other DID patients, Foster led a remarkably stable and productive life. Although pervasive, the effects of his dissociative disorder neither disrupted his functioning nor caused extreme and enduring psychological distress. Thus, whereas his Axis IV (psycho-social stressors: 2-mild) and Axis V (GAF: 65) diagnoses were unusually moderate for DID patients (cf. Horevitz & Braun, 1984), the global pattern of deficits observed was consistent with the symptom picture of DID.

TREATMENT

The pervasive deleterious effects associated with dissociative disorders argue for the pragmatic approach of cautious acceptance of the clinical reality presented by the patient within a treatment paradigm that acknowledges the complex psychobiological consequences of prolonged exposure to trauma in childhood (Donovan & McIntyre, 1990; Kluft, 1993; Loewenstein & Ross, 1992). Unfortunately, much evidence implies that a naive and simplistic model of "archeological" treatment (i.e., uncover the trauma, uncover the hidden dissociative states, and let love and trust heal the wounds), however theoretically doctored, is commonly held by therapists and plots a treatment course that leads to a destructive spiral for the patient, who may never recover (Chu, 1988; Fine, 1989, 1991; Greaves,

1988; Kluft, 1988). Patients suffering from DID must be understood to be the most complex and potentially fragile of all patients because, *by definition*, their condition involves underlying fragmentation of all the basic affective, cognitive, and behavioral structures whose integration is required for the development of self (American Psychiatric Association, 1994, p. 477).

No matter how well adapted and high functioning, DID patients are particularly at risk for misdirected or misguided treatment. Treatment is often long and arduous; great care must be taken to preserve the individual patient's well-being and level of function.[3] Because of its inherent difficulty and the level of risk involved in treatment, where expert care is not available, the clinician is *advised to seek competent, regular consultation or supervision for each case being treated.* Few other conditions warrant this level of warning.

Although the "fusion" or "integration" of separate identities has often come to be seen as the goal of treatment, it is not. The goal of treatment is the integration of cognitive function, affective experience, a sense of personal history, and perception of the environment (including beliefs and core assumptions) to the maximum extent possible for a given individual. A framework for understanding the treatment objectives of DID patients is presented in Table 1.

These treatment goals are relevant in varying degrees to all treatment of DID. Fortunately, Foster's own adaptive capacities allowed him to manage many of these problems without requiring extensive attention to a broad range of cognitive and behavioral skills training or pharmacological intervention that many patients require.

HYPNOSIS IN TREATMENT

Unlike many disorders for which hypnosis can be considered one alternative treatment intervention or strategy, the use of hypnosis has always been regarded as integral to the treatment of DID. Indeed, the history of clinical hypnosis and the diagnosis and treatment of multiple personality disorder have been so intertwined as to be the foundation of much of the criticism of DID as a diagnosis (see Horevitz, 1994, for a review). Hypnosis may be a viable part of treatment because it is believed there are certain commonalities between dissociative disorders and hypnosis. While this is no longer quite as evident a proposition as it once seemed, research gen-

---

[3]Foster's treatment required 4 and a half years of weekly 1-hour sessions to achieve full fusion and integration. Another year of postintegration consolidation followed. Treatment was gradually tapered to once every 3 months by the end of this period. I followed up for another 18 months after termination.

TABLE 1
Treatment Goals

Confront and resolve the use of dissociative defenses:
- Confront the illusion of separateness between identities by increasing shared experience, inner communication, and cooperation.
- Confront the hidden aspects of past history and memory, disavowed behaviors, and traumas of childhood.
- Confront any present–time amnesia for current behavior and denials of responsibility. There is just one person, no matter how many separate identity states.
- Confront present–time active use of dissociation, such as switching between identities to avoid dealing with unpleasant emotion or memory.

Confront and resolve pervasive self–destructive tendencies:
- Suicidal ideation and motivation as both a constant wish and alternative life choice.
- Pervasive indulgence in self–mutilation, self–harm, and parasuicidal behavior designed to reduce stress, relieve pain, or end feelings of numbing emptiness.
- Confront behaviors that threaten the therapeutic relationship.
- Confront self–destructive patterns of living including substance abuse, destructive lifestyles or relationships, impulsive behavior, or propensities to seek being dominated and denigrated in life.

Provide adequate skills for affect mastery and clarification of cognitive distortions:
- The principal affects relevant to treatment are:
  States of fear, terror, panic, and anxiety.
  States of shame and humiliation leading to self–destructive frenzies.
  States of potentially uncontrolled rage and feelings of impotent anger.
- Cognitive distortions:
  Experiencing interpersonal relationships as occasions of manipulation.
  In fear states, severe disorientation to time and place.
  Typical depressive "triad" and other cognitive distortions described in Beck, Rush, Shaw, and Emery (1979) and Fine (1991).
- Provide skills for distress tolerance, impulse regulation and behavioral self control (cf. Linehan, 1993).

Provide an overall integrative treatment structure that is consistent, stable, and directed toward the first three goals, while steering through the myriad of day-to-day crises these patients often present. Keeping an eye on these goals is itself a major treatment goal.

---

erally shows that individuals with dissociative disorders are significantly more hypnotizable as a group than any other diagnostic group (Frischholz, Lipman, Braun, & Sachs, 1992).

In Foster's case, hypnotherapy had already become a cornerstone of treatment, and his hypnotic capacity was well-established. Hypnosis had been used to identify past trauma and internal dissociated identity states. In view of this history, I decided to forgo any use of formal hypnotic inductions or deepening techniques except when hypnosis was used either for *affect mastery* or for *integration work*. From my perspective, too many potentially confusing hypnotic experiences had already been introduced into his treatment, and his stability could be all too readily undermined by continuing to use deliberately regressive and ill-proven techniques such as finger signaling. I chose to rely on his past experience and nothing more complex than "Close your eyes, take a breath, sink in to yourself . . . now, tell me what is going on" or "tell me what part of you is trying to be here." These simple interventions were used to suggest that Foster experience a hypnotic mode of responding. Many will recognize this past-experience induction as that pioneered by Erickson.

Hypnosis was used throughout the treatment, although it was often indistinguishable from any technique that involves self awareness (e.g. experiential focusing). Many instances of the use of hypnosis were so informal that they relied only on past response history. The primary uses of hypnosis were geared to the four treatment goals outlined above.

The remainder of the treatment section will trace the unfolding of treatment, year by year, issue by issue, along with examples of clinical work with Foster.

CHRONOLOGY OF TREATMENT

As mentioned earlier, the first six sessions were devoted to assessing the feasibility of treatment. Foster reported that he was aware of the experience of the "others" but never actually felt their feelings. He reported that, normally, physical pain is attenuated for him and that he could voluntarily dull acute and sharp pain with little trouble. He reported that he experienced no feelings himself, although in the previous year of treatment he had begun to experience a sense of "warmth" in relationship to his wife. He reported no abnormal alterations of perceptual processes or hallucinations (other than inner voices); no somatic symptoms, present time loss, or amnesia; and no anxiety symptoms, except for muscular tension and fear for what the future might bring. He reported that he had never been comfortable with women, rarely dated, and was never able to consummate sex until his marriage to his wife. As noted earlier, this courtship reportedly occurred in a depersonalized, dissociated state associated with an alter identity.

I obtained a careful year-by-year history, which revealed some memory gaps. For instance, Foster's memory of his kindergarten experience was much clearer to him than his first- and second-grade years. The memory for these latter years was described as "a blur." He remembered his mother as a cold, distant disciplinarian, except when the family vacationed and she was not with her mother, who lived with the family. At these times, Foster's mother was much warmer and more loving, which confused the young Foster.

During the fourth session, an alter identity, the Destroyer, emerged spontaneously after much grimacing and bodily contortion to tell me that he had been created to take care of Foster after Foster attempted suicide 35 years before. He told me that there was another "Big Box" who had been created years before to hold all the pain of the abuse. The most terrible thing that he wanted to tell me was that this pain consisted of the memory of having had to participate in the killing of the family house-keeper, who had been his nanny. The memory that he was forced to cut off her breast during a cult ceremony was particularly gruesome. I listened to this story without comment until it was concluded. I assured Foster that I understood how much pain and confusion this event must have provoked in the past, and that I understood that it continued to disturb him in the present. I also thanked him for taking a risk and telling me the story. When this message was delivered Destroyer faded, leaving Foster in a more normal posture but convulsed with sobbing.

From the very first emergence of Destroyer, I began using deeper hyp-notic procedures at the conclusion of sessions to resolve and quiet the emotional turmoil of the session and create a safe and stable internal emo-tional environment during the time between sessions. Beginning with the session described above, for the first year or so of treatment, the closing "ritual" of each session was virtually identical:

> Foster, everyone, listen. Let your eyes close as you float down into yourself, feeling your back against the cushions of the chair and your legs supported by the seat. Feeling your feet on the ground, you can feel the tension and any distress flowing down and out through your legs and feet, into the ground just the way that lightening flows down and is safely grounded. You can hear the sound of my voice, so familiar as its vibrations reach your ears, actually moving the little hairs of your inner ear, so that it is physically present to you, as your inner ear translates it to your brain and the very center of your being. So my voice can flow to you, and you can see and experience it as if there were a special healing balm that like water running down the many layers of rocks seeps down to the many layers of yourself, of your being, all the parts of yourself bringing deeper and deeper comfort and relief. Each moment becoming calmer and deeper, deeper and calmer. Heal-ing moving throughout the whole of your being, layer to layer. Count-ing now, deeper and deeper relief and healing, sealing over all the distress until we meet again, 1 . . . more and more complete, 2 . . . deeper and deeper . . . 3 . . . until all the parts of yourself are resting comfortably together, 4 . . . no conflict, no distress, 5 . . . deeply, resting, undisturbed, 6 . . . Foster there more and more, everyone else more and more quiet, 7 . . . deeper, 8 . . . deeper, until a complete sense of calm reigns, 9 . . . deeply healing, 10 . . . quiet and calm, ready now to return to a state of fully alert awareness and function while retaining this deep sense of calm and healing. 10 . . . 9 . . . 8 . . . 7 . . . 6 . . . 5 . . . 4 . . . 3, more and more alert . . . 2 . . . 1 fully awake and alert, calm and oriented.

From time to time specific suggestions related to upcoming events in the week or in response to particular events during the session would be added as necessary within the overall framework of the imagery described above.

The same simple eye closure instructions were used to elicit alter identity segments that readily appeared in treatment, introducing themselves and presenting their experience. At no time, then, until near the conclusion of treatment, when I attempted deep hypnotic exploration to elicit any otherwise undiscovered dissociative elements, did I use anything other than the suggestion to close his eyes and let whatever part of himself that needed to appear (or was requested to appear) appear.

As might be expected, such simple closing ceremonies were not always sufficient to master the strong emotion that was often expressed during sessions. Nonetheless, the ceremony was always included to provide a sense of consistency and predictability across sessions. However, the general principle described above remained in force throughout the treatment: Deep hypnotic states were only elicited to control affect, stabilize behavior, or foster the integration process. At no time were age-regression procedures used to elicit memory or to work through trauma. Although the appearance of alter identity states most often seemed accompanied by at least light "trance" experience, Foster was always aware of what had occurred. Even if he did not necessarily feel the emotions described, he would often have profound affect in response to what he heard or saw happening. At no time in this treatment was posthypnotic amnesia used to titrate these effects.

DEALING WITH INCREASING DISTRESS IN TREATMENT

Patients with DID experience an array of distressing emotions related to three distinct phenomena: (a) the recovery and reliving of intensely painful, terrifying, and shame-inducing memories; (b) the distress of *present-time* cognitive discontinuities in memory, skills, and knowledge; and (c) the effects of the presence (and dominance) of distinct alternate identities, which are often in conflict and always differ in terms of motive, style, and intention.

Compared with other DID patients, Foster had relatively few problems with overt loss of behavioral control to alter identity states. As treatment progressed, painful affect increasingly came to the fore. Despite the use of hypnotic interventions described above, Foster's memory or emotions could be jarred by a variety of unanticipated triggers, some of which were not readily identifiable.

Shortly after the session described above, we had a 2-week break for the Christmas holidays. During that period (6 weeks into treatment), Foster and his family were watching television, and Foster witnessed a commercial for cat food. This triggered a dissociated memory of his grandmother killing his cat when he was 6 or 7 years old. With this memory came a flood of emotion, and Foster appeared to switch into an alter identity state. His altered behavior greatly alarmed his family. In fact, it was the first time his children had witnessed such an episode.

In our next session, after he reported this episode, I asked Foster if he actually remembered such an event. Foster said that he did not, but he seemed certain that as a child he did indeed have a favorite kitten. When questioned further, he admitted that he had no idea what "became of the cat." However, there was no doubt that Foster remembered the experience of being "taken over" by a childlike state, speaking in a childish voice, "They killed my puddy cat; I want my puddy cat," and crying inconsolably for 10 minutes or so. I asked Foster to close his eyes and describe what had happened. In the same childlike voice, he told me the story of the killing of his cat and all the feelings he felt as a child and still felt in this child identity. The identity was described by Destroyer as "Little Foster," the child who had undergone the original trauma that lead to the formation of alter identities.

Next, I asked Little Foster to describe not only what happened but also how and where it happened. I prompted him to provide a detailed description of the surroundings in the room—who and what was there, along with what was occurring, beyond the specific horror surrounding the slaying of the cat. For the first time since this material surfaced in his previous treatment, Foster himself was able to relate these bizarre and terrible happenings to events he actually remembered.[4] That is, he was able to recall that the killing occurred on the second floor of a building used as a Christian Science Church. Of course, this in itself does not constitute evidence that the events took place. However, when Foster was able to link the dissociated voices and their traumatic reports with events he was able to recall, the emotion generated was overwhelming. I asked Foster to close his eyes and go into a very deep trance. I suggested that he see the room being put into a box, as if in psychological brackets, and that in front of the scene there was a curtain hanging. Behind the curtain, behind the brackets, and within the box all the feeling and the meaning of this event could be and would be contained.

> All the feeling, everything you are afraid that it means is held in by the strong walls of the box, protected from sight by the curtain. However, you will know that it is there for times when you are ready to look at it, little bit by little bit. So that you can be safe and secure

---

[4]The difference between the feeling of "knowing" something and the feeling of "remembering" is very important to people's subjective sense of the reality of events. While feeling things to be "really real" is experientially vital, it is surely no guarantee of the veridicality of the memory. Evidence exists to suggest that plausibility coupled with repeated free recall leads to high rates of "remembering" things that did not occur (cf. Schachter, 1996).

during the week and you don't have to think about any of this until
we meet again. And you can just jot down any notes that you have in
your mind on a piece of paper and put them into a locked cash box,
where the thoughts will rest until we meet again.[5]

The next 24 hours were particularly difficult for Foster. He was able
to recall that the other main culprit in the dissociated cult memories was
a real woman who had been one of his grandmother's friends. He further
recalled that she sexually molested him on one occasion, and he recalled
that his mother was always frightened when she was around this woman.
More than anything, it was this sort of connection in memory that gave
him confidence that his dissociated memories were accurate and productive.

By the next session (number seven), several new alter identities had
emerged spontaneously. A very violent-appearing alter appeared who was
cavemanlike in demeanor. This alter presented with an out-thrust lower
jaw; a wrinkled, scowling brow; and a hunched-over, muscular appearance.
The alter was filled with rage and demanded to be heard. First expressed
as howling and raging at "the women," the anger rapidly subsided as there
was a shift into a very tearful, sobbing state with a whining quality to it.
This character announced that the identities in greatest pain, suffering
from the most shame and paralysis, were Little Foster and another adolescent, who could not appear because they were so humiliated.

Foster was again instructed to close his eyes, this time with the di-
rective:

everyone close your eyes and listen to me. I know that you are filled
with shame, and rage, and hurt, and lots of other feelings. I know that
you feel all alone with this and don't know what to do because you
all feel trapped in time with these things. But each of you knows that
Muriel [Foster's wife] is there, that she has been there for 30 years, and
that she loves Foster and that she says that she will love every part of
him and that all those things that happened in the past do not matter
to her, they do not change her feelings of love. So each of you in your
own way can feel that there is more than just pain, more that just
shame, more than just fear, more than just anger, there are other things
too, there is love that is in this whole person's experience that each
of you, because you are part of the same person, can feel, can feel it
entering into you, calming you, nurturing and soothing you. And each
of you knows, too, that I am here, that you want me to be here, and
that is why you are talking to me and telling me these things so that

---

[5]Throughout the text where I include transcript excerpts, I have condensed the actual content to
provide a flavor of my interventions, more than that of the therapeutic dialogue. When these
interventions actually took place, with the possible exception of the closing relaxation ritual,
dialogue was a part of all hypnotic work. I believe in actively engaging the patient in the decisions
and discussion. No doubt this limits depth of hypnotic experience, which from my perspective is all
to the good.

they too can remind you that you are no longer alone with no one to help, no one to tell. So that it would be all right for all of you to go to sleep and rest and heal. It would be all right for you to rest and heal, letting Foster be there day to day, letting Muriel be there day to day. Resting peacefully until we have a chance to talk again.

Over the next 5 months there were many episodes of intense abreaction during sessions. Despite these exhausting sessions, Foster had only a single episode of switching states at home, and he never missed work. He alternated between periods of desperation and hopelessness and periods of relief and hope that allowed him to consider (but reject) the need for social relations and friendships outside his family. Indeed, the mere mention of having friends was sufficient to produce an intense emotional reaction.

Then in the seventh month of treatment, the memory of the murder of his nanny–family housekeeper reemerged as if it had been a real experience. Intense affect was stirred up, and the memory was interlaced with other memories of his being beaten until he participated in the murder. The second session involving this material brought vivid memories of his attachment to the housekeeper. Foster could scarcely contain his emotions with this rush of memory, and he was unable to contain his turbulent feelings with hypnotic and behavioral procedures. Unfortunately, at this same time his wife had a trip scheduled to visit her mother in another state. The second evening that she was gone, Foster had several glasses of wine and alternately switched between an inconsolable child and the raging Killer identity. In between these state changes, he had the foresight to call his wife, who placed an emergency call to me. When I tried to reach him, there was no answer because he had ripped the telephone from the wall. I called emergency services, and Foster was transported to the local emergency room, where he was held overnight and where he made several serious attempts to cut himself while in restraints. The next day he was released for assessment for a possible admission to a DID inpatient program, but the director felt he was calmer and did not require hospitalization. This single episode was the sole hospital admission during the entire treatment. It was also the first of only two episodes of self-harm over the course of treatment.

At all other times that alter identities emerged, either Foster or his wife reached me by telephone, and he was able to regain self-control using the following hypnoticlike techniques related during a telephone conversation: "Killer, this is Dr. Horevitz. You know who I am, you know the sound of my voice, you can remember how it sounds to you, the things that you experience so that as you become calmer and more centered, you can tell me what it is that is going on right now."

I elicited a discussion of the immediate precipitating event, thought, or feeling and discussed plans and means of gaining control of the situation.

Ordinarily, within a few minutes, Foster regained sufficient control so that whatever alter identity emerged felt that I understood enough to help Foster resolve the problem. Suggestions along the following lines were often quite beneficial in this regard:

> So now that you have told me all these things and you know quite deeply that I understand how you feel and why you feel it, you can see how much calmer you are already feeling and how good it would be just to close your eyes and allow yourself to sleep and go to that safe place we have made and let Foster come back to be in charge. Just letting your eyes close, deeply, even your "inner eyes" can close and as I count from 5 to 1, you can rest and let Foster be here, 5 . . . 4 . . . 3 . . . 2 . . . 1. Foster!

In my experience, this simple strategy is effective in calming and soothing DID patients in crisis. Nevertheless, Foster's response was uncharacteristically rapid and devoid of complications.

Such episodes of uncontrolled switching can be a serious problem in treating DID patients. However, DID patients are even more commonly troubled by disabling internal conflict. Such conflict is characteristically experienced as a cacophony of voices or direct challenges to present behavior often accompanied by "character assassination" (i.e., "negative self-statements"), which DID patients do not experience as arising from the self. Not surprisingly, such manifestations of internal conflict were a part of Foster's symptom picture.

Although such processes can be viewed as cognitive distortions (cf. Fine, 1989, 1991), I approach them as distortions within a "family" system (of alters) that lacks adequate means of communication and problem resolution. To better understand this system, many authorities agree that getting a "map" of the internal world is essential. These maps may take many forms, but they really consist of a log of internal dissociated identities, their descriptions and relations to one another, and other essential information that can be obtained. Most often this is done by the creation of drawings or charts. Foster was unwilling to attempt such a project but hypnotically was able to achieve the same effect using a technique of imagining being in a movie theater and watching the screen develop as a "jigsaw puzzle" that identified all the parts. I transcribed his description.

To facilitate communication between and among alters and to foster problem resolution, in Foster's case, techniques from structural and systematic family therapy, rather than cognitive therapy, were applied to resolve interidentity conflicts. In my experience, this has the advantage of directly increasing the contact between alter identities. This is done by requiring that each alter "be in the other's shoes" and look at things from the other's perspectives and anticipate the consequences of the other's actions and symbolic communications. Often such joint problem solving and co-experiencing successfully diminishes internal dissociative barriers.

For instance, one of Foster's alter identities called himself "Satan's Son" and relentlessly punished the Little Foster child alter. As is commonly the case, this persecutor alter served a "protective" function (i.e., "correcting" Foster) by punishing, humiliating, and blaming Foster. Satan's Son was convinced that he had died when Foster had almost been suffocated on one occasion, and that he had been reborn, according to his grandmother's wishes, as Satan's son. This alter was angry in appearance but, in fact, was frightened and confused. If Foster had died, who were all these other characters and why did he have to punish them if they were already dead? Did he want to do something to "someone" else similar to what was done to him? In hypnosis Satan's Son was asked to briefly reexperience his own feelings of having to be born a "slave" out of pain and torture. He was asked to identify the similarities with Little Foster's feelings by sharing this alter's consciousness (i.e., coconsciousness). By indentifying with Little Foster, it was possible for Satan's Son to realize that he had much more in common with Little Foster than with the descriptions of Satan and Satan's desires he had been told about (e.g., blood, killing, and death).

The next painful memories Foster confronted were of abuse by his mother, which first emerged as a voice telling him that she had abused him. With the recognition of this abuse, Foster began to express intense fear of retribution through various child identities. This was countered with exhortations for his adult identities to comfort him. Foster began to report that for the first time in his life he was actually experiencing pleasure in his daily activities. He, nevertheless, expressed the fear that what had happened in his past would make him unforgivable insofar as he was unable to forgive himself for what he had done or for what had been done to him. We had a session with his wife to deal with this issue, which culminated in Foster allowing all "parties" of him to reach out and take his wife's hand and be reassured that she loved him "through and through" and did indeed forgive him.

This experience of contact with his wife, although initially reassuring, also activated fears that the angriest parts of him would confuse his wife with the terrible women of the past and hurt her as a means of revenge. A few weeks of rapid switching occurred in sessions as he tried to come to grips with this. Many of the angry and hurt identities wanted Foster to feel some of their pain so that he would know what they were going through.

During this period, I introduced several hypnotic techniques to reduce fear and pain, all of which had the same logic: They suggested increased connectedness and diminished barriers between identity states. Thus, fearful child alters were taught to be able to experience the massive, muscular bulk of the adult Foster. They were often "time progressed" to understand that this is who they would become in the future and that Foster's strength could protect them from further harm.

The alters who were anesthetic to emotional pain (like the Man from Mars) were urged to sit with, hold, and console the hurting adult parts. Killer, who was always in extreme pain, described himself as if he was all exposed raw nerves: Because every sensation hurt him, there was no meaningful distinction between pleasure and pain. The following pain-reduction technique was developed to soothe Killer:

> Killer, you know that Foster has had many good things happen in his life; that despite all the things that happened in the past, there is lots of love for him, there is caring, there is [his wife's] love, the kid's love, the good deeds that he has done, therapy, and other things that don't hurt. All these things can be put together, blended together in a giant pitcher filled with "unhurt" from all these things, and as you are able to drink this cool drink, the coolness of the "unhurt" will ease your pain, will flow through you and provide a protective covering around all your nerves, around all those parts of you that used to be so sensitive so that you will be able to rest, easily and comfortably, easily and comfortably.

These sorts of statements were repeated a number of times in the session and in the following session, which his wife also attended. We used the same hand-holding procedure to have all the "unhurt" flow from her to Killer until he felt better with her and increasingly calm. In this session Killer felt able to integrate his wife's love and integrate the evidence of 30 years of caring from her family as well. Suggestions along the following lines were also used to reduce internal tension, so that by the end of the session, Foster was relaxed:

> Killer, you can float easily inside yourself, floating in a sea of "unhurt," able to feel the ebb and flow of emotions and feelings—feelings come and feelings go, moods come and moods go, emotions come and emotions go; just let yourself float and allow feelings to come and go. Fear of feelings is not necessary, just let them come and go.

During this period Foster recalled many more aspects of the traumatic picture that were central to him. This occurred following brief hypnotic inductions described earlier in which Foster was asked to close his eyes and tell me "what was going on." A key memory that surfaced was of his mother's attempt to drown him at the age of 5, during which time he evidently lost consciousness and reawakened in bed convinced that he had died.

As emotional pain began to increase and he began to feel paralyzed by it, I suggested that his pain was like a single small hurt pressing down on a nerve plexus, thus producing a wider pain and paralysis than necessary. In hypnosis, we isolated the hurt, surgically lifted it, and packed it with gauze while cooling it with liquid nitrogen. This allowed the pain to remain localized. This maneuver was so successful that we used it in other contexts to manage pain. Even as we worked at this point, about 2 years into treatment, to reduce pain, I increased the pressure to share experience and obligation for joint outcome. All alter identities' experience was subtly redefined and reframed to suggest that none of them had truly escaped pain or had really succeeded in not feeling. We reviewed Foster's defensive strategies until he was able to see that no matter what he had done, he never really could completely elude emotion and feeling, even when numb. Therefore, it was agreed that all those alters old enough and important enough would be joined together in a league, around a council fire where they would pass the peacepipe, each with their turn to talk and develop joint problem-solving skills.

The major impasse at this point in treatment was that all the alter identities "blamed" Little Foster for their pain—if he hadn't wimped out in the bathtub incident, they would never have had to be created to take all the pain. Their empathy, including Foster's level of empathy, was extremely restricted because all relationships, except that with his wife, were associated with potential pain. This precluded both social relationships and internal interalter relationships.

At a certain point words, hypnotic imagery, and cognitive reframing failed to break the impasse. There was too much anger and contained violence. Therefore, I suggested that Foster make arm protectors out of heavy gloves and thick foam rubber covering, which he did. Sitting very close to me so his range of motion was restrained, he had the freedom to use his considerable strength to strike out at me to release his rage. This provided a safe and constructive outlet for him. Over five sessions with the "gloves" on, his pain and rage diminished dramatically. After displays of intense and exhausting anger during which time I would actively constrain and absorb his blows, he would begin to cry. I would lean over and hold him until the shuddering and sobbing stopped. Not only had the expression of anger become safe, but it also was integrative.

In the following months it became possible to deal with the pain associated with the near-death drowning and the apparent purpose his mother had in mind to convince him he had died and had been reborn to function in the cult. Once all those around the council fire could agree, they went back in time hypnotically and bodily carried Little Foster out of the bathtub, out of the house, and into the present. This was hypnotically dramatized with a great sense of urgency, difficulty, and finally relief at having broken through the emotional time barrier. From then on, Little Foster sat at the council fire and could actually "be carried" on either Killer's or Foster's shoulders and see out of their eyes to get a sense of what life was like in the present.

By Christmas 1990, we were also able to deal with the issues that surrounded Lover's pressing sexual needs. It appeared that the anonymous sex that Foster sought out related to trying to diminish feelings and memories of forced sadistic sex, which included some very vicious incidents and maternal incest. Because these experiences were wrapped up in Lover, and Lover's behavior was closely monitored (as well as despised), Lover was an outcast in the system. Once these issues were clarified, Lover was "affirmed" and included in the council fire. Within a few weeks Foster noticed an important increase in his social relationships—he joined a men's athletic association and became an active participant. All of the angry parts had relinquished their hatred of Little Foster and Lover.

Over the next four months, we addressed more of the sadistic sexual experiences and the incest with his mother. Special hypnotic procedures included "removing" inserted objects and making a trip in time to see his mother's and grandmother's graves to be sure that they were indeed no longer a danger. All the abuse stories were now repeated, looked at from the perspective of all the alter identities, and questioned as to what other outcomes were possible and what level of control he actually had during the experiences. This elicited heretofore unknown alter parts who strongly identified with the sadistic and aggressive mother and grandmother. This was met with nonhypnotic means: Their views were questioned in great detail until incongruities and contradictions began to emerge. I focused, often quite dramatically, on the elements of the cognitive dissonance, until the alters felt forced to admit that they really were not so sure that they wanted to uphold this nihilistic, destructive worldview. Rapidly they turned around and became strong supporters of the Three Musketeers model of treatment: all for one and one for all.

During this same spring, we were able to use hypnosis to age progress Little Foster from the age of 5 first to 8 and then to the age of 12.

> Little Foster, Killer and Angry One helped you out of the bathtub and out of that room in which you lay and thought you had died. Now you know that you didn't die, you weren't reborn as someone who belonged to someone else or to the cult, and you can see, looking around the council fire, that no one who used to torment you or threaten you or be angry with you is that way any more. They are all there for you. Look around at them, at their faces, how do they look, what are they saying, is it angry? [shakes head], are they smiling? [nods]. OK, then. Killer and Angry One are going to walk with you and take you on a journey; Destroyer will be there too. First, Destroyer, I'd like you to help Little Foster feel what it will be like for him to be all grown up, not lost in the past. Let him feel the strength in your muscles, the whole size of your body . . . almost like putting on a costume. Flex your muscles and let him feel their strength, so that no one will ever again be able to hurt you physically.
>
> That's good [as he flexes and postures], so now he knows that it is all right to grow up. Everyone together, walking forward in time, as

each year passes, all the young ones who are that age can come along, bring their feelings, memories, and experience together. Little Foster, growing older and bigger, more and more room for the others to enter with their memories and feelings, guarded and protected, walking up the road of time just like on an autumn day and the wind swirls the falling leaves about your feet and in the air, all the colors swirling around until all is one and you're all together Little Foster because you can remember all there is to remember to share all there is to share and Killer and Destroyer and Angry One are there to protect you.

Over the next sessions, the strength of this fusion of identity fragments was tested, often against Foster's complaints that treatment was not moving quickly enough. However, within a few weeks, Foster was consistently reporting new levels of experiencing his feelings and the environment. He could tolerate much more feeling and was less vulnerable to emotional upset provoked by internal and situational triggers. At the same time, previously unknown dissociated identities emerged, all associated with abuse by his grandmother. These identities included an angry woman who was quite similar to the grandmother—what might be called a sadistic female introject—and a parallel "Little Girl" part that was evidently created as a result of his grandmother's sexual torture of Foster as a young boy. This torture was accompanied by verbal tirades about how bad and awful boys were and that he would not have to experience this from her if he was a girl (but if he was, then without her protection, he would experience it from men).

Naming her "Old Woman," we spent the next 5 months working on Foster's sadistic impulses and fear of integration. Much inner conflict was stirred up, but as this was addressed, the Old Woman's need to appear so threatening began to diminish, and her identity as a hidden protector rather than a literal incorporation of the grandmother was reformulated. Increasingly, the Man From Mars and the Old Woman were addressed as mirror images of each other, as final protective barriers against Foster ever having to grow up and face the world on his own. Whatever hidden trauma they each were masking was approached in hypnosis like a card game—they would take turns, each having to help the other figure out some way to reframe, reinterpret, understand, and integrate the sequestered experience. As this progressed, at a certain point the experiential distinction between them began to diminish and each agreed that their charges, Little Foster and the Little Girl, ought to be allowed to grow up and bring everything they had in their experience together and discover what life had in store for them.

This aspect of integration led to the first period of true calm for Foster. He was visibly relaxed more of the time, smiled spontaneously, and joked with me and his family. After having had much difficulty in the past being around his grown daughter and attending church, he was able to do all of these things with enthusiasm for the first time. Feelings of simmering hatred and rage which had been present for so long, no longer troubled him.

The next step was to integrate Little Foster with Foster. By January 1992 we were ready to accomplish this task. Hypnotic imagery was used to suggest that Little Foster could see himself walking up a country road. Way down the road there was a full length mirror. As we walked toward it, he would see himself getting bigger and bigger in the mirror. Not only would the size of the image change, but all the changes that accompany aging and growing up to be a man would occur as well. Finally, when he reached the mirror, the image in the mirror would be that of Foster, the man whom Little Foster was becoming. As he looked at this reflection of himself in the mirror, I suggested that he touch the mirror with his finger tips, and as he did so, the mirror would become like a perfect reflecting surface of water. Instead of feeling his fingers on glass, he would feel Foster's fingers coming through from the present. Both could enter into the perfect reflecting surface and join together, thus becoming one. After this imagery work was accomplished, for several weeks, I encouraged Little Foster to experiment with this union, while retaining a measure of distance (Little Foster could look through Foster's eyes, feel with Foster's skin, move with his body, and experience sex through him). After a brief period, the need for this distinction ended: Little Foster spontaneously became one with Foster.

Within the month, the Little Girl was able to accept a male role after watching what happened to Little Foster and, together with all the remaining identity fragments, repeated the looking-through experience we engineered with Little Foster and Foster.

A major complication, not mentioned earlier, was that Foster did not, in his experience, actually grow much past his fearful, despairing, suicidal 20s. The alter identity Destroyer, which had been created during his suicide attempt, actually experienced all of the intervening 40 years. Their identities were very much intermingled: Destroyer's voice in treatment was low, gruff, and grumbling, whereas Foster's, although resembling more his day-to-day voice, was more effeminate, tentative, and filled with uncertainty and fear.

Over the next 2 months in late winter 1992, much time was spent having Foster live as a companion of Destroyer, much as we had done with Little Foster and Foster. This brought many issues of sexuality, pleasure, and pain to the surface. Symbolically, much of the confusion about sadistic and masochistic pain was reduced by having the Old Woman redefine herself as distinct from the grandmother and be able to merge with the Man from Mars. By spring, Foster was no longer particularly distinguishable from Destroyer. For the first time, Foster himself began to experience and initiate sex with his wife and began to embrace his children. More and more integrative shared inner experience and problem solving was suggested and cultivated in sessions.

In June, Foster had the spontaneous hypnotic image of a room filled with electricity and pain. In his therapy session he was able to identify that all of the pain, the lightning, and chaos was his own experience of himself as a "beast"—all the terrible things he had done and experienced, all the humiliation he had been forced to undergo, and all the rage that remained. We spent the month working in and out of hypnosis with these feelings. Then, in mid-July his wife reported that Foster had what looked like a seizure episode but that afterwards he reported to her and to me that what was going on was that all of the parts decided to fuse and integrate. This occurred after they had watched the movie, *Regarding Henry*, which Foster identified as his and Destroyer's story. Immediately after this episode, Foster reported a dramatic increase in the ability to feel both emotions and tactile sensations. He no longer had any negative reactions to touch. He also could no longer hear any internal voices as separate, although he felt that his parts were still a part of his make-up but no longer separate.

Over the next 4 months we began a postfusion stage of treatment in which we discussed many complex issues related to the integration of his experience, life choices, and future plans. Hypnosis was used, on average, only twice a month to test the stability of the fusions achieved. Numerous attempts were made to elicit known or possibly unknown alter identities, all of which failed. Foster's condition gradually stabilized over time, and by September, sessions were reduced to biweekly and gradually tapered as his ability to handle arguments with his wife, disappointments at work, and conflict with his children improved. By January 1993 he was being seen on a visit per 3 month basis. Treatment was finally terminated in July of that year. Since then, Foster and his wife have retired and left the state. Nevertheless, his progress has been followed by phone or letter through the end of 1994. After that, he will check in yearly to keep me up to date on his progress.

FOLLOW-UP

As noted above, I followed up on Foster's progress in person and by telephone. He was also evaluated at the conclusion of treatment by a complete battery of psychological tests. Unfortunately, there are no pretreatment data to compare them with, so they must be presented and accepted at face value. The data are less than rigorous, yet they are nevertheless interesting.

When Foster was 62 years of age, in the spring of 1994, I administered the Rorschach Inkblot Test (Rorschach, 1921), Thematic Apperception Test (TAT; Murray, 1938), MMPI-2 (Butcher, Graham, Dahlstrom, Tellegen, & Kaemmer, 1989), MCMI-II (Millon, 1987), Dissociative Experiences Scale (Bernstein & Putnam, 1986), Beck Depression Inventory (Beck et al., 1961), MMPI PTSD Scale (Schlenger & Kulka, 1989), SCID-D (Steinberg, 1993) and SCID-P, Stanford Hypnotic Susceptibility Scale Form C (Weitzenhoffer & Hilgard, 1962), Wechsler Memory Scale-Revised (Wechsler, 1987), and a number of other self-report inventories.

In brief, the structured interviews did not reveal any clinically diagnosable disorders. Foster passed 6 of the 12 suggestions on the SHSS:C, evidencing an average level of hypnotizability, although he did have a vivid age-regression back to second grade (though none to fifth grade). This score is unusually low for someone suffering from a dissociative disorder. The SCID-D failed to provide evidence for a current dissociative disorder, and his score on the DES (3.75) was atypically low for all psychiatric and normal populations. Furthermore, Foster did not exhibit any signs of depression, (3 on the BDI), and no MMPI-2 scales were elevated, with the exception of an L scale at 70. This latter elevation suggested that Foster was over-constricted and exhibited a marked tendency to produce a favorable response. These test scores were all consistent with the impression Foster presented at the time. Whereas the SCID-P was positive for past history of anxiety, alcohol abuse, depression, and posttraumatic stress, and the SCID-D was positive for past dissociative disorder, the posttreatment assessment revealed no current syndromes.

On the TAT, Foster's responses to the pictures were conventional, although they were marked by significant detachment and disinterest between the characters in the stories and relative stoicism and resignation in relationship to loss or failure on the part of individual characters. On the Rorschach, Foster only provided 13 responses, a meager record not adequate for interpretation. He was asked to go through the cards one more time and produce additional responses to the stimuli. With these instructions, he produced 19 responses. He had many poor form responses on the Rorschach associated with reflection responses (which are conventionally interpreted as relating to narcissistic concerns). In Card II he saw an injured cat (recall the lost cat of childhood), and in Card III he saw the wide grinning face of a cat. These are very unusual responses reflecting odd percepts and organization of information. Despite his managerial style and success, his Rorschach revealed rather poorly developed styles for handling emotional situations when he cannot distance himself from emotions. Some traumatic contents were also apparent, but the major theme appeared to be an underlying concern with the injury to his own core sense of self. However, there were no special scores or level 2 scores, and no evidence of depression, obsessiveness, hypervigilance, thought disorder, or gross pathology.

In short, there was no evidence of continued major (Axis I) psychopathology or severe personality (Axis II) pathology. Nevertheless, residues of hurt or trauma remain and were, perhaps, reflected in his cautious style. Alternatively, the testing indicates the capacity to be open to experience, which was definitely not apparent when clinically assessed at the beginning of treatment. I believe that Foster's treatment must be judged an unequivocal success. The treatment provides some evidence for the efficacy of the standard format for treating dissociative disorders, which will be capsulized below.

CONCLUSION

This case illustrates what has come to be accepted as the basic model of treatment of the dissociative disorders (Horevitz, 1993; Kluft, 1993). First, the presentation of dissociated identity states is accepted, rather than discouraged, and the continued presentation of these states and attention to their individual uniqueness is encouraged. Second, the treatment is structured around initial stabilization, followed by a period of work within and outside of hypnosis where symbolic and experiential events are encouraged. Alter identities are encouraged to achieve greater differentiation while they are simultaneously encouraged to cooperate and identify with the person as a "single" individual. Third, trauma is related to the self-definition of these alter identities and to symptomatic presentation. Resolution of the trauma is not geared toward abreaction but, instead, toward an integrative reexperiencing of past events in light of understanding their role in shaping the individual's present experience. Fourth, the clinician's task is to resolutely confront and work through dissociative defenses as they are manifested in treatment and everyday life.

In the service of these goals, extensive use of metaphor, symbolization, and dramatization is used as the vehicle to treat dissociation, even as other interventions ranging from cognitive therapy, dynamic understanding, pharmacotherapy, and hospitalization are used to treat other focal symptoms. This particular case relied little on pharmacotherapy and relatively more on family and marital interventions. Although Foster's treatment was lengthy and spanned over four years, it proceeded carefully and economically. Given the level of problems observed at the beginning of treatment and the progress documented at the end of treatment, a weekly 45-minute session over this time period appears to be neither excessive nor unduly costly.

Like many DID patients, Foster had the experience of the emergence of alter identities and reports of critical life events that were not in his conscious memory. When these events were remembered, they did not have the quality of ordinary memory. Rather, they were upsetting and disorienting. Over the course of 4 years, Foster related a long history of trauma and torture. The emergence of such memories raises the question of whether they were accurate representations of historical reality or were imagined or suggested creations. Although Foster's treatment began long before the eruption of controversy about false memories in psychotherapy, these potential problems were evident from the beginning of Foster's treatment. Indeed, I told Foster that he could view any memories that emerged with respectful skepticism.

For the most part, as Foster was able to talk about memories and resolve his feelings about experiences he believed occurred in his past, the traumatic material ceased to trouble him. Part of the reason why this was the case was that his wife was able to reassure him of her love and devotion and gave Foster considerable support. At any rate, Foster did not become a professional trauma victim. Great pain and shame required working through, but as these feelings were resolved, Foster's functioning improved, as confirmed by both his wife and children.

It is important to note that in this treatment, as in many similar treatments, no verification of the prior history of abuse could be undertaken. Furthermore, the allegations of ritual abuse, although considerably milder than some heard today, could not be verified either. The persistence of "cat" imagery in the Rorschach can hardly be taken of evidence of anything other than the persistent personal importance of this theme. As I remarked in the opening paragraphs, the diagnosis and discovery of trauma history, including the alleged cult abuse all occurred in his previous treatment. How contaminating that treatment might have been, we will never know.

In Foster's case, it seems clear that if the diagnosis and memory responses were "suggested," then the mechanism of that occurring is unrelated to hypnotizability or imagination. For example, Foster scored very low on the ICMI of Wilson and Barber (1983) and the Bett's scale of vividness of imagery (Sheehan, 1967). Although there is no evidence that he had a preexisting disposition to believe that such things as cults exist, he did have a very high degree of faith in his former therapist. Had she handled his report of hearing a voice tell him he was sexually abused by his mother by dismissing it, there is no telling what would have transpired.

It is worth sounding a note of caution about suggestion effects in working with dissociative disorder patients, as well as with any patient. Since I treated Foster, the literature on the potential deleterious effects of suggestive influences in psychotherapy has mushroomed (Ganaway, 1989; Loftus, 1993). It is now fairly well-established (see Lynn & Nash, 1994) that people who are hypnotizable may be particularly vulnerable to sug-gestive influences. Although Foster was not very hypnotizable, many DID patients are. Furthermore, people who are uncertain about past events or who have poor memories for past events may be prone to succumb to suggestive influences. Therapists who treat dissociative patients need to discuss the possibility of false memories emerging in the treatment prior to the use of any memory-recovery techniques. Therapists also should avoid pressuring patients to recall past events and legitimizing the historical re-ality of memory reports while, at the same time, deeply empathizing with their patients' representations of their history.

Therapists need to exert caution in accepting the patient's imagina-tive or symbolic reality for actual reality. The danger lies in the potential for the therapist to enter into the symbolic reality of the patient, taking the vivid presentation of self for the patient's real world. When this hap-pens, the therapy gets diverted into a dangerously complex systematic *folie à deux* where the problems of each alter identity are treated as if they were individual patients in treatment.

Much work remains to be done in the whole area of dissociative disorders and on understanding the increasingly complex and horrifying accounts of abuse these patients present. What role social causation may play has been contested, but no research on the subject exists. Controlled outcome studies are lacking, though some large uncontrolled series of suc-cessful treatments have been reported (Coons, 1986; Coons, Bowman, & Milstein, 1988). In light of the absence of a defined, manual-based treat-ment to test outcomes in a controlled fashion, Foster's treatment, like other reported successful treatment, cannot be counted as proof of either the diagnosis or the efficacy of treatment. Perhaps single case studies that use pooled time-series methodologies can be attempted to weed out such un-controlled factors as maturation and the generalized, nonspecific, positive effects of treatment (see Nadon & Laurence, 1994). In Foster's case, for example, much of the treatment gain evidenced might have been a func-tion of the support his wife lavished on him at various times during his treatment.

On another level, however, I believe that Foster's successful treatment demonstrates what has long been argued: Patients' diffuse pain, suffering, and nameless dread can be transformed through techniques that involve symbolization, dramatic reenactment, and reframing. This approach re-mains as viable today as it did for our Neolithic ancestors and shamans throughout the world. There is something transforming and curative in the treatment model I have set forth. It is not, however, a predictable treat-ment and much depends on the quality of the relationship developed be-tween the patient and therapist and on the therapist's ingenuity and flex-ibility. Success in this endeavor does not tell us anything about causation, only about that which cures what ails us.

REFERENCES

American Psychiatric Association. (1994). *Diagnostic and statistical manual of mental disorders* (4th ed.). Washington, DC: Author.

Beck, A., Rush, J., Shaw, B., & Emery, G. (1979). *Cognitive therapy of depression.* New York: Guilford Press.

Beck, A. T., Ward, C. H., Mendelson, M., Mock, J., & Erbaugh, J. (1961). An inventory for measuring depression. *Archives of General Psychiatry, 4,* 561–571.

Bernstein, E. M., & Putnam, F. W. (1986). Development, reliability, and validity of a dissociation scale. *Journal of Nervous and Mental Disease, 174,* 727–735.

Blake, D. D., Weathers, F. W., Nagy, L. M., Kaloupek, D. G., Klauminzer, G., Charney, D., & Keane, T. M. (1990). A clinician rating scale for assessing current and lifetime PTSD: The CAPS-I. *Behavior Therapist, 18,* 187–188.

Butcher, J. N., Graham, J. R., Dahlstrom, W. G., Tellegen, A. M., & Kaemmer, B. (1989). MMPI–II *manual for administration and scoring.* Minneapolis: University of Minnesota Press.

Chu, J. A. (1988). Ten traps for therapists in the treatment of trauma survivors. *Dissociation, I*(1), 24–32.

Chu, J. A. (1991). On the misdiagnosis of multiple personality disorder. *Dissociation, 4,* 200–204.

Coons, P. M. (1986). Treatment progress in 20 patients with multiple personality disorder. *Journal of Nervous and Mental Diseases, 174,* 715–721.

Coons, P. M., Bowman, E. S., & Milstein, V. (1988). Multiple personality disorder: A clinical investigation of 50 cases. *Journal of Nervous and Mental Diseases, 176,* 519–527.

Donovan, D. M., & McIntyre, D. (1990). Healing the hurt child: A developmental-contextual approach. New York: Norton.

Fine, C. G. (1989). Treatment errors and iatrogenesis across therapeutic modalities in MPD and allied dissociative disorders. *Dissociation, 2,* 77–82.

Fine, C. G. (1991, September). Treatment stabilization and crisis prevention: Pacing the therapy of the multiple personality disorder patient. *Psychiatric Clinics of North America,* pp. 661–675.

Frankel, F. H. (1993). Adult reconstruction of childhood events in the multiple personality literature. *American Journal of Psychiatry, 150,* 954–958.

Fraser, G. A., & Raine, D. (1992, November). *Cost analysis of the treatment of multiple personality disorders.* Paper presented at the ninth International Conference on Multiple Personality/Dissociative State, Chicago.

Frischholz, E. J., Lipman, L. S., Braun, B. G., & Sachs, R. G. (1992). Psychopathology, hypnotizability, and dissociation. *American Journal of Psychiatry, 149*(11), 1521–1525.

Ganaway, G. K. (1989). Historical truth versus narrative truth: Clarifying the role of exogenous trauma in the etiology of multiple personality disorder and its variants. *Dissociation, 2,* 205–220.

Greaves, G. B. (1988). Common errors in the treatment of multiple personality disorder. *Dissociation, 1*, 61–66.

Horevitz, R. P. (1993). Hypnosis in the treatment of multiple personality disorder. In J. W. Rhue, S. J. Lynn & I. Kirsch (Eds.), *Handbook of clinical hypnosis* (pp. 395–424). Washington, DC: American Psychological Association.

Horevitz, R. P. (1994). Dissociation and multiple personality: Conflicts and controversies. In S. J. Lynn (Ed.), *Dissociation: Clinical research and theoretical perspectives* (pp. 434–462). New York: Guilford Press.

Horevitz, R. P., & Braun, B. G. (1984, March). Are multiple personalities borderline?: An analysis of 33 cases. *Psychiatric Clinics of North America*, 69–88.

Horevitz, R. P., & Loewenstein, R. J. (1994). The rational treatment of multiple personality disorder. In S. Lynn & J. Rhue (Eds.), *Dissociation: Clinical research and theoretical perspectives* (pp. 289–316). New York: Guilford Press.

Kernberg, O. F. (1975). *Borderline conditions and pathological narcissism.* New York: Jason Aronson.

Kluft, R. P. (1988). The postunification treatment of multiple personality disorder: First findings. *American Journal of Clinical Psychiatry, 42*, 212–228.

Kluft, R. P. (1991). Multiple personality disorder. In A. Tasman & S. Goldfinger (Eds.), *American Psychiatric Press Review of psychiatry* (Vol. 10, pp. 161–188). Washington, DC: American Psychiatric Press.

Kluft, R. P. (1993). Basic principles in conducting the treatment of multiple personality disorder. In R. P. Kluft & C. G. Fine (Eds.), *Clinical perspectives on multiple personality disorder* (pp. 53–73). Washington, DC: American Psychiatric Press.

Kluft, R. P., Steinberg, M., & Spitzer, R. L. (1988, March). DSM–III–R revisions in the dissociative disorders: An exploration of their derivation and rationale. *Dissociation*, pp. 39–46.

Linehan, M. M. (1993). *Cognitive–behavioral treatment of borderline personality disorder.* New York: Guilford Press.

Loftus, E. F. (1993). The reality of repressed memories. *American Psychologist, 48*(5), 518–537.

Lynn, S. J., & Nash, M. R. (1994). Truth in memory: Ramifications for psychotherapy and hypnotherapy. *American Journal of Clinical Hypnosis, 36*, 194–208.

McHugh, P. R. (1992). Psychiatric misadventures. *The American Scholar, 61*, 497–510.

Mersky, H. (1992). The manufacture of personalities: The production of multiple personality disorder. *British Journal of Psychiatry, 160*, 327–340.

Millon, T. (1987). *Millon Clinical Multiaxial Inventory–II: Manual for the MCMI–II* (2nd ed.). Minneapolis, MN: National Computer Systems.

Murray, H. (1938). *Explorations in personality.* Fairlawn, NJ: Oxford UP.

Nadon, R., & Laurence, J-R. (1994). Idiographic approaches to hypnosis research (Or how therapeutic practice can inform science). *American Journal of Clinical Hypnosis, 37*, 85–94.

North, C. S., Ryall, J. M., Ricci, D. A., & Wetzel, R. D. (1993). *Multiple personalities, multiple disorders: Psychiatric classification and media influence.* Oxford, England: Oxford University Press.

Orne, M. T., & Bates, B. L. (1992). Reflections on multiple personality disorder: A view from the looking–glass of hypnosis past. In C. Pierce, M. Greenblatt, & A. Kales (Eds.), *The mosaic of contemporary psychiatry in perspective.* New York: Springer Verlag.

Persinger, M. (1982). *The personal philosophy inventory.* Unpublished manuscript, Laurentian University, Sudbury, Ontario.

Putnam, F. W. (1989). *Diagnosis and treatment of multiple personality disorder.* New York: Guilford Press.

Putnam, F. W. (1991) Recent research on multiple personality disorder. *Psychiatric Clinics of North America, 14(3),* 489–502.

Putnam, F. W. (1992). Discussion: Are alter personalities fragments or figments? *Psychoanalytic Inquiry, 12(1),* 95–111.

Rorschach, H. (1921). *Psychodiagnostik* [Psychodiagnostics]. Bern, Switzerland Bircher.

Ross, C. A., & Dua, V. (1993). Psychiatric health care costs of multiple personality disorder. *American Journal of Psychotherapy, 47,* 103–112.

Ross, C. A., Heber, S., Norton, G. R., & Anderson, G. (1989). Differences between multiple personality disorder and other diagnostic groups on structured interview. *Journal of Nervous and Mental Disease, 179(8),* 487–491.

Schachter, D. L. (1996). Memory distortion: History and current status. In D. L. Schachter, J. T. Coyle, G. D. Fischbach, M. M. Mesulam, & L. E. Sullivan (Eds.), *Memory distortion* (pp. 1–65). Cambridge, MA: Harvard University Press.

Schlenger, W. E., & Kulka, R. A. (1989). PTSD *scale development for the* MMPI–2. Research Triangle Park, NC: Research Triangle Institute.

Sheehan, P. W. (1967). A shortened form of Betts's Questionnaire upon mental imagery. *Journal of Clinical Psychology, 23,* 386–389.

Spanos, N. P., Burgess, C. A., & Burgess, M. F. (1994). Past life identities, UFO abductions, and satanic ritual abuse: The social construction of memories [Special Issue: Hypnosis and delayed recall: I] *International Journal of Clinical and Experimental Hypnosis, 42(4),* 433–446.

Spanos, N., & Burgess, C. (1994). Hypnosis and multiple personality disorder: A sociocognitive perspective. In S. Lynn & J. Rhue (Eds.), *Dissociation: Clinical and theoretical perspectives* (pp. 136–157). New York: Guilford Press.

Spanos, N. P., Weekes, J. R., & & Bertrand, L. D. (1985). Multiple personality: A social psychological perspective. *Journal of Abnormal Psychology, 94(3),* 362–376.

Spitzer, R. L., Endicott, J., Fyer, H. A., Mannuzza, S., and Klein, E. F. (1985). *The schedule for affective disorders and schizophrenia–lifetime version (Modified for the study of anxiety disorders).* New York: New York State Psychiatric Institute.

Spitzer, R. L., Williams, J. B., Gibbon, M., & First, M. B. (1990, August). The structured clinical interview for DSM–III–R (SCID): I History, rational, and description. *Archives of General Psychiatry*, pp. 624–629.

Steinberg, M. (1993). *Structured clinical interview for DSM–IV dissociative disorders* (SCID–D). Washington, DC: American Psychiatric Press.

Steinberg, M., Rounsaville, B., & Cicchetti, D. V. (1990, January). The structured clinical interview for DSM–III–R dissociative disorders: Preliminary report on a new diagnostic instrument. *American Journal of Psychiatry*, pp. 76–82.

Wechsler, D. (1987). *Manual for the Wechsler Memory Scale–Revised (W.M.S.–R)*. San Antonio, Texas: The Psychological Corporation.

Weitzenhoffer, A. M., & Hilgard, E. R. (1962). *Stanford hypnotic susceptibility scale: Form C*. Palo Alto, CA: Consulting Psychologists Press.

Wilson, S. C., & Barber, T. (1983). The fantasy–prone personality: Implications for understanding imagery, hypnosis, and parapsychological phenomena. In A. Sheikh (Ed.), *Imagery: Current theory, research and application* (pp. 340–387). New York: Wiley.

Young, W. C. (1988). Observations on fantasy in the formation of multiple personality disorder. *Dissociation*, I(1), 13–20.

11

COGNITIVE–BEHAVIORAL HYPNOTHERAPY FOR SMOKING CESSATION: A CASE STUDY IN A GROUP SETTING

JOSEPH P. GREEN

The United States Department of Health and Human Services estimates that as many as 50 million Americans continue to smoke despite the known risks associated with smoking (USDHHS, 1990). Indeed, smoking is a powerful addiction (American Psychiatric Association, 1994) that poses dire health consequences. Death and negative health effects seem especially tragic given that smoking is a voluntary behavior. Although a majority of smokers wish to quit, the odds of successful smoking cessation are discouragingly low if the smoker tries to quit on his or her own. Specifically, although more than 80% of smokers express a desire to quit, and approximately 35% will attempt to quit annually (U.S. Department of Health, Education, and Welfare, 1990), less than 5% will be successful without professional assistance (American Psychiatric Association, 1994).

A more encouraging fact is that there are a variety of tools, techniques, and therapies currently available for individuals interested in smoking cessation. Among these are aversive conditioning, education, group support, nicotine replacement, pharmacology, behavior modification, hypnosis, and role playing (see Lynn, Neufeld, Rhue, & Matorin, 1994). A growing research literature attests to the success of hypnosuggestive interventions as a viable and effective method of achieving smoking cessation (see Cornwell, Burrows, & McMurray, 1981; Crasilneck, 1990; Frank, Umlauf, Wonderlich, & Ashkanazi, 1986; Williams & Hall, 1988). In a recent

223

review of empirical studies published since 1980, Lynn and his associates (Lynn et al., 1994) reported that abstinence rates secured through the use of hypnosis ranged from 14% to 61%. Although the evidence indicates that hypnotic interventions are at least as successful as nonhypnotic approaches (Hunt & Bespalec, 1974; Lynn et al. 1994), the question of whether hypnotic interventions are more effective than nonhypnotic methods remains to be answered (Wadden & Anderton, 1982).

Steven Jay Lynn and his colleagues at Ohio University have developed a cognitive–behavioral, multimodal hypnotic smoking cessation treatment program that emphasizes education, motivation, self-monitoring, self-management, a gradual reduction in smoking, and relapse prevention (for a technical overview and supportive research findings, see Lynn et al., 1994). Generally, participants are seen for two sessions; however, the program was designed to be flexible, allowing clinicians to individually tailor the program to meet particular client needs. The approach can be adapted to an individual or group format.

The following narrative demonstrates an application of Lynn's smoking cessation program within a group format. As will be seen, learning, practicing, and employing self-hypnotic skills are centerpieces of the approach. In addition to illustrating the various cognitive, behavioral, and hypnotic skills germane to Lynn's smoking cessation program, I will highlight relevant historical and interpersonal variables associated with the case.

BACKGROUND INFORMATION

Mrs. Jamie Brooks (pseudonym), a 37-year-old, married Caucasian woman, was referred for smoking cessation by her psychologist. She reported that she had been smoking for nearly 24 years, beginning at age 14. She had unsuccessfully attempted to quit at least five previous times. All of her previous attempts to quit smoking took place without professional assistance. Although she did achieve temporary success during previous attempts to quit, she failed to sustain her efforts and resumed smoking within a couple of weeks. She reported smoking, on average, one and a half packs of cigarettes a day.

Jamie was well aware of the health risks associated with smoking. Her motivation to quit was sparked by a recent diagnosis of chronic obstructive pulmonary disease. The news that she had permanently damaged her lungs did not come as a surprise. She stated, "I've known for a long time that I smoked too much and that I needed to quit. I just couldn't stop." Her physician informed her that if she did not stop smoking she would probably die of lung cancer within 10 years. Although her health was her primary reason to quit smoking, social pressures at work were secondary factors. Her company recently adopted a no-smoking policy for all employees. Jamie complied with this policy only by taking frequent breaks, during which she would slip outside and hastily smoke a cigarette in order to satisfy her nicotine dependence. Aside from one coworker who posted a highly visible "No smoking" sign across from Jamie's desk, Jamie reported that her employer and colleagues were accommodating and tolerated her nicotine dependence.

Past Psychiatric History

Jamie had attended individual counseling for nearly 1 year prior to the referral for smoking cessation. She initially sought psychological treatment for "anxiety attacks" and insomnia. She was diagnosed with generalized anxiety disorder and displayed several symptoms of dependent personality disorder. Over the course of the preceding 6 months, Jamie had achieved moderate improvement in her anxiety symptoms. Her therapy focused on marital issues, and she described a high level of conflict within the home. She characterized her husband as a "drinker" and an emotionally restricted man who rarely shared his feelings. Jamie acknowledged contemplating divorce, but had no immediate plan to do so. Six months earlier, Jamie's 17-year-old son had been charged with underage drinking and cocaine possession. His trial and subsequent court-ordered inpatient treatment for substance abuse were particularly stressful for the family. Finally, Jamie reported that her son had openly smoked cigarettes for about 3 years. Jamie's husband had quit smoking 15 years earlier.

Conceptualization of the Problem and the Goal of Treatment

Pressured by her physician to quit smoking, Jamie requested help from her individual psychologist. Her psychologist referred her to me for short-term adjunctive therapy for smoking cessation. I telephoned Jamie and invited her to an informal meeting during which we would discuss her case and formulate an initial treatment plan. She was somewhat reserved on the phone and appeared hesitant to commit herself to smoking abstinence. However, she agreed to come in, professing, "Something must be done; I have to quit."

During our first session, we discussed Jamie's smoking history and past attempts to quit. Jamie presented as a bright and attractive woman. She was knowledgeable about the health risks associated with smoking and attributed her chronic history of pulmonary infections to her smoking. Despite her understanding of the risks involved and her desire to quit for several years, she continued to smoke. When asked to predict how successful she thought her treatment would be, Jamie cited the number of years that she had smoked (23 years) and her unsuccessful attempts to quit (at least five previous attempts) in the past as evidence that she "just couldn't do it."

When we negotiated a treatment goal, I was careful not to support Jamie's belief that she was unlikely to achieve abstinence. I pointed out that most smokers cycle through smoking cessation and relapse before finally achieving long-term abstinence. I was challenged to encourage Jamie to set a goal that would reflect both the seriousness of her current health problems and an understanding of how difficult it would be for her to achieve complete abstinence.

As Jamie detailed her past attempts to quit she was encouraged to articulate past circumstances that made quitting formidable. By highlighting situational variables that undermined her chances to succeed in the past, I attempted to enhance Jamie's belief that she would succeed with the present treatment program. For example, each of her past attempts to quit was unaided by professional help; she failed to inform family, friends, or coworkers of her goal to quit, bypassing potential sources of social support and encouragement. Furthermore, although she had *wanted* to quit in the past, she *needed* to quit now, as continued smoking was a direct threat to her life. As we shifted away from her "inability" to quit and focused on her previous use of ineffective strategies to abstain, Jamie seemed to gain hope. I was encouraged when she stated that she "probably could have resisted urges to smoke in the past had someone been there to offer support or help."

I highlighted several areas in Jamie's life where she had succeeded through persistence and determination. I voiced being impressed by her ability to successfully complete college while burdened with the demands of working. Equally impressive were the facts that she had rebounded from two permanent layoffs from prominent corporations and she had completed a job retraining program. Finally, I praised her efforts to manage her difficult marriage and sustain her family as best as she could. We concluded that her past successes and accomplishments should be attributed to her own initiative, effort, and perseverance. I then bridged our discussion of past accomplishments and successful achievements to her new goal of smoking cessation.

During our dialogue, Jamie reappraised her conclusion that she simply could not quit. She agreed that her previous strategies to achieve abstinence unintentionally minimized her chances of success. Furthermore, she acknowledged that she had been successful for at least two consecutive weeks during three previous attempts to quit. We reframed her stated "inability to quit" as "unsuccessful past attempts" in an effort to shift her attribution of the cause of past failures away from personal limitations or characterological flaws to inadequate cessation strategies and situational variables. Throughout this dialogue, I emphasized the importance of confident expectations and the link between positive self-predictions and successful behavioral change (Bandura, 1977; Bandura, Adams, & Beyer, 1977).

Jamie's addiction to smoking occurred over many years; undoing this ingrained habit would require much effort on her part. Simply discussing her addiction in terms of a learned behavior as opposed to a personality trait seemed to liberate a growing conviction that it was possible for her to become a nonsmoker. By the end of our one-hour meeting, Jamie seemed more optimistic about treatment. However, her overall self-efficacy (Bandura 1977, 1978) seemed moderate, at best, and her self-confidence in accomplishing a goal of complete abstinence was tenuous. Therefore, we agreed to adopt a "dramatic reduction in smoking" as our treatment goal. We set as our goal a minimum reduction of 90% of the number of cigarettes smoked over the 6 months following treatment.

At the end of the consultation, Jamie signed up for my next smoking cessation program (which was held 10 days later) and joined four other participants.

DESCRIPTION OF TREATMENT

The Lynn et al. approach is a multidimensional smoking cessation program that focuses on developing cognitive–behavioral skills and mastering self-hypnosis (see Lynn et al., 1994).

Session One

The first session commenced on schedule. As part of my introduction, I presented a brief overview of my clinical work in the area of smoking cessation and noted that I had assisted in the development of the Lynn program. In an effort to generate group cohesion, each member of the group introduced him or herself and discussed their reasons for attending. Jamie was the last person to speak. She stated that she "had to attend" treatment and added that she had been unsuccessful in several previous attempts to quit. Cognizant of the fact that Jamie did not say she was unable to quit, as she had in our introductory meeting, I remained hopeful that she would wholeheartedly immerse herself in the treatment protocol.

After about 15 minutes of introductions, I formally began the treatment session by outlining the program:

> I am confident that this program will be an educational experience for each of you. Education, of course, involves learning. Let's get a fix on how you learned to smoke, because smoking is not a natural act. How many of you felt awkward when you first began to smoke? Did you feel sick or nauseated? It often takes weeks or even months of practice and perseverance to condition your body to learn to accept the noxious

agents contained in tobacco smoke. Many of you probably smoked to fill a specific need (for example, to be "in" with your friends, remain alert, or keep awake). What were some of your reasons for smoking?

Each member of the group shared at least one reason why they began smoking. As is so often the case, no one stated that they began to smoke because they enjoyed it. Jamie remembered finding her older sister and a mutual friend smoking behind their family barn. Jamie recalled how, at the age of 14, she earned an invitation to smoke with them by promising not to tell her parents. Regarding her first inhalation, Jamie recalled a burning sensation spiraling down her throat. In an attempt to conceal her inexperience and to impress her sister that she too was "all grown up," Jamie forced herself to smoke three cigarettes that afternoon. Later that evening, feeling sick to her stomach, Jamie recalled eating little of her dinner and going to bed early.

I encouraged the group to refer to their smoking as a "learned habit." To illustrate the strength of each member's habit and to seed the idea that a "smoking habit" can be modified or replaced with a "nonsmoking habit," I presented the following:

> Initially, many of you probably only smoked in very limited situations. However, as time passed, the strength of your habit grew and you probably extended your smoking to many other situations, including on the telephone, while reading the paper, at work, or after you eat. Each time you lifted a cigarette to your lips, you strengthened your habit. Just think of how many times you lifted a cigarette to your lips. Why don't we calculate the number of times you have lifted a cigarette to your mouth. [Using a chalkboard in the therapy room, I wrote out the following formula.] If you smoke a pack a day: (a) 20 cigarettes per pack; average number of inhalations per cigarette is 10; (b) $20 \times 10 = 200$; (c) 365 days per year $\times$ number of years you have smoked; (d) multiply part "b" by "c" to equal the total number of times you have lifted a cigarette to your mouth if you are a pack-a-day smoker. Now, that is a habit!

We then calculated the number of times each participant engaged in this "cigarette to mouth" behavioral repertoire. Jamie had averaged 1-1/2 packs per day over the past 20 years. Not counting the number of times she raised a cigarette to her mouth between the ages of 14 and 17 (she estimated that she "only" smoked about 5–10 cigarettes per day, on average, during her first 3 years of smoking), we calculated that Jamie had reinforced her smoking repertoire well over 2 million times! In disbelief, Jamie asked to recalculate the figures. We did (30 cigarettes per day $\times$ 10 inhalations per cigarette $\times$ 365 days a year $\times$ 20 years = 2,190,000). "Wow!" She sighed.

A key emphasis in this treatment approach is what Lynn et al. have termed, the "edge." The edge refers to a collection of skills and pertinent pieces of information that strengthen participants' ability to break habitual patterns, cope with withdrawal symptoms, and maintain treatment gains.

> We have many ways we will teach you to give you the "edge," the advantage you will need to break this habit. You should know that more than 40 million Americans have successfully quit. So it certainly is possible. Our program will help you turn that possibility into a personal reality.

We will teach you the skills you need to learn to break habitual patterns, deal with any discomfort you might experience, and maintain the gains you achieve. We want you to have many skills and techniques you can choose from. Your task will be to find ones that work best for you. We will not only point out some of the costs of smoking, but make you more aware of the benefits of quitting: How being a nonsmoker can fill you with a sense of pride as you learn you are protecting and preserving your health, being more competitive in sports, more kissable, and keeping your house free of smoke odors. We will make any discomfort easier to deal with by gradually fading out nicotine from your life by moving to fewer and fewer cigarettes over the week and changing to lower nicotine cigarettes.

> And of course, hypnosis will be one part of the program, one way to give you the edge. If you follow through with this program, we are confident that you can quit. We cannot do it for you, but we can make it a lot easier for you to become smoke free for life!

The approach capitalizes on positive self-predictions, borrows from self-efficacy theory (Bandura, 1982), and recognizes that high motivation is essential for successful smoking cessation (See Perry, Gelfand, & Marcovitch, 1979; Perry & Mullin, 1975). Following the program guideline, I obtained a simple index of each member's motivation level.

> We have found that motivation is one of the most important factors in being a nonsmoker. The best hypnotist in the world will not help if you are not motivated to quit. I would now like to pass out a 3 × 5 index card. As you will see, it has a 1–5 scale on it of how motivated you are to quit: 1 = not at all motivated; 3 = somewhat motivated; 5 = extremely motivated. I would like you to complete this scale at the end of our first session. If you are not strongly motivated (at least a 3), then you should consider not coming back for the second session, and I will give you a full refund. Past research has shown that successful participants score between a 3 and a 5 on this scale.
>
> But if you do want to quit and if you are ready to complete the program, then I will ask you to sign a contract and have it witnessed by another group member. The contract will also be signed by your spouse, living partner, or best friend, and also by your employer if you are currently employed. We want you to enlist their support. We want you to announce your intention to quit. We want them to understand

the efforts you are making. We want them to know you are doing your best, and we want them to help you any way they can. How can they help you? Why don't we brainstorm as a group to get some ideas? You can then share these suggestions with the people in your life.

Behavioral contracting and enlisting social support are additional components of the program. Participants contract with a spouse or other significant individual, and are instructed to inform family, friends, and employer of their goal to quit smoking. In accordance with the treatment protocol, we also employed a "buddy system." All participants paired up with one another and exchanged phone numbers. Participants were told to call their buddies during the next week to discuss how things were going. They were especially encouraged to call if they were having difficulty resisting an urge to smoke, or if they just successfully resisted an urge and wanted to share their triumph.

Jamie was especially eager to have a buddy. Given an odd number of participants, we divided our group into a two-person buddy pair, and a three-person buddy system. Jamie requested being in the "three group," stating that she could benefit from all available help. She appeared pleased when asked by two other women to join their network.

Our discussion soon focused on withdrawal symptoms:

In order for you to quit and to conquer the smoking habit, it is important that you let go of blaming yourself, dispense with the sorts of statements you make to yourself like, "I'm weak, I have no willpower." If you smoke 15 or more cigarettes a day, you may be physically addicted to nicotine, and it is possible that withdrawal symptoms will occur when you do not receive your dose of nicotine. We will teach you ways to deal with these withdrawal symptoms if you should experience them.

But there is one thing to remember: Even heavy smokers do not always experience withdrawal symptoms, and withdrawal symptoms are not always very intense. In fact, 20% to 45% of quitters report absolutely no withdrawal symptoms. Our goal is to prepare you for whatever you will face when you quit. This program is designed to help even heavy smokers quit. This program will help you to be a nonsmoker for life.

By gradually cutting down on nicotine content and then the actual number of cigarettes you smoke, any withdrawal you might experience will be reduced in intensity. But what is important to remember is that withdrawal reactions are temporary, and you can learn to combat smoking urges. Consider this: After a month, two thirds of persons who quit do not report strong urges. In fact, several months after quitting, most ex-smokers feel less anxiety and depression than they did while they were smoking.

Let's focus on withdrawal reactions now. Withdrawal is actually a sign that your body is coping with your decision to be a nonsmoker.

It is a short-term reaction that you can deal with. Some of the reactions are a direct result of the body's healing itself. Let's consider some of the uncomfortable feelings some of you have had and what can be done about them.

If you have a cough, this can be a healthy signal, a sign that your lungs are cleansing you. Not being able to concentrate is a short-term reaction; it means that your body is adjusting to a decrease of nicotine. Feelings of depression may arise because of your mistaken belief that you are losing a friend; actually, you are vanquishing a deadly enemy by quitting. Feelings of anxiety may arise because of the association that you have made between smoking and situations in which you feel anxiety. But once again, this is only temporary; in the long run, you will be calmer than when you were smoking. To combat any feelings of lack of energy, eating right and getting exercise will give you the boost you need. And there's the old cure for problems with sleeping—drink milk before you go to bed. It contains a natural sleep-promoting substance—tryptophan—that will also help to calm your nerves. We have no sure-fire cure for irritability, but one reason why we ask you to have other people in your life sign the contract is so they can better understand what you are going through. At any rate, feelings of irritability will pass in a week or two.

What is important to keep in mind is that any discomfort you may experience is short-term, but some of the long-term effects of cigarette smoking are not. The good news is that the body begins to repair itself almost as soon as you stop smoking. After a year of being a nonsmoker, your risk factors for cancer and heart disease return to about what they were before you began smoking. So this should constitute powerful motivation for you to quit.

At this point, I presented a potpourri of medical findings underscoring the health benefits associated with quitting smoking (facts and statistics were obtained from the USDHHS, 1990):

Following 10 years of smoking cessation, the risk of lung cancer is reduced by 30% to 50%. The risk of laryngeal cancer is significantly reduced following smoking cessation. The risks of cancers of the oral cavity and esophagus are reduced by around 50% following just 5 years of abstinence. Risks of pancreatic, bladder, and cervical cancers are all reduced following smoking cessation. Quitting significantly reduces risk of coronary heart disease across all age ranges. After 5 to 15 years of abstinence, risk of ischemic stroke and subarachnoid hemorrhage is reduced to a level comparable with that of nonsmokers. Smoking has been linked with ulcers, premature aging of the skin, and osteoporosis. Smokers who quit before the age of 50 reduce their risk of dying within the next 15 years by 50%, relative to continued smokers. Following 15 years of smoking abstinence, the risk of mortality is nearly the same as that of individuals who have never smoked.

One group member inquired about the link between smoking and pregnancy. I responded:

> Smoking during pregnancy has been associated with low birth weight and a variety of complications. The birth weight of infants from women who stopped smoking before they became pregnant has been found to be comparable with the birth weight of infants from mothers who never smoked. Smoking abstinence, however, appears to be the key. Results from a couple of preliminary studies have shown that simply reducing the amount of smoking during pregnancy does not stave off the risk of low infant birth weight (USDHHS, 1990).

Jamie questioned the possibility of gaining weight as a side effect of quitting smoking. I informed her that about three out of four people who quit smoking will gain weight, however, less than 5% of those will gain more than five pounds (see Lynn et al., 1994; USDHHS, 1990). The increase in weight is largely due to increases in the amount of food consumed and a decrease in resting metabolism. Gaining a couple of pounds is trivial compared to the health risks of smoking. The Lynn script acknowledges that slight weight gain may be a possible side effect:

> Some people get discouraged and begin smoking again when they gain a few pounds after quitting. We have some recommendations for you that are simple but effective. First, be sure that you eat a well balanced diet from the four basic food groups; increase physical activity like walking, jogging, swimming, playing sports; and lose weight slowly, but do not lose more than 2 pounds a week.

Quit Cards

> Index cards were passed out to the group:

> Think for a moment about what it would mean to you to be a non-smoker. I will pass out some index cards, and I would like you to list at least five reasons for quitting, in order of importance. Now visualize two roads: A high road where you imagine your future if you quit successfully. Think of the social rewards, the monetary rewards, and the health rewards. Now imagine a low road where you see your future if you are not truly motivated to quit. [pause] The choice is yours. Which road will you walk down?

> How many think or fear that you may not be able to quit? Raise your hand if you think you will not be able to quit.

Four of the five participants raised their hands. Jamie shrugged her shoulders, passively rolled her eyes, and then slowly raised her hand.

> Those with your hands up, keep them up . . . now, if I were to promise you a million dollars if you could remain abstinent for a year, do you think you could do it? (All agreed that they could.) But the question

I would like you to ask yourself is whether your health is worth a million dollars. Close your eyes now and tell yourself all the reasons you have to quit, and see yourself walking down the road of health and well-being as a nonsmoker. [pause]

What I would like you to do this week is to review your reasons to quit, and to do this on a frequent basis. Carry your quit card on your person. During this week, I would also like you to identify trigger situations. These are places, situations, and times that are loaded with powerful personal smoking cues. An urge can be thought of as an internal smoking cue or a prompt for you to smoke. Smokers tend to have urges linked with specific experiences. When a specific situation is linked with the feeling or urge to smoke, we call it a trigger situation.

What triggers your desire to smoke?

A variety of different triggers were identified. Jamie reported smoking two or three cigarettes during her morning routine of cooking breakfast for her family. She identified several behaviors that she had learned to associate with the urge to smoke: reading the paper, sewing, watching TV, driving, paying bills or doing paperwork, and working at her computer. We brainstormed about coping strategies that the group could use to help them cope with smoking urges. Our discussion included using distractions or doing something else; simply "waiting it out"; and the use of somatic focusing techniques.

The treatment protocol encourages participants to devise their own coping responses. Suggestions include exercising, taking a shower or bath, playing a sport, stretching, touching toes, polishing glasses, doodling, deep breathing, using imagery, bicycling, chewing sugarless gum, exercising with hand grippers or squeezing a rubber ball, playing with worry beads, chewing on carrots or celery sticks, waiting it out, drinking water, and using self-talk or self-hypnotic techniques. We continued with the treatment script:

Now, on the reverse side of your reasons-to-quit card, write your alternative coping responses in the trigger situations you identified.

One technique that many participants in our workshop have found useful is what we call the "urge zapper." First, say to yourself, "I am aware of an urge to smoke." Second, say to yourself, "NO! I do not have to smoke; I am a nonsmoker," or another key phrase that will help you. Three, read your reasons-for-quitting card. And finally, engage in one of the alternate coping responses on the back of your card.

During the first week, and even thereafter, it is important that you avoid high-risk or trigger situations, when possible. Think about those situations that you can avoid and how you can reduce stress in your life this week. There may, however, be some situations you cannot avoid, so I would like you to anticipate a situation this week, imagine it now, and see yourself coping effectively in this situation.

We recommend that after this week you never put a cigarette to your lips again. However, some people do slip. This does not mean that you are a total failure and that you should end your efforts to quit. A slip can be a learning experience; you can realize you have a choice. A slip is a sign of the strength of the smoking habit. But remember this: A lapse does not mean a relapse, which is a return to the original pattern of behavior. Again, you are playing with fire if you think you can control your smoking by "smoking a few here or there." You will begin to feel better sooner when your body is truly convinced that you are serious about quitting. Make that resolve firm! Do it now!

Contingency Management and Self-Reinforcement

To help you to maintain the important gains you have achieved, it is important that you reward yourself. Make a list of things you enjoy and that are easy to obtain. A few can be expensive, but not all rewards have to be material. Make this list of rewards now on the paper provided. One thing you might wish to do is to put money ordinarily spent on cigarettes in a highly visible container and then spend it for a pleasurable activity when it accumulates.

Introduction to Self-Hypnosis

Self-hypnosis is an important part of this program. It is a skill that you can learn. It can help you to be a nonsmoker by promoting relaxation, by strengthening your motivation to quit, by helping to change your self-image from a smoker to a nonsmoker, and by providing you with a vehicle for administering useful self-suggestions that have the power to change your life.

The first part of the script is taken from Gorassini and Spanos's (1986) hypnotizability modification program, which has been shown to increase the hypnotizability of even initially low-hypnotizable individuals and is presented in Lynn et al. (1994). In this part of the program, participants are disabused of misconceptions about hypnosis, including the idea that hypnosis is a sleep-like trance state that involves relinquishing control to the hypnotist. Instead, hypnosis is presented as involving imaginative skills that anyone can learn with proper motivation, instruction, and practice. The remainder of the script is presented below:

Because I will only be acting as your guide, and you will be creating the experiences called for the suggestion yourself, it is fair to say that what we will be doing today is "self-hypnosis."

Later, you will be able to create a self-hypnotic experience for yourself . . . So, if you will, let us begin by your simply closing your eyes. Please close your eyes and take a deep breath. And as you breathe out you can begin to feel a sense of calm, feel the calmness spreading. You will not fall asleep, although you may notice that you are more relaxed than when you are asleep. And you can listen to my voice, and you can move into an even deeper state of calm and at ease, because, you see, there's nothing to disturb you, nothing to bother you, there's lots of time, lots and lots of time. Perhaps you can feel time slowing down . . . time slowing down to a most comfortable pace. And as you notice this, you can also notice that your breathing has slowed down to meet the resting requirements of your body, or perhaps you notice that your breathing is a bit faster because you anticipate what will happen next, just how relaxed and at ease you can become, how much involved in your self-hypnosis you can be. It doesn't matter really, the only thing that matters is your comfort, because your breathing will take care of itself, as your conscious and unconscious mind work together.

Now imagine yourself on a magnificent staircase with 10 steps to the bottom. At the bottom is a place where you feel safe and secure, where you will feel just wonderful. And as you probably have guessed, in a few moments, I will ask you to walk down the staircase, with each count, you will move one step down the staircase. Take a nice deep, full, filling, and relaxing breath. Good, now take another, with each step down the staircase, your body will relax more and more, more and more, but neither you nor I know just how relaxed you will be, but even that doesn't matter, all that matters is that you are comfortable, with nothing to bother you, nothing to disturb you. OK, I am going to start counting, guiding you down the staircase, deeper and deeper into a most comfortable state of mind, a most comfortable state of being, with nothing to bother you, nothing to disturb you. You don't have to do anything, just listen to my voice. Let my voice go with you.

One. One step down the staircase. Let your feet relax as you move down the staircase, feel the calmness spreading. There's lots of time. *Two.* Let your legs relax. Do you feel more relaxed than when you are asleep or would you rather not think at all? Deeper and deeper calm and feeling quite secure. *Three.* Three steps down the staircase. . . . Can you feel your thighs relax? Can you feel yourself letting go just a little bit more with each breath? Can you feel waves of gentle relax-ation? Or are you not thinking at all, just feeling open and receptive? Do you feel more heavy and warm or an easy floating feeling? *Four.* Can you let the area around your pelvis relax? There is lots of time. Do you feel as relaxed as when you are very tired and just about to fall asleep? Or as relaxed as you feel after waking up from a deep, sound sleep? *Five.* Five steps down the staircase. Half way down. Can you feel a sense of calm in your stomach area? Do you want to experience a deeper level of hypnosis, of openness to ideas, receptivity to images, feeling sure and in-control, aware of possibilities for yourself? Or are you so comfortable with your level of hypnosis now that you want to just maintain that feeling in an easy, effortless way? You know you don't have to do anything, unless you want to, like adjust your position to get even more comfortable.

Six. Down the staircase. Six steps down the staircase. . . . Can you feel the calm, easy feeling spreading to your chest? Can you feel that some parts of your body are catching up with other body parts that are even more relaxed? *Seven.* Down the staircase. Can you feel your arms relax? Nothing to disturb, nothing to bother you. Can you feel time slowing down? Do you think you are ready to go even deeper? Would you like to be even more calm and secure within yourself? And yet it really doesn't matter just how deep you feel, or even if you feel hypnotized at all, just that you feel comfortable. *Eight.* Eight steps down the staircase. Almost near the bottom, soon you will arrive at that place where you feel so comfortable and secure, so much at ease. Can you feel a still, quiet point between inspiration and exhalation of your breath? Can you feel quiet and still inside? I really don't know and it really doesn't matter, because soon you will arrive at your special place, where you are so deeply centered within yourself. *Nine.* Nine steps down the staircase. Are you aware of just how relaxed your face and eyes feel or are you in a dreamy state of mind, perhaps not thinking at all? I wonder what it will feel like for you to be in that place where you feel protected, secure . . . perhaps you feel that you are there already . . . maybe you are alone, maybe you are with a special companion . . . perhaps you are on the beach, near the water, or in a forest or meadow, perhaps you are in your favorite chair at home, or some other inviting place, a place in your past, or a place in your future. There's lots of time, so good to be alive! Are you aware of the sounds in this place? Are you aware of a pleasant, gentle caress of a soft breeze, or the reassuring pressure of the surface you are resting upon? Time will take care of itself, your breathing will take care of itself. If you are not already there, soon you will be there.

Ten! Ten steps down the staircase. You have arrived! Experience this place in your consciousness, in your experience, fully, deeply, feel your mind at peace. You are more and more ready to retain those ideas that I will give you, as you will let them go deep in the back of your mind, and use them as you wish. Deep into your unconscious mind, where they can have a profound, a meaningful and important effect on you . . . Think of a word or a key phrase that expresses how you feel . . . words like "clear and calm" or "warm and relaxed" . . . whatever word or words will work best for you as cues or as reminders of who you are, what you can be at a deep level, the level of potential, the level of self-creation, the you that will be a nonsmoker. But you don't even have to think of that, because the idea is now in the back of your mind, in your unconscious. You are on your way . . . you are moving, moving toward the reality of what you want to be . . . learning and understanding on a deep level as I speak to the open, receptive, and healthy center of yourself, as you open yourself to new ways of thinking and being. You can use your key word at any time, at any place, you can imagine your special place at any time, at any place to recreate the feelings you have now. And with practice, you will become even better at doing this. I will give you a tape to practice what you have learned, and perhaps you will learn some new things . . . as you move, you are on your way to being a nonsmoker.

But you don't even have to think about this now, as you learn another way to anchor these pleasant feelings . . . And anchor these feelings of mastery, security, and a deep sense of inner confidence and motivation to succeed at becoming a nonsmoker. The person within you. Magnify these feelings of mastery, security, inner confidence, motivation. Feel them swell within you. Register and remember these feelings on a deep, deep level within the very core of your being. Take a deep breath, say your key phrase to yourself. Hold the breath. Hold it. When you release it, say your key phrase. Do this now. Good. Feel a surge of strength and confidence.

Now make a fist, with either hand, a tight fist. Feel this sense of strength, confidence, and motivation to be a nonsmoker grow even more. Make this tight fist, and when you release the fist when you are ready, you can feel a sense of calm, relaxed security spread throughout your body, and your mind can feel clear and free and light. Good. Now you can use this anchor in situations where you want to feel confident, secure, and increase your motivation.

Some of you will be able to use this anchor immediately, even after one session, and reap obvious benefits. Some of you may require a bit more practice. Practice with your tape, learn the self-hypnosis skills, become a master. You have that power within you. Each of you. Practice will also help those of you who have learned the skill in one session to use your anchor in a more automatic fashion. You will learn how to manage any urges you have with coping skills. Self-hypnosis skills are one important set of coping skills that you will learn today and next week. You will get better and better, better, and better.

Here is something else I would like to teach you. You can, if you wish, use another anchor that is a little less obvious. Take a deep breath, say your key phrase. Hold the breath. Hold it. When you release it, say your key phrase again. Do this now. Good. Feel a surge of strength and confidence. Simply bring your thumb and forefinger or your thumb and ring finger together. Do this now. Good. Make a circle, an anchor or cue to bring you into contact with the feelings you wish to magnify. Good. When you release contact between your thumb and finger, when you are ready, you can feel a sense of calm, relaxed security spread throughout your body, and your mind can feel clear and light and free. Good.

Now think of all of the reasons that you have to quit smoking. All of the many reasons why you are motivated to be a nonsmoker. And when you have done this, imagine yourself as a nonsmoker in different places and situations and with different people. Make an image of yourself as the person you will be as a nonsmoker. In time all urges to smoke will fade away, fade away, fade away. The urge to smoke is fading, fading, fading away, like clouds breaking up in the sky, you feel the need to smoke fading, fading, fading away, you are learning more and more about taking control, taking charge of your life, as you see yourself as a nonsmoker in different places, situations, with different people, the urge to smoke fades away, it passes, and you go on with your life, you feel a sense of pride and accomplishment, and now you see yourself rewarding yourself in some small way for being a nonsmoker, as you become aware of your senses coming alive, which is a reward in itself, and all that matters now is your comfort, there is nothing to disturb you, your body is healing itself, as you feel a sense of hope, a sense of pride, a feeling of being worthwhile, and as you experience these feelings, take a deep breath, say your key phrase. Hold the breath. Hold it. When you release it, say your key phrase again. Do this now. Good. Feel a surge of strength and confidence. Simply bring your thumb and forefinger or thumb and ring finger together. Do this now. Good.

Make a circle, an anchor or cue to bring you into contact with the wonderful feelings of being a nonsmoker. Good. When you release contact between your thumb and finger, when you are ready, you can feel a sense of calm, relaxed security spread throughout your body, and your mind can feel clear and light and free.

When you are ready, you can end the exercise and come out of your self-hypnosis by counting backward to yourself slowly from five to one, just as I will be counting for you in a little while. At the count of two your eyes will open; and at the count of one you will be fully awake, alert, feeling pleasantly refreshed, and with your usual sensation and control. You should flex and relax your muscles a few times before standing up.

The more you practice this exercise the easier it will become to do and the more effective it will be to help you achieve your goals. And on a final note, remember that it is important to use your anchor not only in your imagination, in the privacy of your home, or your place of comfort, but also in everyday situations.

I am now going to give you instructions to gradually wake up. I will count backwards from 5 to 1 and you will gradually wake up. When you awaken, you will feel fresh and awake. Ready: 5 . . . 4 . . . 3 . . . 2 . . . open your eyes. 1. Wide awake. Any remaining drowsiness will quickly pass.

Homework Assignments

Homework assignments focused on 10 areas. Participants were instructed to:

1. Monitor their smoking and to record each cigarette smoked. In addition to recording the frequency of cigarettes smoked, record the time of day, situation (e.g., reading the paper, driving to work), and emotional state at the time (e.g., upset, fatigued, anxious, pressured). Past research (Abrams &

Wilson, 1979) has found that self-monitoring may result in a reduction in smoking among highly motivated individuals.

2. Review their newly composed reasons for quitting, on a daily basis; to keep their reasons-for-quitting-cards with their cigarettes and to read their cards before smoking.
3. Buy cigarettes by the pack, not the carton.
4. Start a "butt jar" and place cigarette butts in that jar.
5. Practice self-hypnosis on a daily basis.
6. Use urge-management techniques when starting reduction.

In addition to the above assignments, I detailed a seventh: reduction guidelines for the next week:

Day 1: Begin recording smoking behaviors; review reasons for quitting; read quit card before smoking.

Day 2: Analyze their smoking habit by reviewing the times and circumstances of yesterday's smoking. Record a list of triggers and compose a corresponding list of alternative behaviors. Switch to a lower tar and nicotine brand and plan a 10% reduction in cigarettes the next day.

Day 3: Continue with trigger analysis, and review or edit list of alternative behaviors. Reduce lower tar and nicotine cigarettes smoked by 10%. Plan another 10% reduction for the next day.

Day 4: Reduce cigarettes and plan a 20% reduction for next day. Begin to plan rewards.

Day 5: Switch brands again. Reduce number of cigarettes by 20% and plan to reduce another 20% the following day. Review reasons for quitting. Add to the list your planned rewards.

Day 6: Switch brands and reduce by another 20%.

Day 7: Quit day! Second session day. Participants instructed to bring with them their last pack of cigarettes (it may be empty).

Prior to terminating the first session, I passed out the contracts for participants to complete instruction 8. I reemphasized the importance of motivation, and encouraged (instruction 9) telephone contact with "buddies" during the week. I passed out a tape of the self-hypnosis script and instructed subjects to practice their new skill at least twice a day (instruction 10). We rescheduled to meet the following week.

Session Two

The second session began with a brief review of how each participant fared over the course of the preceding week. At the time of the second session, all but one member reported being abstinent that day. Jamie reported chewing nearly two packs of sugarless gum earlier in the day to help her successfully resist urges to smoke. She found that chewing cinnamon flavored toothpicks also helped her "wait out the urge." Although she reduced her cigarette consumption each day as instructed, Jamie's confidence in sustaining her success was tenuous. "I can't go through another week like the last one!" I pointed out that the first week is always the most difficult. In particular deference to Jamie, given her dependence on nicotine, I explained that her body was becoming less dependent on nicotine, and that each day she did not smoke, she would feel stronger and find it easier to resist urges to smoke.

Jamie reported that she did not ask her husband to sign her smoking cessation contract until 2 days after the first session. To her surprise her husband was supportive. He not only signed the contract but asked her several times during the week how she was doing. Her coworkers were also supportive. Her employer was especially helpful. He encouraged Jamie to periodically take a 5-minute break, walk outside, call her "buddy," or stretch when attempting to manage an urge to smoke.

Quitting Ceremony

The second session officially began with a quitting ceremony:

Welcome to our second session! By coming here you again affirm your wish to become a nonsmoker. We will start our work today with a quitting ceremony. What we will do is start off by walking one by one to the front of the room, crumpling up your last pack of cigarettes, and throwing it in the wastebasket that you see here. If you would like, feel free to make a statement, a positive affirmative statement about your feelings about quitting as you throw out your last pack. If you are willing, say this in front of the group, along with the statement, "I am a nonsmoker," and we will all show our support by clapping as you toss your last cigarette away.

Before we do this, though, let's briefly review our reasons for quitting. Let's share a bit and talk about what we became aware of during the week, about how our lives can change for the better when we quit. I know that throwing your cigarettes away may seem to some of you like you are losing your best friend. But as we talked about last week, cigarettes are not really your friend but a deadly enemy. Reviewing our reasons for quitting will firm our resolve. Let's take a few minutes to review our reasons.

Each member, in turn, walked to the front of the room and discarded a pack of cigarettes. Somewhat comically, Jamie stomped on her carton before throwing them into the trash. She chanted, "Never again, never again." We all applauded.

Hypnotic Suggestions to Become a Nonsmoker

I would like us to start with your experiencing hypnosis again. You have had some practice doing this. I will give you suggestions for deepening this experience you are already familiar with. So just close your eyes now and begin to relax, with nothing to worry, nothing to disturb, moving and moving, and moving into the familiar ground, the territory of your private experience . . . your hypnosis . . . you can close your eyes, yes, you can close your eyes . . . so easily . . . so gently . . . eyes closing, closing, closing. I wonder if you can let yourself go even deeper into your experience, your mind and body working together, your conscious and your unconscious mind working together for your best good, in their own way . . . partners . . . partners to protect your health, your well-being, your life . . . your breath. With each breath you can begin to move deeper and deeper, although you may not know exactly how you do it. But I can tell you one thing, you don't even have to try . . . in fact, you don't even have to do anything but listen to my voice . . . let my voice move with you, with your own sense of what is good for you . . . what you need. You can probably already feel yourself flowing with the experience. . . . Would you like to imagine a favorite scene, your spot where you feel so centered and so secure? . . . I wonder if you could do that . . . I know you can. And you will find that you will not fall asleep . . . you will remain awake yet so deeply relaxed, just on the edge, with me communicating with the deepest levels of your understanding . . . all the while knowing on that level of deep, perhaps even subliminal awareness . . . you will take the strength that you need from inside yourself . . . to be what you can be . . . to do what you need to do . . . to be a nonsmoker as you were for so many years before you first smoked.

Yes . . . get more and more of a deep fulfilling sense that strength is within . . . you move toward this place in your mind . . . in your imagination . . . in your being . . . this place where you are centered and secure . . . where you can return to anytime you wish . . . anytime you want . . . moving and moving and moving . . . flowing and flowing and flowing . . . change your position anytime you want to go even deeper, go even deeper into your desire to preserve your health to be a nonsmoker . . . get into your need to free yourself from this habit . . . yet nothing to bother now . . . nothing to disturb . . . you can do this . . . you can be smoke free . . . you can do this . . . yes . . . learning to do this . . . more and more . . . more and more . . . on so many levels . . . your mind is calm and clear even as I speak . . . different muscle groups relaxing in their own way . . . I wonder which muscles are more relaxed . . . your neck or your eyelids . . . it doesn't matter for now . . . does it . . . it really doesn't matter . . . as you approach this place . . . or are you there now . . . I don't really know . . . and is your breathing becoming slower . . . as you relax . . . as you let go . . . or are you feeling heavy or light, floating or heavy . . . or perhaps a relaxed, heavy floating feeling all in one . . . can you feel comfort and security wrapping around you like a blanket that is so comfortable . . . or is your conscious mind wandering while your unconscious mind tunes into the deepest meanings, your deepest desires to be a nonsmoker . . . or are you ready to relax even more?

Let's go deeper now . . . or are you so relaxed that you would just like to maintain where you are? . . . So comfortable and at ease . . .

strength is within . . . you are moving toward that place or maybe you are there . . . you are taking the steps you need to take . . . learning . . . taking just the steps you need to take to get where you are going . . . to where you want to go . . . can you notice some words and images coming easily and naturally to you . . . healing words and images . . . cleansing words and images . . . freeing words and images . . . perhaps a key phrase is coming to you . . . something you can say any time you want . . . any time you wish . . . a phrase that touches the deepest core of your being . . . a phrase that helps to cushion you . . . support you . . . or maybe it's an image . . . I don't know . . . but you can say this phrase or visualize your image any time you want . . . say it now . . . use it to anchor your resolve to be a nonsmoker forever.

As you do this . . . think of all the many reasons you have to quit smoking forever. Can you see a writing board? . . . Is it black or is it green? . . . I don't know . . . write and hear your words reading your reasons . . . write why you will quit smoking . . . listen to your voice saying to yourself . . . talking to yourself . . . about why you will quit smoking . . . think of all the benefits . . . so much to gain . . . health . . . money saved . . . so many benefits . . . you will think of even more reasons . . . let them move you deeper and deeper . . . let them swell your confidence . . . let them help you as you move and step toward your goal, how much your life can mean to you . . . how much you have to look forward to.

Are your hands more relaxed than your feet? . . . Is your breathing so easy? . . . Perhaps you can feel your head moving ever so slightly . . . moving up and down ever so slightly . . . it is saying yes, yes . . . your unconscious mind is somehow communicating with your con-scious mind your desire to be free of smoking . . . yes . . . yes . . . but you don't even have to do anything for this to happen . . . for you to be free of smoking . . . yes . . . yes . . . you don't even have to move, although you could if you wished . . . to create a sense of yourself, perhaps an image of yourself as a nonsmoker . . . Can you see yourself with others? . . . Or are you alone? . . . feeling a sense that you can say yes, yes to your health . . . to your body . . . to your feeling at ease without smoking . . . say yes to yourself . . . yes . . . take a few minutes to see yourself as a nonsmoker . . . see this image unfold . . . it somehow begins to become more and more real to you . . . I don't know exactly how this happens but notice it happen anyway . . . I wonder whether you can feel a sense of the strength that is within . . . can you feel it . . . or is it becoming so much a part of you that you do not notice it?

So comfortable now . . . your need to smoke is fading . . . any urges to smoke once a part of you are fading . . . they are dissolving . . . detaching from you . . . breaking up . . . like clouds in the wind . . . like clouds on a day that the sun begins to shine through . . . the light . . . the diffuse light . . . the breeze . . . the wind . . . the gentle calm . . . it all helps you to think that you can do so much other than smoke . . . you can see yourself doing something else in situations in which you smoked . . . you know you have the power . . . the power to flow with your strength to resist any urges that come up . . . they will fade . . . fade . . . like clouds in the wind . . . you can use your key phrase now . . . you know your strength is within . . . you can see yourself as a nonsmoker . . . it is coming clearer to you . . . the light is illuminating you, your reasons to quit . . . your will . . . your resolve . . . the power is within you . . . you know that smoking is a poison . . . you respect yourself . . . you will protect your body . . . you need your body . . . it needs you . . . your strength . . . your will power.

You can think about what you can do besides smoking . . . so many things . . . your conscious working with your unconscious mind to help you to decide what to do . . . you know that you are capable of taking care . . . taking good care . . . of others . . . of yourself . . . you can get in touch with your kindness . . . your caring . . . you can direct this toward yourself . . . you can feel so good . . . you can learn the art of controlling an urge . . . you can learn to ignore it . . . by admitting it, but at the same time remembering your commitment to respect your body . . . lock them together . . . If you emphasize one, you have to ignore the other and you can commit yourself to your body . . . emphasize your commitment to your body, ignore the urge to smoke . . . you can feel so relaxed and in control . . . your body is so important . . . you are your body's keeper . . . so many things you can do beside smoking as you ignore the urge . . . you notice it passes . . . it fades away . . . like clouds in the wind . . . you can think about how choosing not to smoke . . . and you will do this . . . will lock into your strength . . . your pride. Do this now . . . feel . . . experience . . . get to know yourself . . . you are a nonsmoker . . . see yourself this way . . . experience it.

See yourself in social situations . . . see yourself this way . . . notice others supporting you . . . noticing you are not smoking anymore . . . you feel their respect for you . . . you feel serene . . . calm . . . comfortable . . . nothing to bother you . . . nothing to disturb you . . . feel this sense growing . . . you don't have to do anything now . . . but later today . . . and tomorrow . . . and the tomorrows thereafter you will become more and more aware that you are in control . . . you will avoid one or two or more situations in which in the past you were perhaps likely to think about smoking . . . you will do this . . . you will do this . . . for you care about yourself . . . relax . . . deeper . . . deeper . . . quitting smoking is a way to be good to yourself . . . to care for yourself . . . yes . . . say yes to this.

Feel good about yourself . . . reward yourself for not smoking . . . you are saving money . . . you are preserving your health . . . you are resisting urges . . . you are not gaining weight . . . you are exercising . . . or eating in moderation . . . you are taking care of yourself . . . you feel pride . . . you can reward yourself . . . you do deserve it . . . how can you do this? You want to do this, to be good to yourself . . . so you can think of some things you can do . . . what will it be . . .

think of what it will be now . . . no need to deny yourself a reward for not smoking . . . feel good about what you have done . . . about coming here . . . how can you show yourself that you can like yourself . . . yes . . . say yes to liking yourself . . . see yourself as the person you want to be . . . do this now . . . moving and moving toward strength . . . to be that person . . . see that person . . . get a sense for that person's essence.

Can you begin to feel your senses awakening? Begin to let your senses come alive . . . your sense of touch . . . of smell . . . you can begin to smell better . . . you begin to taste . . . really taste . . . you smell fresh . . . you are free of the stench of cigarettes . . . you are free of their clinging odor . . . you are fresh . . . you are beginning to regain your senses . . . you are becoming aware . . . like a newborn baby . . . before your senses were dulled . . . your body is healing . . . healing . . . you are opening up . . . you are able to taste your foods . . . you can chew them slowly . . . with enjoyment . . . you are exercising . . . if you wish . . . you are a nonsmoker today . . . from this moment on . . . say this to yourself . . . yes . . . say yes to it . . . yes!

Go deeper into your hypnosis . . . moving and moving and moving . . . learning and firming your resolve . . . comfort . . . your mind clear and calm now you are moving and moving and flowing with your experience . . . nothing to bother as you go deeper and deeper and deeper, aware of what you are and what you can be . . . how you can use what you have learned in your life of learnings . . . how you can use what you have learned about self-hypnosis . . . how you will help yourself to remain a nonsmoker . . . as you see yourself not smoking in situations in the past in which you were tempted to smoke, you can see yourself substituting healthy behaviors for smoking . . . you see yourself choosing health and well-being . . . you feel different . . . your senses are alive . . . you feel a sense of pride . . . you are in control . . . you do it . . . you give yourself positive suggestions . . . you use your key phrase . . . your anchor . . . you find many ways to reinforce your sense of accomplishment . . . in this situation in which, in the past, you had thoughts of smoking . . . you realize you can control what you do and what you do not do . . . no longer a slave to smoking . . . yes . . . you are in charge of your life . . . you can say this firmly to yourself . . . I am in charge . . . I am in control . . . my strength is within . . . I am a nonsmoker . . . until you feel even better about what you can do . . . yes . . . capable of so much . . . perhaps now you can absorb the fact that every day of your life you are a nonsmoker . . . you do not smoke when you sleep . . . perhaps for eight hours a day you did not smoke . . . perhaps more . . . perhaps less . . . you do not feel deprived yet you are not smoking . . . you are coping . . . your conscious and unconscious minds working together . . . your body is relaxed . . . your body healing . . . now when you do not smoke during the day . . . your body will heal even more . . . you can relax, too . . . with what you have learned . . . with what you have learned.

Perhaps you can let go even more . . . feel time slowing down . . . time slowing down to a most comfortable pace . . . a sense of feeling really good . . . a flowing feeling . . . moving more and more toward hope and peace . . . a sense of feeling worthwhile . . . and as you experience these feelings, what I'd like you to do is to bring your thumb and forefinger together . . . or perhaps you would like to touch a ring that has special significance for you . . . make your anchor . . . just lightly touch . . . make your anchor and feel so good and relax . . . more and more . . . more and more . . . feel more confident . . . even better . . . flowing wave upon wave . . . gentle relaxation . . . gentle waves of relaxation as you feel calm, and at ease, and secure . . . deep . . . deep . . . so good . . . yes . . . can you feel this in your entire body . . . relax even deeper . . . so deep . . . you can create this feeling . . . your strength . . . your security . . . is within . . . let yourself create these feelings . . . make these feelings move and flow together with your need to be a nonsmoker . . . relaxing . . . coping effectively . . . that anchor . . . a symbol of your conscious and unconscious mind working together . . . your mind and body working together . . . to help you control your thoughts and feelings in ways that are productive . . . good for you . . . for your health . . . for your self-respect.

The more you practice . . . the more you develop your skills, the better you will feel . . . practice early in the morning . . . practice during the day . . . as you do the things you do in your life . . . as you live and learn . . . more and more and more . . . more and more . . . you can give yourself suggestions . . . program your mind . . . to be a nonsmoker . . . tune yourself . . . tune your feelings . . . like you tune a precision instrument . . . an instrument you take good care of . . . each morning . . . and at times during the day . . . use your anchor . . . say your key phrase . . . review your reasons for not smoking . . . if you have any urges . . . use your lifetime of learnings to emphasize your health and well-being as you ignore them . . . remember that strength comes from within . . . you can use your anchor . . . perhaps take a deep breath and hold it in for four counts, and then as you slowly exhale, say your key phrase . . . be sure to anchor those feelings . . . you are a nonsmoker!

Go even deeper . . . deeper still . . . time slowing down . . . calm and at ease . . . anchored . . . grounded in your being . . . centered in yourself . . . visualize yourself in a situation in which you might in the past have been tempted to smoke . . . and anchor your resolve to be a nonsmoker . . . this sense of yourself as a nonsmoker . . . you can feel so good knowing that you can lock your resolve to be a nonsmoker with good feelings . . . and the knowledge that any thoughts of smoking will fade away . . . until they are gone and you can feel good and whole and together . . . with your body . . . with your unconscious . . . working together with your conscious mind . . . all of your senses working together to help you do what you need to do.

Of course, this is the essence, the basis of suggestion. [pause]

Termination of Hypnosis

In a little while, I will give you instructions to wake up. Before you do, however, I want to talk to you a while longer. I want to encourage each of you to continue to practice your self-hypnosis. Build on the skills which you have developed over the last week and give yourself suggestions to become the person that you want to be . . . to become that nonsmoker that you know that you can be. Practice all of the techniques, and all of the things that you have learned here in real-life, everyday situations. You have the power to resist the urge to smoke and you will become a nonsmoker . . . for life!

In a moment, I will begin counting backwards from 10 to 1, and you will gradually wake up. You will open your eyes when I reach the count of five. At one, you will be wide awake. You will feel fine and have no aftereffects.

Ready: 10 . . . 9 . . . 8 . . . 7 . . . 6 . . . 5 . . . open your eyes . . . 4 . . . 3 . . . 2 . . . 1 . . . wide awake. Any remaining drowsiness will quickly pass.

Conclusion of Treatment

At the end of the second session, Jamie expressed her gratitude and affirmed her motivation to successfully avoid smoking. She particularly enjoyed the self-hypnosis tape and promised to use it on a regular basis. I encouraged all members, with the permission of their "buddies," to continue to call on one another for periodic support. I informed the group that I would be contacting them in approximately 6 and 12 months to assess their progress. As Jamie exited the room, I expressed my hope that she would not only reach her goal of 90% reduction but achieve total abstinence. She simply smiled and walked away.

OUTCOME

Six months after our last meeting, a questionnaire was sent to each participant. Jamie reported smoking a total of 10 cigarettes since treatment. She smoked more than half of those cigarettes over the course of one evening following an argument with her husband. Fortunately, she stopped herself from relapsing by calling her buddy and playing her hypnotic tape several times the next day. Over the preceding 4-1/2 months, Jamie had achieved complete smoking abstinence! She wrote that she was "very proud" of herself. Furthermore, she expressed an enhanced sense of overall confidence in her ability to accomplish goals. Jamie's success in smoking cessation apparently strengthened her overall self-efficacy. On the back of her response form, Jamie wrote that she "knew all along" that the ultimate treatment goal had to be total abstinence. She thanked me for not insisting on total abstinence in the beginning noting, ". . . part of me, I guess, was hoping that after meeting with you that first time, you would agree that I couldn't stop smoking and excuse me from the program. The gradual approach and your confidence in me helped a lot." On the 12-month follow-up questionnaire, Jamie reported complete abstinence from smoking. She had not smoked a cigarette in over 10 months. Although I do not know if Jamie sustained her smoking abstinence beyond the 1-year follow-up, it was clear that she surpassed her stated goal to achieve at least a 90% reduction in smoking within 6 months after treatment.

Results from the other participants were as follows: One member achieved total abstinence across the entire 12-month time span; two significantly reduced their smoking; and one, having achieved only minimal gains immediately following treatment, returned to her baseline level of smoking. All of the participants enjoyed the hypnosis script and found the treatment protocol to be informative and helpful.

CONCLUSION

The clinical application of a two-session cognitive–behavioral smoking cessation program utilizing hypnotic suggestions both to resist urges to smoke and to visualize oneself as a nonsmoker was demonstrated in a small group format. Abstinence rates achieved were generally consistent with results reported by the authors of the program (see Lynn et al., 1994). The chapter followed the treatment course of one individual who had unsuccessfully tried a variety of smoking cessation approaches in the past. With encouragement and application of a graduated approach to smoking cession, the client successfully achieved her objective by reducing cigarette consumption by at least 90% over a 6-month period of time. Furthermore, at time of last report, she had achieved total abstinence from smoking over a 10-month time span.

REFERENCES

Abrams, D. B., & Wilson, G. T. (1979). Self-monitoring and reactivity in the modification of cigarette smoking. *Journal of Consulting and Clinical Psychology, 51,* 226–233.

American Psychiatric Association. (1994). *Diagnostic and statistical manual of mental disorders* (4th Ed.). Washington, DC: Author.

Bandura, A. (1977). Self-efficacy: Toward a unifying theory of behavioral change. *Psychological Review, 84,* 191–155.

Bandura, A. (1978). The self-system in reciprocal determinism. *American Psychologist, 33,* 344–358.

Bandura, A. (1982). Self-efficacy mechanism in human agency. *American Psychologist, 37,* 122–147.

Bandura, A., Adams, N. E., & Beyer, J. (1977). Cognitive processes mediating behavioral change. *Journal of Personality and Social Psychology, 35,* 125–139.

Cornwell, J., Burrows, G. D., & McMurray, N. (1981). Comparison of single and multiple sessions of hypnosis in the treatment of smoking behavior. *Australian Journal of Clinical and Experimental Hypnosis, 9,* 61–76.

Crasilneck, H. B. (1990). Hypnotic techniques for smoking control and psychogenic impotence. *American Journal of Clinical Hypnosis, 32,* 147–153.

Frank, R. G., Umlauf, R. L., Wonderlich, S. A., & Ashkanazi, G. S. (1986). Hypnosis and behavior treatment in a worksite cessation program. *Addictive Behaviors, 11,* 59–62.

Gorassini, D. R., & Spanos, N. P. (1986). A social cognitive skills approach to the successful modification of hypnotic susceptibility. *Journal of Personality and Social Psychology, 50,* 1004–1012.

Hunt, W., & Bespalec, D. (1974). An evaluation of current methods of modifying smoking behaviors. *Journal of Clinical Psychology, 30,* 431–438.

Lynn, S. J., Neufeld, V., Rhue, J. W., & Matorin, A. (1994). Hypnosis and smoking cessation: A cognitive–behavioral treatment. In S. J. Lynn, J. W. Rhue, & I. Kirsch (Eds.), *Handbook of clinical hypnosis* (pp. 555–585). Washington, DC: American Psychological Association.

Perry, C., Gelfand, R., & Marcovitch, P. (1979). The relevance of hypnotic susceptibility in the clinical context. *Journal of Abnormal Psychology, 89,* 598–603.

Perry, C., & Mullin, G. (1975). The effects of hypnotic susceptibility on reducing smoking behavior treated by an hypnotic technique. *Journal of Clinical Psychology, 31,* 498–505.

U.S. Department of Health and Human Services. (1990). *The health benefits of smoking cessation: A report of the surgeon general.* Rockville, MD: Public Health Service, Centers for Disease Control, Center for Chronic Disease Prevention and Health Promotion, Office of Smoking and Health.

U.S. Department of Health, Education, & Welfare. (1990). *Smoking and health: A report of the surgeon general* (DHEW Publication No. PHS79-50066). Washington, DC: U.S. Department of Health, Education, and Welfare, Public Health Service, Office of the Assistant Secretary for Health, Office on Smoking and Health.

Wadden, T. J., & Anderton, C. H. (1982). The clinical use of hypnosis. *Psychological Bulletin, 92,* 215–243.

Williams, J. M., & Hall, D. W. (1988). Use of single session hypnosis for smoking cessation. *Addictive Behaviors, 13,* 205–208.

III

HYPNOTHERAPY WITH CHILDREN AND ADOLESCENTS

12

NARRATIVE AND IMAGINATIVE STORYTELLING: HYPNOTHERAPY IN THE TREATMENT OF A SEXUALLY ABUSED CHILD

JUDITH W. RHUE, STEVEN JAY LYNN, and JUDITH PINTAR

Child abuse has existed for centuries. In 1874, the case of Mary Ellen, an 8-year-old girl who was chained, beaten, and starved by her adoptive parents, marked the real beginning of recognition of child maltreatment in the United States (Zelikovsky & Lynn, 1994). However, it is only within recent years that it has become a focal point of social concern. This concern is surely justified in that each year a disturbing number of children are sexually abused in the United States. The National Center on Child Abuse and Neglect (1991) reported 838,232 substantiated cases of child abuse (e.g., physical, psychological, sexual) and neglect. Furthermore, statistics reveal that 20% to 30% of female children, and 9% to 12% of male children are victims of sexual abuse (Finkelhor & Hotaling, 1984; Herman, 1981; Russell, 1983). The Clearinghouse on Child Abuse and Neglect Information (1989) reported that physical child abuse is associated with high morbidity (psychological distress) and a mortality rate of 10% to 15% (cited in Kolko, 1992).

Given these alarming statistics, it is no wonder that therapists are frequently called upon to treat the aftermath of sexual abuse. Indeed, sexual abuse has been associated with a variety of sequelae ranging from precocious sex play to nightmares, sleep disturbances, compulsive masturbation, school problems, depressed appetite, anger, tantrums, disaffiliation, and regressed and clinging behavior (see Brandt & Tisza, 1977; Gomes-Schwartz,

Horowitz, & Sauzier, 1985; Zelikovsky & Lynn, 1994). In response to the serious problems that often follow in the wake of abuse, many different treatments have been applied including family therapy, group psychotherapy, interpersonal skills training, and psychopharmacological treatments (see Kolko, 1987). With the exception of play and art therapy, experiential treatments, including hypnosis, have generally not been used to treat the repercussions of child abuse. This is unfortunate because abused children have much to gain from psychotherapeutic procedures that facilitate access to their feelings and thoughts, in general, and about the abusive events in a safe and protected treatment context, in particular.

In this chapter and elsewhere (Rhue & Lynn, 1991a, b) we argue that hypnotic storytelling techniques can play a pivotal role in the assessment and treatment of sexually abused children. We have found that storytelling techniques have been useful in our treatment of more than 40 sexually and physically abused children. Storytelling has helped us to pace psychotherapy; to establish rapport with frightened children and learn about their fears and aspirations; to alter children's mood and direct their stream of thought, while using powerful symbols and metaphors to stimulate insight and behavior change; and to engage children's fantasy and imaginative abilities. To illustrate how this can be accomplished, in this chapter we present a case of a 6-year-old boy, John, who was treated by one of the authors (Rhue) with storytelling techniques.

Storytelling has a rich psychotherapeutic tradition that dates back to Despert and Potter's clinical work (1936). More recently, Richard Gardner's (1977) psychoanalytic work with children reflects a sophisticated approach in which their stories are treated as analogous to adult dream productions. Storytelling with children in a more explicitly hypnotic context has been richly described by G. Gardner and Olness (1981), and an inspection of Milton H. Erickson's (Erickson & Rossi, 1980) writings reveals how creative storytelling and the use of metaphors can diminish resistance to change and forge a path to personal growth. Furthermore, hypnotic storytelling has been used to advantage in the treatment of children in acute pain (Kuttner, 1988) and in helping children endure difficult medical procedures (Hilgard & LeBaron, 1984).

Like more conventional hypnotic techniques, storytelling capitalizes on children's fantasy and imaginative abilities, and on their natural tendency to appreciate listening to and weaving interesting, meaningful stories. The techniques described in this chapter are informal, naturalistic, client-centered, permissive, and hypnotic insofar as they enhance qualities of imagery, absorption, and the involuntary, spontaneous quality of ideation, behavior, and affect (Rhue & Lynn, 1991b). Storytelling can proceed with or without a formal induction, or with or without being defined as hypnosis. Such techniques can combine direct and indirect suggestions in creative ways, and can be used with other therapeutic techniques. All in all, storytelling techniques afford a remarkable degree of flexibility that is appropriate to the changing attentional, emotional, and behavioral aspects of the child's reaction to trauma.

Our impression is that stories work so well because they tap into a basic truth about adults and children alike: When we tell stories, we create something from nothing. When we tell stories we shape and edit our experience of ourselves and the world. Through stories, we continually create ourselves. Hence, what seems real to us, and what is meaningful, is, in no small measure, a constructed rather than a given reality.

This truth is expressed in a growing narrative psychology (see Meichenbaum & Fong, 1993; Sarbin, 1986; Spence, 1984) based on the premise that feelings, thoughts, and memories are, in essence, organized along narrative lines. As Bonanno (1995) has written, narrative reconstructions integrate the past, present, and anticipated future and are intimately bound up with our present sense of identity and purpose (McAdams, 1985). We think along time-lines with beginnings, middles, and ends. We think about whether outcomes will be happy or sad. We exaggerate and minimize our report of our experiences. We try to anticipate how things will turn out—how the story will end. Stories ultimately are important means by which we to come to know and define ourselves. We learn about who we really are by way of the stories we hear from our parents and significant people in our lives; we come to see ourselves, and find our niche, in their stories about us and the world. As children, the boundary between ourselves and others is especially permeable, so the stories we hear and formulate are especially compelling and formative.

Through the construction of narratives, we impose order and continuity on events as they unfold and on how we react to them. For instance, in describing a traumatic event—in telling a story about it—we give coherence, structure, and meaning to what may be fragmented and chaotic strands of experience. Order and continuity of the stream of life's experiences can also be achieved by anticipatory coping in relation to probable but unpredictable natural disasters such as earthquakes. With respect to such events, Meichenbaum and Fong (1993) maintain that persons engage in a wide variety of mind games or stories they tell themselves and others to control dysphoric feelings, protect their view of self and the world, and interpersonally influence others. For instance, persons may adopt a fatalistic attitude about the event (e.g., when your number is up, it is up), justify why they live in high risk areas (e.g., no place is completely safe), and minimize the possible personal threat involved (e.g., I never drive on expressways).

Virtually every characteristic we attribute to ourselves—goodness, badness, intelligence, shyness—has stories associated with it embedded in generalizations about persons, events, and outcomes in the past, present, as well as the projected future (e.g., I am not intelligent, so I will never amount to much). What at first blush might appear to be a simple self-statement (e.g., "I am not intelligent"), might be associated with a rather elaborate network of themes involving the self and others. These themes encompass complex explanations or rationalizations for past and present actions, wishes, fantasies, feelings, and behavioral scripts.

Our discussion suggests that the self is more than the sum total of personal characteristics. Indeed, many attributes are not fixed entities so much as dynamic action potentials that change in response to our expectations, the challenges we face, the roles we enact, the outcomes we achieve, and the important relationships in our lives. However, in the absence of fresh stories, new ways of conceptualizing ourselves and our lives, or input that somehow perturbs the way we view ourselves and our fate, we are likely to view the self as an inevitable byproduct of the past.

One reason why behavior is recalcitrant to change is that it is easy to mistake the stories we tell about ourselves for some absolute reality—failing to appreciate the degree to which we are the unconscious authors of our experience. But another reason why narratives may be difficult to modify is because of their social nature. That is, narratives are often deeply embedded in the bedrock of our relationships, which are, themselves, not necessarily easily modified. Pintar and Lynn's (1995) narrative model of dissociation suggests that personal identity is constructed through individuals' constant and complex relationship to the social world. They argue that dissociation is a mechanism that mediates identity in the face of traumatic conditions that present an individual with contradictory social narratives. These contradictions are inevitably reflected in resulting personal narratives. In this sense, the subjective experience of having many "selves," which appears to be a distortion of reality, can also be seen as an accurate reflection of actual social conditions.

Because of the social basis for the construction of personal narratives, traumatic conditions must change before an individual's narrative-of-self can change; still, changing the social condition does not guarantee that the personal narrative will automatically change as well. It can be difficult for a traumatized individual to reconstruct a personal narrative to reflect new nonabusive social circumstances. Storytelling in a therapeutic setting can have considerable healing power because it helps to replace images, symbols, and metaphors that drain, deplete, and diminish the self with images, symbols, and metaphors that empower the self. This dynamic is made evident in our discussion of the case of John presented below.

BACKGROUND INFORMATION

John was a 6-year-old boy who was brought to the therapist by his mother. She was concerned about John's behavior change since an episode of alleged sexual abuse by her sister's husband, and related that John might have to testify in court at the trial of the abuser. Since the abuse incident, John had become angry and difficult to manage. His mother stated that he had begun to talk back to her, and had violent temper tantrums during which he kicked her and threw things at her. She stated that he was not like this prior to the abuse incident. John's mother also felt that he had become "hyper" since the alleged abuse, stating that he was always moving and was difficult to get to sleep, in contrast to a previously lower level of activity and no notable difficulty with bedtime. John's mother stated that for the first 2 weeks after the incident, John would recount it to her, to the police, and to the child protective agency personnel that were involved in the case. However, around the time John learned that he might have to testify in court, he began to avoid talking about the incident. At first, he simply avoided answering questions by busying himself with other activities or changing the topic. During the past 2 weeks, John had refused to discuss the incident altogether, and said that he could remember nothing about it.

John's mother was a 24-year-old single parent who worked as a secretary, and was the sole support of the two of them. She had grown up in a rural, impoverished setting and was pregnant with John when she graduated from high school. She had maintained herself and John on public assistance until job training had led to her current secretarial job. John's biological father, whom his mother had lived with for less than a year and never married, had left the area shortly after John's birth and had instigated no contact over the years. John's mother was faced with constant financial struggles, and often depended on her parents and siblings for financial help and child care. Her family was large (six siblings), with numerous extended family members, many of whom acted as baby-sitters for John. John and his mother had a close relationship, and she had not been involved in a dating relationship for nearly 2 years.

Approximately one month earlier, John's mother had left John in the care of her sister (John's aunt) while she went to work. During the late afternoon, John's aunt had to go to the grocery and left John in the care of her husband, an unemployed 30-year-old construction worker. During the hour John's aunt was gone, her husband allegedly molested John, attempting anal intercourse and having him perform oral sex. John's mother arrived from work to find John crying by the swing in the backyard. Her sister had not yet returned from her grocery shopping, and her sister's husband offered no explanation for John's crying. John clung to his mother wordlessly for the next 2 hours. When she noticed a small spot of blood on his pants, John told her that his uncle "hurted me" and showed her his bruised bottom. John told his mother what his uncle had done and what his uncle had forced him to do. John's mother took him to the hospital emergency room for treatment. The emergency room staff called Children's

Services and the police. At the hospital John had to repeatedly recount the events surrounding the abuse incident. Based on John's injuries and his brief account of what happened, police picked John's uncle up for questioning. The uncle immediately confessed what had occurred, but later retracted his confession, creating the possibility of a trial at which John would be the chief prosecution witness. At the time of the initial contact with the therapist, a court date was pending.

ASSESSMENT

The initial phase of the assessment process consisted of a clinical interview with John's mother and a separate interview with John. The interview with John's mother was conducted first in order to obtain a clear understanding of the parameters of John's acting out, and the responses of his mother and others in his environment to episodes of anger and misbehavior. It was also important to gain as much collateral information about the alleged sexual abuse incident as possible, as John's mother stated that since his emergency room visit, John had not spoken about the abuse or the alleged abuser. In fact, in response to any questions about it, John simply responded "I can't remember anything." John's mother described his tantrums as beginning with yelling, "I hate you" and "You don't love me," and progressing into throwing and breaking toys.

If she tried to physically restrain John, he would attempt to kick and hit her. A tantrum might last from 15 minutes to an hour, and they occurred on an average of once per day. Even mild frustrations such as being told "no" might precipitate a tantrum, and they were worse when John was tired.

In describing her response to John's upsets, his mother cried and said that she felt guilty because she often yelled at John, and had slapped him in the face once or twice when he said particularly hurtful things. She reported that when she lost control and hit John or cried hysterically, John actually seemed to regain control and to try to comfort her. She said that she knew John's upsets were related to the abuse and felt that she had no right to be angry at him when he was having a tantrum. John's mother stated that sometimes she sent John to his room, sometimes she ignored the behavior, and that at other times she spanked him or yelled at him. She stated that John used to be an "easy" child to manage, although she reported that he always had "a bad temper."

With these inconsistent maternal behaviors, it was difficult for John to develop new organizing themes or ways of thinking about himself and his mother. Indeed, her occasionally slapping him could only reinforce the perception that his mother did not love him. His provoking her, in seemingly countless ways, might have been John's way of not only expressing his anger but also giving his mother a "reason" to not love him, thereby regaining a measure of control in the situation. This control was also evidenced in his comforting his mother after she was upset.

John's mother reported that John was also having increased difficulty at school since the abuse incident. John had always been somewhat difficult for the teacher to manage. She had complained from the beginning of school that John failed to listen to her or follow instructions and would talk back to her when she tried to correct him. Recently, his teacher reported increased angry acting out by John. After John's mother talked with her about the abuse incident, John's teacher began to let his increased acting out occur without responding with attention or consequences on all but the most severe occasions in order to give John some adjustment time. Unfortunately, this had not been a successful strategy, and the teacher was now asking for an evaluation to see if John qualified for a severely behaviorally handicapped designation.

Testing was performed by a colleague of the therapist's, and consisted of the Wechsler Preschool and Primary Scale of Intelligence, Thematic Apperception Test, Childhood Depression Inventory, and two measures of imaginative involvement, the Inventory of Childhood Memories and Imaginings and the Children's Fantasy Inventory. John was cooperative and pleasant during each of the three testing sessions. His full scale IQ was 109, with no notable differences between the subscale scores. His Thematic Apperception Test stories were characterized by themes of aggression, response to physical threat, and anger. He depicted maternal figures as weak and unable to protect him, whereas adult males were depicted as hurtful and violent. He seemed to identify with victims who needed to be constantly wary and who were outwardly threatening.

On measures of imagination and fantasy, John appeared to be a child who enjoyed imaginative activities and was moderately involved in fantasy. He spontaneously told a story about having gone fishing with his grandfather recently. John said,

> We sat in the boat and waited and waited for something to bite. I pretended that there was a big fish keeping all of the others away. If any of the other fish came too close, the big one would get them. I named that big one 'tough Tommy.' Finally, tough Tommy saw our boat and thought it was a space ship and it scared him. He went away. Then I caught a fish.

On the inventory of childhood memories and imaginings for children, he positively endorsed 18 items, which was in the middle range of fantasy involvements. In order to assess his depression, the Reynolds Childhood Depression scale was administered to John. His score was high for children of his age group, but did not reach the level required for a diagnosis of clinical depression.

The initial conceptualization of this case, based on the presenting information, interview data, and assessment, was to view John as a child of normal intelligence who was acting out in response to the trauma of an uncontrollable abusive episode. As with many other abused children, John's problems following in the wake of abuse emerged from both a rupture in the sense of security in the world and in important social relationships. For John, the world was no longer the safe place it once appeared to be. The narrative truth that the world is a safe place and Mom can protect you from lurking dangers was contradicted by the basic truth that terrible things can and do happen, and Mom is not omnipotent. Because John was angry with his mother for not protecting him, and perhaps for not loving him enough (otherwise why would she have let him be abused?), he was not willing to share his story and his pain with her. Hence, he could not ease his burden nor begin to develop a narrative in which he was, once again, safe and powerful, and protected by a caring mother. Lacking a sense of mastery over his experience of abuse and a sense of safety in the present, John was not able to view the event as truly in his past. With these narrative themes organizing his emotions and behaviors, it was no wonder that John sometimes reacted in a violent way to his mother.

Further, it seemed that John and his mother had several dysfunctional factors in their relationship. John's mother often seemed to view him as a small adult, and to seek adult reactions from and support from him. When he could not behave in ways to meet her needs, and acted out angrily toward her, John's mother responded in an immature, egocentric manner, feeling that he "shouldn't" be childish or do things that were stressful to her. John, in turn, appeared to be highly dependent on his mother. He seemed to be acting out his anger over the incident of abuse and his blame toward his mother for not protecting him, by throwing tantrums over relatively minor issues. When John's mother lost control by crying or yelling and trying to physically control him, John had her full attention and a sense of control over her behavior. John learned that he could be powerful in this way, which appeared to reinforce the occurrence of these incidents. Further, "make-up" times after his mother had been angry involved nurturant, loving times during which John's mother cried and held him, told him how much she really loved him, and was sorry that they fought. These actions only served to reinforce John's attention-seeking behaviors. Under these circumstances, intervention was clearly necessary.

THERAPY CONSIDERATIONS

In considering what therapeutic strategies would be most helpful to John and his mother, it appeared that John was a good candidate for storytelling. Testing revealed that John was reasonably bright and verbal. Furthermore, he was imaginative and enjoyed fantasy and storytelling. This natural predisposition toward creative thinking and imaginative involvement boded well for a therapeutic strategy that utilized these natural abilities, allied him with the therapist, and facilitated trust in their relationship. John's "memory loss" for the alleged abuse incident seemed more related to the anxiety of having to repeatedly recount the incident, and apprehension about facing a courtroom setting, than an artifact of dissociation. The storytelling process seemed particularly appropriate because it avoided direct confrontation of the abuse incident, while allowing "difficult" material to be dealt with through the context of the story. In short, it provided a buffer for anxiety, was nonthreatening, and potentially the swiftest route to restoring more appropriate functioning.

It is notable that formal hypnotizability was not assessed. We do not routinely measure children's hypnotizability. As in the case of John, it is only necessary that a child be absorbed in the story and participate in the unfolding narrative and that useful insights and the working through of difficult issues ensue from our efforts.

However, despite the many "pros" cited above for using an imagery-based technique, the therapist faced a significant "con" to selecting this approach. That is, the therapist was forced to consider the impact of this hypnotic-like procedure on a witness, in this case a child, who would later have to testify in a criminal courtroom proceeding. To compound the problem, the use of fantasy and storytelling is easily portrayed in a negative light in a courtroom, with clever attorneys associating storytelling with "lying" and fantasy with "making things up." This situation created an ethical dilemma that was quite troubling to the therapist. If the therapist elected to use storytelling, which the therapist felt was clinically the most efficacious approach, then the court case might be damaged or lost.

In view of this situation, it was decided that because John's mother was his legal guardian, she should be fully apprised of the dilemma. This apprisal would involve explaining the rationale for using storytelling and its potential advantages for John, while fully discussing the possible effect of such techniques on criminal proceedings (i.e., having the case dismissed because of court's view of "hypnosis").

John's mother met with the therapist the following day to discuss the therapy options. After listening to the therapeutic dilemma, John's mother said that she wanted "the best therapy" for John and that she felt that the storytelling technique should be used. However, she felt that she should speak with the prosecutor in the criminal case to apprise him of the therapeutic issues. She called the therapist later in the week to say that the prosecutor felt that no therapy should be implemented that might interfere with the court case, and that she felt compelled to go along with his request. The therapist offered to give John's mother a referral to a therapist who specialized in play therapy for John, or to see John when the court case was resolved.

John's mother recontacted the therapist one month later and asked that the therapist work with John using storytelling procedures. She stated that the day before the trial was to begin, the prosecutor had accepted a plea bargain in which the defendant pleaded guilty to a lesser charge. This seemed an acceptable resolution to the legal case, particularly in light of the fact that John continued to say that he could not remember the incident and would have been a difficult witness for the prosecution. Over the previous month, John had become more withdrawn, refusing to talk with anyone except his mother. John's mother felt that the pressure on John to testify at the trial had exacerbated his unwillingness to talk. John had also experienced two incidents of bedwetting during the prior month, a problem he had never had since his toilet training at age 2 1/2 .

THERAPY

The therapist decided to work with John on a weekly basis, seeing him individually for approximately 40 minutes during each session. The therapy for John was conceptualized as occurring in three stages, with the goals shifting as John was able to progress to the next stage. The first stage would involve the use of storytelling to build a positive relationship with John and to provide a safe environment as the cornerstone to the eventual task of dealing with the trauma of the abuse incident.

One of the best ways to provide a safe haven for children like John is to encourage them to describe their favorite place. This may be an actual place or a fantasized, idealized place. What is important is that the child feels safe, secure, and comfortable in this place. The therapist may expect a wide range of favorite places, some of them improbable. So as not to provide an excessive degree of structure or to create demands for reporting only positive affect, we avoid suggesting that the child feel "happy" in the favorite place, nor do we stipulate whether the child is alone or with a special companion. We do, however, often suggest that the child fill this place with the trappings and creatures that he or she likes best (e.g., stuffed animals, family pets, imaginary companions, articles of self-defense). As children become more comfortable and familiar with fantasizing in line with suggested stories, it is possible to introduce new stories from the safety of their favorite place. Stories involving children and adults can be introduced, while encouraging the child to suggest various plot endings.

The therapist felt that when John could evidence comfort in the therapy setting and could actively provide his own stories, it would be time to move on to the second stage. The goal of the second stage would be to work through the trauma of the abuse through the use of protective images, distancing techniques, and metaphor to help John gain a sense of mastery of the situation.

Protective images can be derived by simply asking children how they can feel better or safer in their place of comfort and security, or by suggesting specific images for them and testing their protective value. For instance, props or devices such as magic wands, rings, or magic with special powers can provide protection, as can invincible suits of armor, invisible shields, cloaking devices, and weapons. These power images can be used to explore children's wishes (e.g., "What three wishes would you like to be granted") or to create certain effects such as relaxation or amnesia for selected events (e.g., "When the magic wand touches you, you will forget everything about . . . . it will seem as if you dreamed it all, only to recall it perfectly when the magic wand touches you again"). Protective images can also involve distancing and escape from threat or danger. To control the emotional and physical distance from a feared person, object, or event, children can talk on telephones, communicate by way of computers, hover over places that are frightening, or escape by way of flying horses or rocket ships, for example (Rhue & Lynn, 1993).

When children are pressured to reveal details of the abuse, resistance can be expected. Of course, this was the case with John, and expressed by his statement, "I can't remember." Metaphors can be used to establish trust and to promote insight by creating a structure that is analogous to that of existing difficulties, personal issues, and possible solutions to problems. (Brown, 1993). For instance, children can connect what happens to story characters with events in their own lives.

In most cases, metaphors introduced by the therapist (or child) precede more direct encounters with conflict-laden issues and events. As rapport and comfort build, there is a movement from metaphor to real-life problems. If they do not do so spontaneously, children can be encouraged to relate stories to themselves or stories of real-life events that have happened to their friends or to "imaginary friends." The children's stories are never questioned. However, because a goal of treatment is to spell out the metaphor in terms of its connection to real-life events, the therapist can promote insight by nondirective questioning (e.g., Do you see any connection between the magic rabbit and yourself?), with interpretations made following the child's insightful observations.

Storytelling is a collaborative (ad)venture. Regardless of their content, stories are always valued, accepted, and respected by the therapist. The child is always free to chart the course of the story. The therapist might invite the child to tell a story, to select a story from among one or more alternatives for the therapist to tell, or to choose a story in which the therapist and child alternate assuming responsibility for the narrative. It is sometimes useful to tell stories about how other children have coped with physical and psychological problems similar to those of the abused child. The child can have the opportunity to finish the story or to modify the ending in some significant respect. This can serve as a useful barometer of the degree to which the child experiences a sense of mastery versus lingering fear and helplessness.

When the child is empowered and a positive sense of self is restored or cultivated, other issues can be addressed. In John's case, the third and final stage involved helping him to accept his role as a child and to seek healthy ways to gain attention from his mother. The end of this stage would be marked by the termination of therapy. The therapist set no time line for the occurrence of these stages or the length of the therapy.

It also seemed advisable to work with John's mother for approximately 15 minutes of each therapy hour. The goal of this work with Mom was threefold: (a) To help her understand the storytelling process and to make her an active participant in the therapeutic process; (b) To help her respond more appropriately to John's behavior at home; and (c) To monitor the occurrence of therapeutic changes at home and at school.

Session 2

This session followed the assessment session and was focused on relationship building and avoiding the pressure of trying to get the anxious, nonverbal John to talk, much less to tell a story. Rather, the therapist modeled storytelling and used some paradoxical and mildly challenging suggestions.

> Therapist: John, I think it's still too soon for you to talk to me much, so I'm going to ask you to just listen today. How does that sound to you?
>
> John: OK.
>
> Therapist: Would you prefer to listen with your eyes open or closed?
>
> John: Open.
>
> Therapist: Good. If you notice that they begin to feel heavy while I'm talking, it will be OK to shut them, but that's up to you. I like to shut my eyes while I'm telling a story because then I can picture what I'm talking about. It's almost like I have a TV that comes on when I shut my eyes. OK?
>
> John: (nodding OK)
>
> Therapist: Now, I'm going to share a favorite story of mine with you. I don't think you're ready to share anything with me yet, but if I'm wrong, you can jump in with a comment or two. I'll be surprised, but I can handle it. This story is about a fish named Henry. Henry lives in a large lake. He is a young fish, but not a baby fish. My story today, for I have many stories about Henry, is about Henry's bad bite. Henry's mother had swum away early that bright sunny morning to help Henry's older brother, Garth, learn to feed on the bottom of the lake. Garth was spending more and more time swimming away from the school of fish in their

neighborhood, and Henry's mother wanted to be sure that Garth knew what sorts of things he could and couldn't feed on that lie on the bottom of the lake. Anyway, Henry was swimming up toward the surface of the lake to catch a few rays of sunlight, when he saw the best looking worm he had ever seen. Now Henry had not had breakfast and that worm looked pretty good to him. The worm glistened in the sunlight and it actually seemed to sparkle. Can you picture that?

John: Uh-huh.

Therapist: Have you ever seen a sparkling worm?

John: No.

Therapist: Well then you have something in common with Henry, because he had never seen a sparkling worm either. And I'm here to tell you it was just beautiful. Henry swam closer to the worm. It was just floating along, but he noticed that it seemed to have a red ribbon attached to its head. What do you think that means?

John: I don't know, but it might be a lure.

Therapist: Tell me what you mean.

John: Well, I don't know, but somebody might be fishing and trying to catch him.

Therapist: You're right John. But let's continue and see what happens. Henry swam closer. The worm was a big one all right. It was irresistible. Henry took a bite. Almost immediately he felt a sharp sting on his mouth and he was being dragged through the water. You were right John, someone was fishing and they now had Henry on their line. What do you think will happen to poor Henry?

John: I don't know.

Therapist: Henry was being dragged toward the shore. As he reached the shallow water, he saw what looked like a rock. But the rock seemed to be moving. What do you think it is?

John: I don't know. Maybe it's a crab.

Therapist: Well, lets shut our eyes and look closer. (Therapist shuts eyes without checking to see if John has complied). No, its a turtle. Can you see it?

John: Yeah.

Therapist: As Henry flounders by still caught on the hook, the turtle sticks its head out of its shell and says (pause) . . . What do you think the turtle says??

John: (some hesitation) . . . the end.

Therapist: John that was very good, but I heard the turtle say, "jump up and twist sideways."

John: What??

Therapist: Jump up and twist sideways. Just as he was being dragged from the water by a hand, Henry jumped up and twisted sideways. With a rip and a sharp pain, Henry was free and swimming toward the bottom of the lake. His mouth hurt, but he was going home. As he passed the turtle, she nodded and smiled at him. He didn't even know her, but he had trusted her and she had helped him. He was going to ask her name, but the turtle had swum away. Another day, Henry thought, I'll come back and ask her name, and he swam home. The end. That's all we have time for today. Maybe we'll have more adventures with Henry soon. OK?

John: OK.

Despite his initial anxiety, John clearly enjoyed Henry the fish. In this story, the therapist attempted to help John identify with Henry, and used metaphor to deal with the issue of trust. Over the next few sessions, the therapist drew John into becoming more and more involved in weaving the story. On no occasion was a formal induction used. Over sessions, as John grew more comfortable in the therapy, he would mimic the eye closure modeled by the therapist. However, as children often do, he would spontaneously open his eyes on occasion, shifting rapidly between levels of involvement.

Session 16

By this time John had established a favorite place from which he shared stories with the therapist. He also had protective images which he introduced into the stories. Both the imaginary favorite place (a treehouse in the jungle) and the protective images (a tiger named King Kahn and a bear named Balou) seemed to be related to the location and characters of *The Jungle Book*, which was a favorite story of John's. However, the therapist did not question the origin of protectors or attempt to tie them to the *Jungle Book* story.

The focus of this session was John's opportunity to deal with the abuser. In the prior session, John had described the abuse incident. He did this from the safety of his favorite place, pretending to talk to the therapist over the phone. He did not want her to look at him while he was talking about the abuse. The therapist had offered him the opportunity to confront the abuser this week. The material from this and the previous session was very meaningful and represented a clear movement to the second stage of therapy. The material from these two sessions was replayed and reinterpreted in many other sessions by John and the therapist.

Therapist: Where are we? You told me to close my eyes and follow you until you said, "Stop."

John: (Laughing) In my place, you know.

Therapist: You mean the treehouse in the jungle?

John: Yep.

Therapist: Are we alone?

John: No, they're here.

Therapist: Who's here?

John: You know. (With exasperation) Kahn and Balou.

Therapist: OK, last week you told me about what X (John's aunt's husband, who molested John) did to you. As I promised, this week you can tell a story about what happens to him. Do you want to watch this on TV?

John: Yeah. I'll switch it on. (John reaches out his hand and turns a switch on an imaginary TV.) OK, Balou and I are after him. He's real scared, running through the jungle. He's shakin'. He knows we're after him. Old Balou and I are following his tracks. We're gettin' closer. Balou's growlin'.

Therapist: What will you do if you catch him?

John: Balou has him. He's yellin' and cryin'. Balou's gonna hit him right in the head. Smack, smash. I'm gonna hit him. Kahn will rip his head off and eat him.

Therapist: Is there anything you want to tell him?

John: Yeah. I hate you. I'm gonna hurt you. My tiger's gonna kill you.

Therapist: How does X feel now?

John: Now he's real sorry he hurted me. Now he wishes he hadn't done it.

Therapist: How do you feel now?

John: I'm gonna make him sorry. I'm glad.

Therapist: Glad?

John: Yeah, look at him (John is looking intently at the imaginary screen). You wanta hit him too?

Therapist: Do you want me to hit him?

John:	Yeah, and I want my Mom to hit him too. She don't like him no more.
Therapist:	What will happen next?
John:	Kahn will eat him. That's it. He's gone. He can't hurt nobody nomore.
Therapist:	OK, are you ready to turn off the TV for today?
John:	Yeah.
Therapist:	Next week I'd like you to make up a story to help other little boys who have been hurt by someone like X. Are you ready to do that now?
John:	Yeah. Can I have a copy of it like you said I could?
Therapist:	Sure. What do you want to do with it?
John:	I want to be able to watch it on TV at home.
Therapist:	OK.

Session 29

In the third stage of therapy, the therapist felt that it was paramount for John to work on his relationship with his mother. She felt that it was particularly important for John to learn to express anger in more appropriate ways and to avoid hitting his mother and throwing tantrums when she frustrated him. This excerpt illustrates John's increasing ability to work with the therapist in using storytelling. However, it is worth noting that throughout therapy there were sessions when John was tired or grumpy and was not active or not willing to be involved in storytelling. At these times the therapist did not push him at all, but provided a brief, entertaining story using some metaphors and characters John liked.

Therapist:	Today I will start a story, then you can make up part of it and then I will make up some more and then you can finish it. OK?
John:	Sure.
Therapist:	This is a story about Tyler the opossum. Tyler, as you remember from our other stories about him, is a young opossum who lives in a street drain with his mother. Every evening when it gets dark they climb out of the drain and walk through the neighborhood looking for food. After they have dinner, they like to hang upside down by their tails and talk to each other. Tonight, while they were hanging upside down Tyler's mother said, "Tyler, I am up-

set about something you do when you feel angry." OK, John, you make up part.

John: When he's mad Tyler likes to yell and throw things and his mother don't like it. So Tyler promises her he won't do it no more.

Therapist: Good. Now its my turn. When it's time to go back to the drain, that very night, Tyler doesn't want to come down from the tree. He feels angry and wants to stay outside. He starts to cry and swing wildly back and forth by his tail. His mother feels really upset. I wonder what she can do and I wonder what Tyler can do differently to stop this tantrum. OK, it's your turn to finish it.

John: Well, Tyler begins to think. His mother tells him that if he goes in he can have a popsicle and watch TV. So he gets down and goes in. The end.

Therapist: Is that what your Mom would do if you were having a tantrum?

John: Yeah, sometimes.

Therapist: What if she doesn't have a popsicle or candy or it's too late to watch TV? Would you just keep on having a tantrum?

John: No.

Therapist: Why not?

John: Well, now if I throw things she won't sing to me at bedtime and sometimes she won't even read to me. She used to cry and be real upset, but she don't no more.

Therapist: So you can show your Mom how you don't need tantrums so much anymore and still get her to sing at bedtime.

John: Yeah.

Therapist: Can you close your eyes and think really hard and come up with a way to help Tyler the opossum to stop tantruming? And can you tell him?

John: [closes eyes] Hey, Tyler, you little hairball. You gotta learn to think, like me. You'll make your Mom feel bad and she'll cry and you'll cry. So, ask for a popsicle and TV and go in.

Therapist: How will Tyler feel then?

John: Happy.

CONCLUSION

Therapy was concluded after three more sessions with John and a termination session with John's mother to acknowledge her efforts and consolidate treatment gains. It was evident that John gained a sense of mastery and personal control as he was able to confront and prevail over his abuser in imaginative stories. In these sorts of stories, John also invoked his mother as an ally. In so doing, his anger and resentment toward his mother dissipated in real life. The narratives developed in therapy appeared to translate into a more secure sense of self and into more secure attachments with others. It was also apparent that with these changes, John was able to put the traumatic event where it belonged: in his past.

John's mother, in turn, was increasingly able to recognize the contribution of her inconsistent behaviors to John's problems. She no longer reinforced his tantrum behaviors and felt that his behavior was under good control. She recognized the importance of continuing to praise her son for asking for things appropriately, for talking in a "soft voice," and for expressing his feelings in a modulated way.

Summing up her feelings, John's mother stated, "I feel I have my son back. We will make it." According to her report, progress was made on the school as well as the home front. John's attention span was reported to have improved dramatically, and he no longer "talked back" to the teacher. A year follow-up indicated that John was no longer a behavior problem at home and was progressing normally, at or above his grade level in all areas at school.

REFERENCES

Bonanno, G. (1995). Accessibility, reconstruction, and the treatment of functional memory problems. In A. D. Baddeley, B. A. Wilson, & F. N. Watts (Eds.), *Handbook of memory disorders* (pp. 615–638). Chichester, England: John Wiley & Sons Ltd.

Brandt, R., & Tisza, V. (1977). The sexually misused child. *American Journal of Orthopsychiatry, 44*, 80–87.

Brown, P. (1993). Hypnosis and metaphor. In J. W. Rhue, S. J. Lynn, & I. Kirsch (Eds.), *Handbook of clinical hypnosis.* (pp. 291–308). Washington, DC: American Psychological Association.

The Clearinghouse on Child Abuse and Neglect Information. (1989). *Child abuse and neglect: A shared community concern.* Washington, DC: National Center on Child Abuse and Neglect.

Despert, J. L., & Potter, H. W. (1936). Technical approaches used in the study and treatment of emotional problems in children. *Psychiatric Quarterly, 10,* 619–638.

Erickson, M. H., & Rossi, E. L. (Eds.). (1980). The collected papers of Milton H. Erickson on hypnosis: Vol. 1. The nature of hypnosis and suggestion. New York: Irvington.

Finkelhor, D., & Hotaling, G. T. (1984). Sexual abuse in the national incidence study of child abuse and neglect: An appraisal. *Child Abuse and Neglect, 8,* 23–33.

Gardner, R. (1977). *Therapeutic communication with children: The mutual storytelling technique* (2nd ed.). New York: Aronson.

Gardner, G. G., & Olness, K. (1981). *Hypnosis and hypnotherapy with children.* New York: Grune & Stratton.

Gomes-Schwartz, B., Horowitz, J. M., & Sauzier, M. (1985). Severity of emotional distress among sexually abused preschool, school-age, and adolescent children. *Hospital and Community Psychiatry, 36,* 503–508.

Herman, J. (1981). *Father–daughter incest.* Cambridge, MA: Harvard Press.

Hilgard, J. R., & LeBaron, S. (1984). *Hypnotherapy of pain in children with cancer.* Los Altos, CA: Kaufman.

Kolko, D. J. (1987). Treatment of child sexual abuse: Programs, progress, and prospects. *Journal of Family Violence, 2,* 303-318.

Kolko, D. J. (1992). Characteristics of child victims of physical violence: Research findings and clinical implications. *Journal of Interpersonal Violence, 7,* 244–276.

Kuttner, L. (1988). Favorite stories: A hypnotic pain-reduction technique for children in acute pain. *American Journal of Clinical Hypnosis, 30,* 289–295.

McAdams, D. P. (1985). *Power, intimacy, and the life story: Personological inquiries into identity.* New York: Guilford.

Meichenbaum, D., & Fong, G. T. (1993). How individuals control their own minds: A constructive narrative perspective. In D. M. Wegner & J. W. Pennebaker (Eds.), *Handbook of mental control* (pp. 473–490). Englewood Cliffs, New Jersey: Prentice Hall.

National Center on Child Abuse and Neglect. (1991). *National child abuse and neglect data system* (Working Paper No. 2). Washington, DC: U.S. Department of Health and Human Services.

Pintar, J., & Lynn, S. J. (1995). *A narrative model of dissociation.* Unpublished manuscript, University of Illinois.

Rhue, J. W., & Lynn, S. J. (1991a). The use of hypnotic techniques with sexually abused children. In W. Wester & D. O'Grady (Eds.), *Clinical applications of hypnosis with children* (pp. 69–84). New York: Brunner/Mazel.

Rhue, J. W., & Lynn, S. J. (1991b). Storytelling, hypnosis and the treatment of sexually abused children. *International Journal of Clinical and Experimental Hypnosis, 39,* 196-214.

Rhue, J. W., & Lynn, S. J. (1993). Hypnosis and storytelling in the treatment of child sexual abuse: Strategies and procedures. In J. W. Rhue, S. J. Lynn, & I. Kirsch (Eds.), *Handbook of clinical hypnosis* (pp. 455–478). Washington, DC: American Psychological Association.

Russell, D. (1983). The incidence and prevalence of intrafamilial and extrafamilial sexual abuse of female children. *Child Abuse and Neglect, 7,* 133–146.

Sarbin, T. (1986). *Narrative Psychology: The storied nature of human conduct.* New York: Praeger.

Spence, D. (1984). *Narrative truth and historical truth: Meaning and interpretation in psychoanalysis.* New York: W. W. Norton & Co., Inc.

Zelikovsky, N., & Lynn, S. J. (1994). The aftereffects and assessment of physical and psychological abuse. In S. J. Lynn & J. W. Rhue (Eds.), *Dissociation: Clinical and theoretical perspectives* (pp. 190–214). New York: Guilford Press.

13

NEUROTHERAPY AND ALERT HYPNOSIS IN THE TREATMENT OF ATTENTION DEFICIT HYPERACTIVITY DISORDER

ARREED BARABASZ and MARIANNE BARABASZ

Attention deficit disorder (ADD), also known as attention deficit hyperactivity disorder (ADHD) when hyperactivity is present, has a long history and is one of the most frequently diagnosed disorders among school children. The principal feature of the disorder is the inability to self-regulate focused attention. ADD/ADHD is a developmentally disabling condition that, if left untreated, persists into adolescence and adulthood. This biologically based behavioral disability has a pervasive negative impact on a wide range of adaptive functioning.

Until recently, treatment has been limited to management through the use of powerful stimulant drugs, such as methylphenidate (Ritalin), and behavior modification. Medication has significant side effects, and even the most elaborate behavior modification programs do not generalize to nontrained behaviors or carry over to the school environment (Gaddes & Edgell, 1994). Cessation of either treatment results in the rapid return of pretreatment symptoms and dysfunction. In contrast to symptom management approaches, neurotherapy (brainwave biofeedback) provides a rehabilitative approach, but may take as many as 40 to 80 sessions. In this chapter, we introduce a new hypnotic–attentional instruction procedure to facilitate normalization of EEG and to accelerate neurotherapy retraining by reducing the number of sessions required by half. We also review the most recent diagnostic considerations, prevalence issues, and traditional treatments.

DIAGNOSTIC CONSIDERATIONS

The *Diagnostic and Statistical Manual of Mental Disorders* (DSM-IV; American Psychiatric Association, 1994) reflects several major revisions regarding the diagnosis and subtyping of ADD/ADHD. Exhaustive empirical clinical trials and expert consultations have generated a much more reliable diagnosis than the earlier DSM-III-R (American Psychiatric Association, 1987). The DSM-IV criteria are more rigorously grounded in the aspects of functional impairment that constitute the disorder. It is important to remember that the diagnosis is made by an accumulation of several symptoms with a typical onset after age 7. No single symptom is required to make a diagnosis, nor is any single symptom definitive of the syndrome.

Although attention-deficit-disordered children may exhibit more neurologic soft signs in both gross and fine motor coordination, there is no specific signature on standardized neurological tests nor do they show significant memory deficits. Problems in task performance arise if the task demands require executive function processing to solve complex problems. Difficulties in organizing and controlling their own behaviors are expressed in great variability in school work or task performance. Contrary to popular notions, these children can become thoroughly absorbed and focused on certain tasks for long periods of time but not on others. Children we have seen have been able to concentrate completely on computer or reading activities for over an hour at a time, yet are unable to adequately complete chores, homework, or school tests. Such performance variability is characteristic of the attention-deficit-disordered child, adolescent, and adult (Barkley, 1990). This variability helps to explain difficulties in social functioning and the apparent 10 to 20 point lower IQ scores shown by some of these individuals in contrast to normal children or siblings (Douglas, 1983). Because of their impulsivity, ADD/ADHD children may respond prematurely without appreciating what is required by a specific task. The result is a high careless-error rate. This response pattern is shown by the high risk-taking behaviors of those with the disorder if potentially destructive or even life-threatening situations are not evaluated.

Demographics

ADD/ADHD prevalence rates range from 5–15% in community samples and 50% or higher among clinical referrals (Whalen & Henker, 1991). Prevalence appears to be increasing, especially for girls and adolescents (Szatmari, Offord, & Boyle, 1989). The DSM-IV states that the disorder is substantially more frequent in males than in females, with male-to-female ratios ranging from 4:1 to 9:1. This apparent differential prevalence rate may be erroneous. Barabasz and Barabasz (1993a, b) noted that if males and females are compared with their same-sex normative groups and appropriate controls are added for symptoms of hyperactivity and antisocial behavior, the occurrence of ADD in males and females may be equal. Females with ADD present with problems in mood, affect, and emotion, while showing considerably less difficulty than boys with aggression. Girls are more socially withdrawn and show more internalizing symptoms, such as depression and anxiety, than are found in boys (Brown, Abramowitz, Mada-Swain, Eckstrand, & Dulcan, 1989). The majority of ADHD children are referred to mental health clinics because of aggression and other forms of misbehavior that are more common in boys. ADD children without hyperactivity are more frequently shy, socially withdrawn, and moderately unpopular (Lahey, Schaughency, Frame & Straus, 1984). Because of these biases and the earlier DSM-III-R (American Psychiatric Association, 1987) diagnostic criteria favoring hyperactivity, girls may have been denied needed treatment more frequently than boys. Prevalence rates may become more balanced with the use of the new DSM-IV, which provides for subtyping of both predominantly inattentive and predominantly hyperactive impulsive patient populations.

Neurological Basis and Assessment

In contrast to a plethora of correlational studies that provide speculations about the role of food additives, dietary sugar, smoking, allergies, and alcohol use during pregnancy, considerable serious research has been progressing systematically that forms a possible basis for a neurological understanding of attention deficit disorders. The data clearly implicate frontal lobe involvement and help to provide a rationale for the use of hypnosis in neurotherapy. Frontal lobe functions are executive in nature, and are involved in developing plans and organizing resources. They also are critical in mustering inhibitory behaviors such as controlling motor behavior and inhibiting attentional focus on distractor or irrelevant stimuli. The evidence suggesting right frontal lobe dysfunction as the basis of attention deficit disorders appears to be considerable (Chelune, Ferguson, Koon, & Dickey, 1986; Gualteri & Hicks, 1985; Hynd, Semrud-Clikeman, Lorys, Novey, & Eliopulos, 1990; Lou, Henriksen, Bruhn, Borner, & Nielsen, 1989; Schaughency & Hynd, 1989; Voeller & Heilman, 1988;).

Recent research using advanced neuro-imaging morphological procedures has shown that ADD/ADHD children fail to show the normal right-greater-than-left asymmetry in the mass of the frontal lobes (Hynd, Hern, Voeller & Marshall, 1991). Consistent with this finding, computerized quantitative electroencephalographic (QEEG) analysis (referred to as "neurometric assessment" in clinical psychology practice) shows significantly greater slow wave (theta) activity and significantly less beta activity predominantly in the frontal regions for ADD/ADHD boys (Mann, Lubar, Zimmerman, Miller & Muenchen, 1992) and for ADD/ADHD girls and boys (Barabasz, Crawford, & Barabasz, 1993) compared with age- and sex-matched normals. Independent of the neurotherapy research, Chabot, Merkin, Wood, Davenport, and Serfontain (1996) conducted a comprehensive investigation of 310 children and found that those with the disorder were distinguished by excess theta relative power, especially in the frontal regions, as well as frontal and central hemispheric hypercoherence.

TREATMENT OF ADD/ADHD

Current treatments can be divided between the traditional approaches aimed at symptom management (stimulant medication, behavior modification, and cognitive–behavior therapy) and the more recent approaches focused on neuropsychological rehabilitation (neurotherapy or EEG biofeedback and active alert hypnosis or instantaneous neuronal activation procedure [INAP]).

Stimulant drugs such as methylphenidate (Ritalin) are prescribed for 600,000 to 1 million school children in the United States. A "review of reviews," conducted by 15 coauthors (Swanson et al., 1993), comprehensively examined 341 reviews and found that medication "does absolutely nothing" for 25% to 40% of children with the disorder. However, the failure rate can be greatly reduced if pretreatment QEEG neuromatic assessment is utilized. Chabat et al. (1996) showed that this methodology could distinguish with high levels of accuracy between ADD/ADHD children who responded to dextroamphetamine and those who responded to methylphenidate. For those who do respond, temporary management of overactivity and inattention can be expected, but there will be no improvement in long-term adjustment (such as improved academic achievement), nor any reduction in antisocial behaviors or arrest rates (Swanson, et al. 1993).

The side effects and limitations of stimulant medications include (a) short length of action (4–5 hours); (b) problems with the child's self-esteem due to taunting by peers; (c) stunting of growth; (d) insomnia; (e) poor eating; (f) tics; (g) cardiovascular problems; (h) development of Tourette's syndrome; (i) cognitive impairment with high doses; (j) no residual effect once medication is terminated; and (k) a small, but significant, number of cases show negative physiological side effects that do not diminish over time despite cessation of the medication (Whalen & Henker, 1991). Some side effects are dose dependent and disappear if the dose is lowered. Growth suppression effects are essentially growth delay effects, and stimulant treated ADD/ADHD children may grow up to be the same size as normals. It could also be argued that at least some of the side effects are far less impairing than the ADD/ADHD-related functional problems. Failure to take the medication as directed may pose the most significant problem. Barkley (1990) indicated that compliance rates are typically poor and particularly problematic for low socioeconomic families. Adolescents are frequently unwilling to take psychostimulants.

Behavior modification is undoubtedly the next most widely used therapy to manage the disorder. One of the strengths of the behavioral approach is the typical collaborative involvement of both parents and teachers. Starting with the seminal work of B. F. Skinner, behavior therapy researchers have published in excess of 5,000 articles, many of which are applicable directly or indirectly to the management of ADD/ADHD. Therapists train parents to use token economies and positive attention for appropriate behaviors and time out or other punishments for noncompliance (Gaddes & Edgell, 1994; Whalen & Henker, 1991). Teachers use classroom contingency management where verbal praise and other rewards are administered for appropriate attentive behaviors, and privileges are withdrawn or punishments administered for undesirable behaviors. Barkley (1990) believes that medication helps to potentiate the benefits of this approach.

Limitations of behavior modification include the following: (a) not all children respond to the treatment, (b) there is no carryover to the classroom of behaviors learned only with parents, and (c) pretreatment behaviors rapidly return to baseline or pretreatment levels upon cessation of the interventions. Probably the greatest limitation lies in the complexity of the approach and its dependence on both parental and teacher cooperation. Consistent with behavioral interventions for other disorders, failures are blamed on noncompliance (Barabasz, 1987). Firestone, Kelly, Goodman, and Davey (1981) reported that 50% of parents failed to continue behavior modification treatment. This is consistent with the noncompliance rate for most psychosocial treatments and medical treatments such as diets for diabetes.

Cognitive–behavior therapy has greater flexibility than behavior modification or medication. For example, self-talk coping skills can be taught, which should be applicable to a wide range of situations that the child might face. In theory, cognitive–behavioral therapy should go beyond symptom management by providing a basis for continued growth and rehabilitation. Unfortunately, the present adaptations of cognitive–behavioral therapy to the treatment of ADD/ADHD have produced few positive outcomes or have failed to demonstrate any lasting effects (Conte, 1991). Further research is needed before cognitive–behavioral therapy can be considered useful. Kirsch, Montgomery, and Sapirstein's (1995) meta-analysis showed that the addition of hypnosis to cognitive–behavioral therapy greatly improved treatment outcomes and long term effects. To date, research has not yet tested the addition of hypnosis to this approach in the treatment of ADD/ADHD.

Neurotherapy (EEG *feedback*) is a relatively new rehabilitative approach to the treatment of ADD/ADHD. It is reviewed here in some detail because it is directly relevant to the new hypnotic intervention presented in the case study. The goal is permanent normalization without dependence on drugs or continuous behavioral management therapy. Neurotherapy accepts the neurological basis of the disorder (i.e. frontal lobe dysfunction). Recognizing that the attention deficit disordered child, adolescent, or adult seems to produce greater EEG slow wave (theta) activity (4–8 Hz) and less beta (14–32 Hz) activity compared with normal controls, neurotherapy is intended to teach patients to normalize their brainwave responses to stimuli (Barabasz, et al, 1993, 1995; Mann, et al, 1992). The procedure is an extension of a breakthrough by Sterman and Friar (1972), who discovered that brainwave feedback made it possible to learn to inhibit epileptic seizures by enhancing low beta while simultaneously minimizing theta in patients who did not respond to medication, which is usually the treatment of choice for this population.

If a normal person is presented with an attentional task, such as reading, doing simple arithmetic, or listening to a story, his or her EEG's usually shift to the beta frequency band with an increase in magnitude with projection to the frontal (particularly right frontal) regions. In contrast, Lubar (1991) noted that persons with attention deficit disorder typically do just the opposite. Instead, they shift down into the slow theta frequency band without any significant increase in frontal activity (Barabasz et al., 1993, in press; Lubar, 1991; Mann et al., 1992). The slow activity (e.g., remaining in alpha 8–14 Hz or dropping down to theta) is characteristic of the wandering mind, nonvigilance, and unfocused thought.

Before commencing neurotherapy, a neurometric evaluation involving a computer analysis of a minimum of 19 active scalp electrode sites must be conducted to confirm or disconfirm the above reactivity to key attentional tasks. Details of this procedure are reported elsewhere (Barabasz & Barabasz, 1995). Clients who demonstrate EEG responses to attentional tasks that are characteristic of those with attention deficit disorder are appropriate candidates for neurotherapy.

In neurotherapy, EEG responses to stimuli displayed on a computer screen are real-time analyzed. Then the computer provides feedback information, in the form of visual displays and stereophonic auditory tones or verbalizations showing how well the subject is doing. Problems inherent in the EEG biofeedback apparatus of the 1970s and '80s have been overcome. Patients are now only provided with reinforcement for EEG responses that are essentially artifact-free. Recently, Allen Pope of NASA's Human Engineering Group and Edward Bogart of Lockheed Sciences developed the concept further by producing a video game that becomes more difficult as the attention deficit disordered child's brain waves show attention is waning (Pope & Bogart, 1991, in press). As in the more established forms of neurotherapy, this approach teaches children to decrease the time spent in slow wave activity and increase the time spent in the fast activity required for focused attention and concentration on tasks. Rossiter and La Vaque's (1995) controlled experimental research showed that significant improvements can be achieved after 20 sessions. However, it usually takes 40–80 sessions (40 minutes to 1 hour each) for neurofeedback therapy to produce lasting EEG and clinical changes. Follow-up neurometric and clinical assessments should be conducted upon completion of the course of treatments and at 1 month, 6 month, and 1 year follow-ups.

Chartier and Kelly (1991) reviewed the effects of neurofeedback for ADD/ADHD from over 200 children treated by Dr. Joel Lubar at the University of Tennessee, Dr. John Carter at the University of Texas, and Dr. Michael Tansey of Sommerville, New Jersey. Consistent with our own findings, Chartier and Kelly found neurofeedback training to provide significant and sometimes "dramatic" clinical improvements in children with attention deficit disorder. Using an A-B-A design, Lubar and Shouse (1977) treated groups of ADD children with the standard protocol (reinforce beta and inhibit theta). The protocol was then switched to inhibit beta and enhance theta. The subjects, parents, and teachers were kept blind regarding the switch, but within two weeks they began reporting that childrens' behaviors and attentional skills were deteriorating. Returning to the standard protocol at 4 weeks, the children, parents, and teachers noted resumption of academic and behavioral improvements.

Barkley (1992) criticized these early clinical outcome studies of neurotherapy because of small numbers of subjects, lack of appropriate control groups, ambiguous diagnostic criteria, and confounding of treatments by use of multiple interventions. Several recent experimental investigations have been conducted that address these valid criticisms.

Cartozzo, Jacobs, and Gevirtz (1995) compared a pseudo-treatment control with neurotherapy. Neurotherapy produced a significant reduction in theta and significant increases in attention and freedom from distractibility on standardized tests, whereas the control group showed a significant increase in theta and no significant changes on the test scores. Scheinbaum, Zecker, Newton, and Rosenfeld (1995) used a plausible cognitive therapy control group and found that only the neurotherapy group showed significant positive posttreatment changes on the test of variables of attention (TOVA). Rossiter and La Vaque (1995) compared neurotherapy with psychostimulant medication using 46 patients matched for age, IQ, gender, and DSM-III-R diagnoses of attention deficit hyperactivity disorder and undifferentiated attention deficit disorder. Both groups showed equivalent significant improvements on independent measures of inattention, impulsivity, and information processing. Neurotherapy was found to be an effective alternative to stimulant medication. Linden, Habib, and Radojevic (in press) found that neurotherapy produced significant increases in IQ and decreases in parental reports of inattentiveness in contrast to the control group.

Gaddes and Edgell (1994) reported that 80% of children treated show significant measurable improvements on IQ tests, standardized tests of academic achievement, and teacher–parent ratings of behavior. The series of very recent experimental investigations, noted above, seem to address Barkley's (1992) well founded concerns. A substantial body of evidence now appears to support Lubar's (1995) conclusion that neurotherapy leads to a "normalization" of behavior, enhancing both long-term academic performance and social functioning.

Limitations of neurofeedback include (a) the need for a greater number of controlled and replicated experimental studies demonstrating effects that are independent of developmental maturation and the potentially confounding effect of the therapist's and parents' attention during the course of treatments; (b) the large number of sessions (up to 80; 6–8 months) required for permanent clinical and academic changes to occur; and (c) overenthusiasm by some practitioners, who may be willing to apply the treatment on the basis of a DSM-IV diagnosis without a QEEG neurometric evaluation.

Hypnosis as an Adjunct to Neurotherapy

There are many theories of hypnosis; however, there is virtually universal agreement that hypnosis involves the subject's attentional processes (Barabasz, 1980a, 1980b, 1982, 1985; Barabasz, Baer, Sheehan, & Barabasz, 1986; Barabasz & Barabasz, 1989, 1992, 1994a, b; Barabasz, Crawford, & Barabasz, 1993; Barabasz & Lonsdale, 1983; Brown & Fromm, 1986; Crawford & Gruzelier, 1992; Hilgard, 1979; Holroyd, 1985-1986; Kirsch & Council, 1992; Lynn & Sivec, 1992). Hypnosis is a state of attention that may be focused, to exclude distractors, or diffuse, depending on the instruction (Fromm, 1987; Hilgard, 1965, 1986).

Hypnosis can also serve to facilitate the more general attentional processes involved in vigilance. Barabasz (1980b) used hypnosis to enhance military target detection in a radar simulator. Military pilot instrument flight reliability has been improved with active alert hypnosis to help optimize pilots' situational awareness with regard to cockpit navigation cues (Barabasz, 1985). Recently, Barabasz (in press) used a refined form of active alert hypnosis to enhance an airline pilot's performance in both simulator and actual flight conditions.

Most recently, the hypnotic active alert attentional instructions that previously produced behavioral human performance enhancement effects in radar operators and pilots (Barabasz, 1980b, 1985, 1993, in press) have been applied in more refined forms to modify EEG topography and enhance focused attention for reading tasks. Using 19 active electrode sites, we were able to demonstrate normalization of EEG during reading, with shifts to beta and shifts toward frontal regions following active alert hypnosis (now referred to as *instantaneous neuronal activation procedure* [INAP]) in children with ADD/ADHD (Barabasz & Barabasz, 1993; Barabasz, Crawford, & Barabasz, 1993). All of the children participating in the study were highly hypnotizable.

The INAP intervention has also demonstrated significant effects in a more carefully controlled experiment with normal young adults of average hypnotizability. Barabasz and Barabasz (1994a) embedded the procedure in an EEG neurological screening aspect of another study unrelated to hypnosis. Eleven subjects were exposed to counterbalanced conditions of waking, attentional instructions, and INAP hypnosis instructions emphasizing speed and memory retention, prior to reading parallel forms of a standardized reading comprehension test. Both attentional instructions and INAP hypnosis significantly increased beta magnitude at key frontal sites while significantly increasing reading speed, but only INAP hypnosis served to significantly increase reading comprehension performance. Unfortunately, testing of long-term effects was beyond the scope of the study.

Case 1 is presented in abbreviated form (complete report in Barabasz & Barabasz, in press) to provide an understanding of the intervention and its usual effects, so that these can be contrasted with the new hypnotic approach to neurotherapy. Case 2 represents an attempt to integrate INAP hypnosis with standardized neurotherapy training protocols in the treatment of attention deficit disorder.

CASE 1—STANDARD NEUROTHERAPY WITHOUT HYPNOSIS

Mike (pseudonym), who was 8 years old when we saw him, had been on Ritalin since the age of 6 1/2 years, when he was diagnosed as having ADHD by a child psychologist. Mike's parents were trained in behavior modification for the disorder. Despite medication, understanding, and special attention from his health care providers, parents, and teachers, Mike had to repeat the 2nd grade because of failing grades and impulsive behaviors.

Assessment

Mike met DSM-III-R (and as later reviewed DSM-IV) criteria for ADHD. Mike's Stanford Hypnotic Clinical Scale for Children (SHCS:C) (Morgan & Hilgard, 1978) score was 4. His Wechsler Intelligence Scale for Children III (WISC-III) revealed a verbal IQ of 92 and a performance IQ of 78. His Bender motor gestalt test performance was consistent with that of a 5-year-old.

Our neurometric EEG assessment of Mike was conducted using our standardized procedure with 19 active electrode sites (see Barabasz & Barabasz, in press). Mike showed brain wave patterns characteristic of attention deficit disorder in response to 5 of the 6 attentional task conditions. Compared with normal responding and to the patient's own eyes-closed record, Mike showed excessive theta (3 1/2–7 1/2 Hz.) and deficient beta (13 1/2–32 Hz.) activity at the frontal regions, particularly the right frontal FP2 site, and insufficient sensory motor rhythm (SMR) (12–20 Hz) at the central CZ site.

Treatment

Mike was seen 2 to 3 times per week for a total of 67 single-channel (right frontal pole FP2) neurofeedback training sessions, using the above apparatus and Lexicor Medical Technologies, Boulder, Colorado, BIOLEX Software. In each session, both Mike and the psychologist were provided with instantaneous visual and auditory feedback as to the patient's EEG activity. Audio tones combined with simultaneous color computer monitor displays were provided, and the psychologist provided verbal reinforcement for attending behavior coincident with beta enhancement and theta inhibition.

The Lexicor BIOLEX package we use makes it possible to both specify and interactively observe processed EEG based on continuous performance of fast Fourier transforms. Progress in each session is adapted to the patient's own level. The clinician adjusts criteria such as inhibit levels and thresholds, as well as visual displays and audio feedback characteristics, to meet the unique needs and progress levels of each patient. EEG frequencies and band information are computed continuously to provide smooth feedback.

By the 25th session, Mike began to produce beta while inhibiting shifts to theta. Parents' reports and responses on the attention deficit disorders evaluation scale (ADDES; McCarney, 1989) showed slight improvement but little if any improvements were noted in general behavior or academic achievement.

Academic achievement reflected by teachers' grades and comments showed significant improvement by session 45, as did parent reports and ADDES scores. A full neurometric assessment confirmed that Mike had made significant improvement in the ability to enhance frontal beta and central SMR.

Neurofeedback continued for 22 additional sessions (67 total). Mike's neurometric assessment at termination could not be differentiated from normal. School grades had gone from failing to C's (arithmetic), B's (reading and spelling), and A's (science and social studies).

Outcome and Follow-Up Data

Parent and teacher forms of the ADDES revealed dramatic improvements in all measured areas. Mike's WISC-III verbal score had increased 11 points to 103, and his performance IQ rose 17 points to 94. Ritalin had been terminated completely during his last 2 months of treatment. Mike's self-esteem seemed greatly enhanced: "I can do it now all by myself and no more pills at school." The academic and behavioral improvements had also been maintained.

CASE 2—NEUROTHERAPY WITH INAP HYPNOSIS

Juan (pseudonym) was 9 years old when we first saw him. He had been diagnosed as having ADHD by a school psychologist–counselor team 2 years earlier. Ritalin, prescribed by a family physician, had been the primary form of treatment for the past 20 months. As in Case 1, failing grades and impulsive–aggressive behavior resulted in repeating a grade (3rd) and placement in the "resource room," where a teacher with training in special education had a reduced class size and support for implementation of a token-economy behavior modification program.

Juan's father held a master's degree in business administration. His mother was a high school graduate who had been admitted to college but never attended due to a first marriage pregnancy that ended in a miscarriage. Juan was the product of the second pregnancy of his mother's first marriage, which ended in abandonment by his biological father before Juan reached the age of 1 year. Juan had two sisters, age 6 and 7, from his mother's current marriage. Juan's father attended only the initial interview session, during which time he expressed his disappointment with Juan's academic failures and attentional problems. He was quick to contrast Juan with his half-sisters who were described as "perfectly behaved 'A' pupils." Juan's mother had had experience as a teacher's aide years ago. She felt the experience helped her to remain dedicated to the resource room behavior modification program despite its apparent minimal effects. She worried about the use of Ritalin but noted "he can be impossible when he's off the drug for more than half a day."

Assessment

Juan met DSM-III-R (and as later reviewed DSM-IV) criteria for ADHD. Juan's SHCS:C score was 4. His WISC-III verbal IQ was 84 and his performance IQ was 80. As in the previous case, Juan's Bender motor gestalt test was consistent with significantly younger normal children. Juan's impulsive responses to the Bender cards may have contributed to this clinical assessment. The parent report form of the ADDES was consistent with ADHD and showed more severe symptomatology than was apparent in Case 1.

Neurometric assessment was carried out using the identical procedures described in Case 1. No signs of pathology were observed for hyperventilation, photic flash, or eyes-open resting conditions. Quantitative EEG evaluations of the responses to the attentional tasks revealed brainwave patterns that were clearly characteristic of attention deficit disorder and similar to Case 1's initial evaluation. Beta activity was remarkably greater during Juan's eyes-closed resting condition than any of the five tasks demanding focused attention. Juan showed excessive theta and deficient beta when he was required to attend to the various tasks, particularly at the frontal sites. A topographic map comparison between Cases 1 and 2 appeared to indicate that Juan was more greatly impaired than Mike at central and frontal regions.

Treatment

Juan was seen for a total of just 32 neurotherapy sessions, which in this case included INAP hypnosis as an adjunct to the computer feedback. Juan's neurofeedback protocol followed our standardized procedure as described for Case 1.

INAP hypnosis is an experimental clinical procedure developed to enhance vigilance performance for either focused attention or optimal situational awareness, depending on the specific hypnotic instructions given (Barabasz, 1985; Barabasz & Barabasz, 1993b, 1994a). As discussed earlier in this chapter, experimentally controlled studies show that INAP increased frontal EEG beta activity independent of neurofeedback (Barabasz & Barabasz, 1993b; 1994a, b; Barabasz, Crawford, & Barabasz, 1993). Thus far our INAP research has been primarily aimed at the achievement of immediate attentional effects with those of average to high hypnotizability. Long-term effects and potential effects for individuals with below average hypnotizability scores remain to be tested. Because of these limitations on our knowledge of INAP's effects, the procedure was used repeatedly during Juan's neurofeedback therapy.

Using standard procedure, INAP was conducted in two distinct phases (Barabasz & Barabasz , 1994a, b). In the training phase, Juan was instructed to roll his eyes up, as if trying to look at his forehead. Then his eyes were led to this position by instructions to focus on the psychologist's thumb. The thumb was then moved slowly from 10–15 cm in front of Juan's nose to the approximate center of his forehead. Speed of movement was carefully coordinated with the patient's ability to follow without swimming of the eyes or obvious loss of focus. If eyes darted or focus was lost the procedure was reinitiated. Normal adults seldom have a problem with this procedure (Barabasz & Barabasz, 1994b), but clinical experience and patience may need to be brought to bear in the treatment of hyperactive children to get their eyes as fully rolled up as possible and then kept steadily rolled up, as required for successful INAP effects. Initially, Juan required only two trials. However, in sessions 9 through 12 during the later half of the treatment hour, Juan required 3–5 trials and verbal reinforcement ("good, that's it" or "good job") to maintain an eyes-steady rolled-up position for about one third of the INAP inductions. Once the eyes were fully and steadily rolled up, instructions were given to take notice of breathing and of the relaxation, confidence, and special alertness felt at this point.

Once subjective signs of hypnosis were observed by the clinician, the patient was asked to raise a finger upon perception of the suggested responses: "Juan, just lift a finger on this hand [clinician touched patient's left hand] when you feel the comfortable relaxation and special alertness." Upon observation of the patient's signal, which occurred within 5–10 seconds, the patient was given attentional process specific suggestions such as "in this special state of alertness you will be able to focus your attention anyway you like, and you can concentrate as completely as you desire."

In the adult reading speed and comprehension enhancement study we (Barabasz & Barabasz, 1994a, b) used the suggestion, "Now in this special state of alertness, you will be calm and confident—finding it easier to concentrate completely—reading faster than ever, and retaining what you read." Variations of these suggestions were used with Juan. Upon completion of the suggestion, he was told to let his eyes roll down and enjoy the feelings. Then the specific attentional task was begun. Once the patient began to learn exactly what each of the graphic video feedback displays represented (e.g., beta, theta), suggestions were tailored to specific levels of understanding that emphasized "more and better (higher amplitude) beta, less theta." As Juan progressed in his later sessions, he was able to use INAP on his own (self-hypnosis) and the above suggestions to excellent effect.

In contrast to Mike, little progress was made in the first two sessions owing, we believe, to the use of time for INAP introduction and practice. Remarkably, during sessions 3–12, where INAP was used before each EEG feedback computer trial, Juan's progress was better than twice the rate of Mike. Despite the apparent greater severity of ADHD symptoms, Juan doubled Mike's times on task in session by session comparisons and began to show measurable EEG changes in the desired direction by session 11–12.

To provide an A-B-A clinical test of INAP effects, sessions 13, 14, and 15 did not include INAP. Progress stagnated. There were no significant improvements in time on task or in enhancement of frontal beta with inhibition of theta from the beginning of session 13 to the end of session 15. Session outcome data comparisons were made by a psychologist blind to the alternation of treatments. INAP was reintroduced in session 16. Juan responded by immediately increasing his average time on task by nearly 50% with a 10% increase in beta production, while maintaining theta inhibition during all above-threshold beta scoring periods.

Coincident with sessions 18–20, Juan's mother reported the best report card she had ever seen and noted that Juan was back in the regular classroom on a trial basis. Medication vacation periods, as ordered by Juan's family physician, were no longer filled with the pretreatment level of impulsive and noncooperative behaviors.

At session 21 we commenced the final phase of INAP (Barabasz & Barabasz, 1994b), where INAP is self-induced by the patient and practiced in the office. By the end of the session Juan was using the procedure before each task without intervention by the therapist. A medication free (24 hours) neurometric assessment conducted 2 days later revealed significant improvements toward beta–theta normalization (beta-theta ratios greater than 2/2.5 to 1) in response to all attentional tasks.

Outcome and Follow-Up

Neurometric assessment results after session 32 showed essentially normal responding. Ritalin had been terminated "on a trial basis" by session 26, but never resumed. Parent and teacher forms of the ADDES showed dramatic improvements in all areas, as did teachers' subjective deportment ratings. Juan's mother remarked that "he does his chores now even better than his sisters, and you hardly have to ever remind him now, and we don't have to mess with the tokens (behavior modification) anymore." Juan's WISC-III verbal score increased 9 points to 93, and his performance score rose 21 points to 101. He felt proud to be in a regular class at school. Success at after-school sports activities was also noted; peers had, for the first time, asked him to participate. Juan's grades had gone from failing to average in all subjects. As in Case 1, follow-up neurometric assessment at 6 and 12 months showed normal beta–theta responses to all attentional tasks. His mother's reports of school performance showed continued improvements in grades, deportment reports, and social relationships. Juan's father had "become more involved" and was reportedly planning to take Juan to a major league baseball game.

DISCUSSION

Hypnosis is known to alter attentional processes, and recent experiments demonstrate that INAP significantly enhances EEG beta as well as attentional performance in normal young adults. Consideration of these data in the broader context of the neurological basis of attention deficit disorder led to our hypothesis that INAP would serve as an adjunct to standard neurotherapy with verbal reinforcement for appropriate beta–theta responses by significantly improving beta and theta production, thereby decreasing the length of treatment.

Case 1 and Case 2 were chosen from our clinical experience because of matching for gender and hypnotizability scores. The patients were also close in age and similar in verbal and performance IQs. Both patients had also failed a grade as a direct effect of their attention deficit disorder, and both began treatment with us while on stimulant medication. Families were intact, and both had histories of active parental participation in behavior modification programs over 2-year periods, with little if any positive effects. The cases were dissimilar in that Juan (Case 2) represents an ethnic minority (Mexican-American) with symptomatology which was somewhat more severe than Case 1 (Mike).

Using the standard neurotherapy protocol without hypnosis, Mike completed the treatment without need for maintenance sessions after 67 sessions (2–3 per week). After this very typical course, Mike's EEG theta–beta ratios were consistent with normals in response to attentional tasks. Medication was no longer used, and significant gains in IQ, school grades, and parent–teacher deportment ratings had been realized. All gains were maintained at a 1-year follow-up.

INAP hypnosis used in conjunction with neurotherapy for Juan resulted in outcomes equivalent to or better than those obtained with Mike. In contrast to Mike, the addition of INAP hypnosis appeared to be the key therapeutic ingredient to produce these same lasting positive effects in only 32 (2–3 per week) sessions. It is especially noteworthy that the progress in the enhancement of frontal beta and reduction of theta stagnated in sessions when INAP was not used (sessions 13–15) and resumed upon reinitiation of INAP. We speculate that had the A-B-A test not been incorporated into Juan's treatment, the number of sessions required to meet EEG and behavioral normalization criteria might have been even further reduced.

Our continued clinical tests of INAP following Juan's treatment have produced additional findings that may be useful to clinicians. Juan's treatment included a procedure that asked him to confirm experiencing feelings of relaxation, confidence, and special alertness by raising a finger during the INAP inductions. We no longer see the need for this additional procedure because it appears to have no measurable effect on the beta enhancement produced by INAP, nor does it seem to have any unique value in building hypnotic rapport. An alternative procedure appears to be helpful when treating patients who have special difficulties with obtaining or maintaining an eyes-rolled-up position. Normally, the patient is asked to focus on the clinician's stationary thumb held 10–15 cm in front of the patient's nose. Then the patient's eyes are led to the rolled-up position by following the clinician's slow movement to the center of the patient's forehead. An alternative to this method is to continuously wiggle the first digit (index finger) to help maintain the patient's focus and attentiveness throughout the upward movement of the hand, which is kept at 10–15 cm from the patient's head rather than descending to the patient's forehead. This variation of the technique can be used alternately with the original procedure or exclusively with patients experiencing difficulty in maintaining eyes rolled up for the minimum period of 30 seconds.

Success or failure of INAP induction is easily determined on the basis of QEEG criteria. Using a simple QEEG feedback protocol, with frontal electrode placement, the increase in beta and decrease in theta from pre- to post-INAP should be obvious in terms of time in beta and theta production.

One of the criticisms of neurotherapy (Barkley, 1992) has been the lack of control for maturation during the heretofore lengthy, 40–80-session and 5–8-month course of treatment. Barkley argued that the successful alleviation of the negative responses of those with attention deficit disorder may not be due to neurotherapy, but rather simply to a "growing out of it" effect coincident with the long treatment. Apparently, this issue has not been raised with respect to the traditional stimulant medication and behavior modification treatments because the goal of these treatments has been limited to immediate symptom management. Even after "successful" treatment, the patient rapidly returns to baseline behavior upon cessation of the intervention. Assuming that further clinical trials and experimental research continue to support the substantial effect of INAP's reduction in treatment duration, the maturation position becomes less defensible.

Perhaps the greatest limitation of our knowledge of INAP effects in the treatment of attention deficit disorder lies in our inability to directly tie its clearly demonstrable effect on EEG beta–theta ratios to hypnosis. Just because we administer what we believe to be a type of active alert hypnotic induction and then observe effects in the predicted direction by no means demonstrates that such effects are due to hypnosis per se. As noted in our work on experimental and clinical research design considerations (Barabasz & Barabasz, 1992), little can be said about the specificity of hypnosis if hypnotizability is not measured. The cases we presented were both moderately high in hypnotizabilty as determined by the SHCS:C. Children with ADD/ADHD and low hypnotizability scores are difficult to find and the only rigorously controlled experimental research on INAP (Barabasz & Barabasz, 1994a, b) used moderately hypnotizable adults. This means that thus far we do not know whether hypnosis per se can be viewed as the causal factor. Perhaps other nonhypnotic aspects of INAP account for the significant changes observed in Juan's case. Further research is needed employing subjects of both high and low hypnotizability.

Of course, further research is essential to the evaluation of the efficacy of neurotherapy as well. At the present time the empirical basis for neurofeedback is less than that for medication for short-term gains, for most clients. Just as placebo effects have been found in ADD/ADHD medication studies, neurotherapy is also likely to produce placebo effects working in combination with the sometimes intense therapeutic relationships that can develop among clinicians, ADHD children, and their often dedicated parents. Neurotherapy clinical outcomes and the very recent experimentally controlled studies are very promising, but more work is needed to document the effectiveness of neurotherapy and the potential of INAP as an adjunctive procedure.

REFERENCES

American Psychiatric Association. (1987). *Diagnostic and statistical manual for mental disorders* (3rd ed., Rev.). Washington, DC: Author.

American Psychiatric Association. (1994). *Diagnostic and statistical manual for mental disorders* (4th ed.). Washington DC: Author.

Barabasz, A. (1980a). EEG alpha, skin conductance and hypnotizability in Antarctica. *International Journal of Clinical and Experimental Hypnosis, 28,* 63–74.

Barabasz, A. (1980b). Effects of hypnosis and perceptual deprivation on vigilance in a simulated radar target detection task. *Perceptual and Motor Skills, 50,* 19–24.

Barabasz, A. (1982). Restricted environmental stimulation and the enhancement of hypnotizability: EEG alpha, skin conductance, and temperature responses. *International Journal of Clinical and Experimental Hypnosis, 30,* 147–166.

Barabasz, A. (1985). Enhancement of military pilot reliability by hypnosis and psychophysiological monitoring: In-flight and simulator data. *Aviation, Space and Environmental Medicine,* March, 248–250.

Barabasz, A. (1993, February). *Presidential address: Antarctic isolation and attentional processes—Research implications for practitioners.* Presented at the Fifth International Conference on Restricted Environmental Stimulation Therapy, Seattle, WA.

Barabasz, A. (in press). Instantaneous neuronal activation procedure (INAP): Reduced stimulation and psychophysiological monitoring in the treatment of phobias. *Experimentalle und Klinische Hypnose.*

Barabasz, A., Baer, L., Sheehan, D. V., & Barabasz, M. (1986). A three year follow-up of hypnosis and restricted environmental stimulation therapy for smoking. *International Journal of Clinical and Experimental Hypnosis, 34,* 169–181.

Barabasz, A., & Barabasz, M. (1989). Effects of restricted environmental stimulation: Enhancement of hypnotizability for experimental and chronic pain control. *International Journal of Clinical and Experimental Hypnosis, 37,* 217–223.

Barabasz, A., & Barabasz, M. (1992). Research design considerations. In E. Fromm & M. Nash (Eds.), *Contemporary Hypnosis Research* (pp. 173–200). New York: Guilford Press.

Barabasz, A., & Barabasz, M. (Eds.). (1993a). *Clinical and experimental restricted environmental stimulation: New developments and perspectives.* New York: Springer-Verlag.

Barabasz, A., & Barabasz, M. (1993b, November). *Neurometric assessment of attention deficit disorders, neurofeedback and active alert hypnosis.* Paper presented at the Portland Academy of Hypnosis, Portland, OR.

Barabasz, A., & Barabasz, M. (1994a, October). *EEG responses to a reading comprehension task during active alert hypnosis and waking states.* Paper presented at the annual Scientific Meeting of the Society for Clinical and Experimental Hypnosis, San Francisco.

Barabasz, A., & Barabasz, M. (1994b, August). Effects of focused attention on EEG topography. In Jan Wickram (Chair), *Symposium: Behavioral Medicine, Psychophysiology and Hypnosis.* Symposium conducted at the annual convention of the American Psychological Association, Los Angeles, CA.

Barabasz, A., & Barabasz, M. (1995). Attention deficit hyperactivity disorder: Neurological basis and treatment alternatives. *Journal of Neurotherapy, 1,* 1–10.

Barabasz, M., & Barabasz, A. (in press). Attention deficit disorder: Diagnosis, etiology and treatment. *Child Study Journal—Special Issue on Attention-Deficit Disorder.*

Barabasz, A., Crawford, H., & Barabasz, M. (1993, October). *EEG topographic map differences in attention deficit disordered and normal children: Moderating effects from focused active alert instructions during reading, math and listening tasks.* Presented at the annual meeting of the Society for Psychophysiological Research, Rottach-Egern, Germany.

Barabasz, A., & Lonsdale, C. (1983). Effects of hypnosis on P300 olfactory evoked potential amplitudes. *Journal of Abnormal Psychology, 92,* 520–525.

Barabasz, M. (1987). Trichotillomania: A new treatment. *International Journal of Clinical and Experimental Hypnosis, 35,* 146–154.

Barkley, R. A. (1990). *Attention deficit hyperactivity disorder: A handbook for diagnosis and treatment.* New York: Guilford Press.

Barkley, R. A. (1992). Is EEG biofeedback treatment effective for ADHD children? *Ch.A.D.D.er Box,* 5–11.

Brown, D., & Fromm, E. (1986). *Hypnotherapy and hypnoanalysis.* Hillsdale, NJ: Erlbaum.

Brown, R. T., Abramowitz, A. J., Mada-Swain, A., Eckstrand, D., & Dulcan, M. (1989, October). *ADHD gender differences in a clinic referred sample.* Paper presented at the annual meeting of the American Academy of Child & Adolescent Psychiatry, New York,.

Cartozzo, H. A., Jacobs, D., & Gevirtz, R. N. (1995). EEG biofeedback and the remediation of ADHD symptomatology: A controlled treatment outcome study. *Proceedings of the 26th Annual Meeting of the Association for Applied Psychophysiology and Biofeedback, USA, 21*–25.

Chabot, R. J., Merkin, H., Wood, L. M., Davenport, T. L., & Serfontein, G. (1996). Sensitivity and specificity of QEEG in children with attention deficit or specific developmental learning disorders. *Clinical Electroencephalography, 27,* 26–33.

Chartier, D., & Kelly, N. (1991, August). *Neurofeedback treatment of attention deficit-hyperactivity disorder.* Grand Rounds Presentation, Rex Hospital, Raleigh, NC.

Chelune, G. J., Ferguson, W., Koon, R., & Dickey, T. O. (1986). Frontal lobe disinhibition in attention deficit disorder. *Child Psychiatry and Human Development, 16,* 221–232.

Conte, R. (1991). Attention disorders. In B. Wong (Ed.), *Learning about learning disabilities* (pp. 60–96). New York: Academic Press.

Crawford, H. J., & Gruzelier, J. H. (1992). A midstream view of the neuropsychophysiology of hypnosis: Recent research and future directions. In E. Fromm & M. Nash (Eds.), *Contemporary Hypnosis Research* (pp. 227–266). New York: Guilford Press.

Douglas, V. I. (1983). Attention and cognitive problems. In M. Rutter (Ed.), *Developmental Neuropsychiatry.* New York: Guilford.

Firestone, P., Kelly, M. J., Goodman, J. T., & Davey, J. (1981). Differential effects of parent training and stimulant medication with hyperactives. *Journal of the American Academy of Child Psychiatry, 20,* 135–147.

Fromm, E. (1987). Significant developments in hypnosis during the past 25 years. *International Journal of Clinical and Experimental Hypnosis, 35,* 215–230.

Gaddes, W. H., & Edgell, D. (1994). *Learning disabilities and brain function.* New York: Springer-Verlag.

Gualteri, C. T., & Hicks, R. E. (1985). Neuropharmacology of methylphenidate and a neural substitute for childhood hyperactivity. *Psychiatric Clinics of North America, 8,* 875–892.

Hilgard, E. R. (1965). *Hypnotic susceptibility,* New York: Harcourt.

Hilgard, E. R. (1979). Consciousness and control: Lessons from hypnosis. *Australian Journal of Clinical and Experimental Hypnosis, 7,* 107–115.

Hilgard, E. R. (1986). *Divided consciousness: Multiple controls in human thought and action* (Rev. ed.). New York: Wiley.

Holroyd, J. (1985–1986). Hypnosis applications in psychological research. *Imagination, Cognition and Personality, 5,* 103–115.

Hynd, G. W., Hern, K. L., Voeller, K. K., & Marshall, R. M. (1991). Neurobiological basis of attention–deficit hyperactivity disorder (ADHD). *School Psychology Review, 20,* 174–186.

Hynd, G. W., Semrud-Clikeman, M., Lorys, A., Novey, E. S., & Eliopulos, D. (1990). Brain morphology in developmental dyslexia and attention deficit disorder/hyperactivity. *Archives of Neurology, 47,* 919–926.

Kirsch, I., & Council, J. R. (1992). Situational and personality correlates of hypnotic responsiveness. In E. Fromm & M. Nash, (Eds.), *Contemporary Hypnosis Research* (pp. 267–291). New York: Guilford Press.

Kirsch, I., Montgomery, G., & Sapirstein, G. (1995). Hypnosis as an adjunct to cognitive-behavioral psychotherapy: A meta-analysis. *Journal of Consulting and Clinical Psychology, 63,* 214–220.

Lahey, B. B., Schaughency, E. A., Frame, C. C., & Straus, C. C. (1984). Teacher rating of attention problems in children experimentally classified as exhibiting attention deficit disorders with and without hyperactivity. *Journal of the American Academy of Child and Adolescent Child Psychiatry, 23,* 302–309.

Linden, M., Habib, T., & Radojevic, V. (in press). A controlled study of EEG biofeedback effects on cognitive and behavioral measures with attention-deficit disorder and learning disabled children. *Biofeedback and Self-Regulation.*

Lou, H. C., Henriksen, L., Bruhn, P., Borner, H., & Nielsen, J. (1989). Striatal dysfunction in attention deficit and hyperkinetic disorder. *Archives of Neurology, 46,* 48–52.

Lubar, J. F. (1991). Discourse on the development of EEG diagnostics and biofeedback for attention-deficit/hyperactivity disorders. *Biofeedback and Self-Regulation, 16,* 201–225.

Lubar, J. F. (1995). Neurofeedback for the management of attention-deficit/hyperactivity disorder. In M. S. Schwartz & Associates (Eds.), *Biofeedback: A Practitioners Guide* (2nd ed., pp. 493–522). New York : Guilford Press.

Lubar, J. F., & Shouse, M. N. (1977). Use of biofeedback and the treatment of seizure disorders and hyperactivity. *Advances in Child Clinical Psychology, 1,* 204–251.

Lynn, S. J. & Sivec, H. (1992). The hypnotizable subject as a creative problem-solving agent. In E. Fromm & M. Nash, (Eds.) , *Contemporary Hypnosis Research* (pp. 292–333). New York: Guilford Press.

Mann, C. A., Lubar, J. F., Zimmerman, A. W., Miller, C.A., & Muenchen, R. A. (1992). Quantitative analysis of EEG in boys with attention deficit hyperactivity disorder: Controlled study with clinical implications. *Pediatric Neurology, 8,* 30–36.

McCarney, S. B. (1989). *Attention deficit disorders evaluation scale.* Columbia, MO: Hawthorne Educational Services.

Morgan, A. H. & Hilgard, E. R. (1978). The Stanford hypnotic clinical scale for children. *American Journal of Clinical Hypnosis, 21,* 148–169.

Pope, A. T., & Bogart, E. H. (1991, December). Extended attention span training system. *Technology 2001 Conference Proceedings, San Jose, CA,* 368–374.

Pope, A. T. & Bogart, E. H. (in press). Extended attention span training system: Video game neurotherapy for attention deficit disorder. *Child Study Journal—Special Issue on Attention-Deficit Disorder.*

Rossiter, R. R., & La Vaque, T. J. (1995). A comparison of EEG biofeedback and psychostimulants in treating attention deficit/hyperactivity disorders. *Journal of Neurotherapy, 1,* 48–59.

Schaughency, E. A., & Hynd, G. W. (1989). Attention and impulse control in attention deficit disorders (ADD). *Learning and Individual Differences, 1,* 423–449.

Scheinbaum, S., Zecker, S., Newton, C. J., & Rosenfeld, P. (1995). A controlled study of EEG biofeedback as a treatment for attention-deficit disorders. *Proceedings of the 26th Annual Meeting of the Association for Applied Psychophysiology and Biofeedback, USA,* 131–134.

Sterman, M. B., & Friar, L. (1972). Suppression of seizures in an epileptic following sensorimotor EEG feedback training. *Electroencephalography & Clinical Neurophysiology, 33,* 89–95.

Swanson, J., McBurnett, T., Wigal, T., Pfiffner, L., Lerner, M., Williams, L., Christian, D., Tamm, L., Willcutt, E., Crowley, K., Clevenger, W., Khouzam, N., Woo, C., Crinella, F., & Fisher, T. (1993). Effect of stimulant medication on children with attention deficit disorder: A "review of reviews." *Exceptional Children, 60,* 2, 154–162.

Szatmari, P., Offord, D. R., Boyle, M. H. (1989). Correlates, associates impairments, and patterns of service utilization of children with attention deficit disorders: Findings from the Ontario Child Health Study. *Journal of Child Psychiatry, 30,* 205–217.

Voeller, K. K. S., & Heilman, K. (1988). Attention deficit disorder in children: A neglect syndrome? *Neurology, 38,* 806–808.

Whalen, C. K., & Henker, B. (1991). Therapies for hyperactive children: Comparisons, combinations, and compromises. *Journal of Consulting and Clinical Psychology, 59*(1), 126–137.

14

HYPNOTHERAPY IN THE TREATMENT OF ADOLESCENT ENURESIS

EDMUND THOMAS DOWD

Enuresis is a complex and multifaceted problem that has physical, psychological, and social–relationship aspects. Because of this complexity, a thorough history of the presenting problem, as well as the relationship and family context in which it is embedded, should be taken prior to actual treatment. For example, enuresis may be caused by such physical problems as a small bladder capacity, by psychological factors such as emotional immaturity or hostility towards parent or self, or by relationship problems such as sibling rivalry or rebellion against parents; the cause often includes strong manifestations of secondary gain (Calof, 1982; Gibbons, 1979; Kroger, 1977). Few problems illustrate more graphically the dictum that hypnosis is a specialized technique, not a therapy itself, and should be used as an adjunctive intervention within a complete psychological and perhaps medical treatment package. It is especially important that a physical and possibly a neurological examination be conducted before beginning psychological treatment, so that the possibility of these problems can be ruled out (Kroger & Fetzler, 1976).

BACKGROUND INFORMATION

For the purposes of this case presentation, the client will be referred to as "John Smith" and his parents as "Mr. and Mrs. Smith," although those were not their real names. John was referred to me for hypnosis treatment by another professional. I should note that a specific referral for hypnosis is not uncommon for one who is known to practice hypnotherapy. Hypnosis is often viewed as "magic" or as a last resort where other treatments have failed (e.g., "You're our last hope, doctor!"), and the hypnotherapist should be wary of being "set up" for possible failure. John was a 14-year-old boy who seemed to be both socially and physically immature. He spoke little and did not look at me, although he did not appear to be hostile and resistant in other ways. Mr. Smith was a tall, forceful, and athletic-looking man, who clearly dominated the interview. Although he had definite opinions about the nature and cause of John's problem, he did not seem resistant to listening to and considering other opinions. Mrs. Smith was not nearly as articulate or as extroverted as her husband and deferred to him on most issues. However, he often seemed to covertly solicit her approval or at least her nonverbal acquiescence. Both parents appeared to be genuinely concerned about their son, and the family in general seemed to be supportive and close-knit. The family did not appear to be obviously distressed or dysfunctional.

The following information was gleaned from two sessions alone with Mr. and Mrs. Smith. They described John as mentally mature but socially immature, as introverted and eager to please, and as doing well in school. He was active in sports and similar activities and generally seemed to have a good relationship with his parents, his teachers, and other students at school. However, they did mention that he had some difficulty expressing anger and would often express it indirectly by such activities as slamming doors. Otherwise, he appeared to be a well-adjusted, although shy, boy.

John had been enuretic all his life and Mr. and Mrs. Smith had taken him to a urologist on several occasions. These evaluations had indicated no medical problems, but the parents were told that John had a small bladder. He had been given medication at various times for enuresis, but the problem had persisted (although it was reduced), and the medication had made him even more introverted and had given him headaches. Therefore, it had been discontinued. They had not taken John to a urologist recently and had never taken him to a psychologist.

The following family history was elicited. John was adopted as a baby, a fact that Mr. and Mrs. Smith had never attempted to hide from him. John had one other sibling, a brother (who will be called Joe) who was four years younger. Joe in several ways was quite different from John, being described by the parents as extroverted, somewhat loud, and lazy. John was the better student, whereas Joe had more friends. There did appear to be conflict between the brothers, which the parents described as "teasing, competition, and fights." Joe had never been enuretic but was quite aware of John's problem and would often tease him about it. Mr. and Mrs. Smith seemed aware of the potential for sibling rivalry and stated that they tried hard not to show favoritism towards either boy.

The parents described their own relationship as good. Mr. Smith traveled extensively, so that Mrs. Smith was in charge of the household for extended periods of time. Although there did not appear to be many disagreements over family life, Mrs. Smith did feel that the conflict between John and Joe was excessive, whereas Mr. Smith did not. There was, however, a significant disagreement regarding John's problem. Mr. Smith saw the enuresis as John's fault and felt that "he could stop it if he really wanted to." Mrs. Smith, on the other hand, thought that it was not John's fault and that Mr. Smith became excessively angry over it.

I next inquired about the immediate context in which the enuresis typically occurred. Often, either Mr. or Mrs. Smith would awaken John during the night so that he could urinate; if they did, he would not wet the bed. Otherwise, he typically wet the bed between midnight and 3 a.m. This would awaken him and he would either sleep on the floor for the rest of the night or go to his mother's room and sleep with her (usually the latter). In the morning, Mrs. Smith would change and wash John's sheets. Mr. Smith did not sleep with his wife, but slept in a separate room on another floor. He said that the reason was that he preferred the waterbed in that room, which his wife did not like. Mr. Smith felt that John's problem was due to a small bladder and an excessive intake of sugar. Mrs. Smith did not agree, but, rather than confront her husband directly, she quietly arranged to supply John with cookies, ice cream, and soda each evening. Because of Mr. Smith's frequent absences, this was not difficult.

I also saw John individually for one session to determine his view of the problem. He appeared relatively undistressed by it, but did agree that he would like to "get rid of it" because of the teasing by his younger brother and because it prevented him from spending nights at his friends' houses. Although it was becoming increasingly uncomfortable as he grew older, he still seemed to see it as someone else's concern. He said that he typically watched TV in the room that he shared with his brother until about 10:30 P.M., drank a soda, and went to bed. He said that he urinated frequently during the day. He characterized his relations with his brother as "OK," but said that they fought a lot. He said that, although he loved both his mother and his father, he felt closer to his mother.

PROBLEM CONCEPTUALIZATION

Calof (1982) has elegantly described how psychosomatic problems in children can be caused by functional inclusion in the spousal system, resulting in a triangulation of mother, father, and child. In this frame of reference, the child's problem is viewed as an expression of marital conflict. This case seemed to fit that model well. In certain ways, the bond between John and his mother appeared to be stronger than the bond between Mr. and Mrs. Smith. Mr. Smith's frequent absences from home, the fact that they slept in separate bedrooms, Mrs. Smith's apparent protection and rescuing of John (as well as Joe) from his father, and her covert alliance in providing John with the nighttime snacks, all seemed to support this conceptualization. This was exacerbated by Mrs. Smith's uncomfortableness with conflict, thus leading her to sabotage her husband's wishes rather than confront him directly about their disagreements. Previous medical assessment had indicated that the problem was likely to be psychosomatic, exacerbated by the existence of a small bladder. John's enuresis could therefore be seen as an attempt to bond himself more closely with his mother, especially as it gave him a reason to sleep in her bed. In addition, part of the family's energy was focused on John's problem, thus providing him with attention and concern that he might not otherwise have had.

John's behavior had also effectively maintained the enuresis in several ways. Not only did he drink fluids just before bedtime, he also urinated frequently throughout the day, thus preventing mature bladder-training from occurring. However, his enuresis was becoming distressing to John in a way that it had not been before. Not only was he increasingly the butt of his brother's teasing, but it was preventing him from enjoying the company of his friends at "sleep-overs," a popular adolescent pastime. In addition, the marital conflicts between the parents appeared to be relatively circumscribed and localized in the area of child-rearing practices and Mrs. Smith's avoidance of conflict. Although this incident was distressing to them, they seemed to have a good relationship in general. Although Mr. Smith was forceful and articulate, he was not dogmatic and I found him to be genuinely interested in what I had to say. Thus, although the enuretic behavior had been effectively maintained in the past by aspects of the family system, I had reason to think that the maintaining factors were weakening. Previous medical evaluation had not shown there to be a medical problem. Therefore, it appeared that psychological intervention at this time might be effective.

Although the family had come to treatment requesting hypnosis, I did not think that it would be best used immediately. Hypnotherapists are often in a conundrum over this point. To immediately use hypnosis if it is requested essentially concedes the selection of the treatment modality to the client, with possible negative consequences for future course of therapy. Not giving clients what they request, however, can lead to disappointment and possible premature termination. Although I believed that hypnosis at this point might prove only moderately successful at best, I decided to use it initially to "hook" the client and his parents. If it worked, fine; if not, I could make adjustments as needed.

HYPNOSIS TREATMENT

Therapeutic goals for a psychosomatic problem such as enuresis are obvious: cessation of bedwetting behavior. Partial gains (e.g., significant reduction of the problem) are not likely to be acceptable. I told Mr. and Mrs. Smith that treatment success for this type of problem, barring medical complications, was good, but that I could not predict the length of treatment nor its course at this point. They seemed to accept this. Because I saw John's enuresis as embedded in a context of inappropriate loving and relating (to his mother especially), and because I saw him as gradually outgrowing his problem, I initially planned a hypnotic intervention structured around metaphors (Gordon, 1978) involving appropriate ways of growing, loving, and relating. These were designed not only to address the enuresis itself, but also the unduly close relationship with his mother and the inappropriate ways of expressing that closeness. At the same time, I wished to help John relate more closely to his father. Because of John's apparent ambivalence towards change and possible resistance, I initially used an indirect induction that he could control. The next session was with John alone:

> You know, don't you, John, that you can close your eyes or not while in a trance; talk or not while in a trance; relax or not while in a trance. You can go into a trance regardless if you wish. Now, as I count from 1 to 10, concentrate on my voice and experience whatever level of trance you wish right now. As I count, you may, if you wish, go deeper into a trance.

Somewhat to my astonishment, the indirect suggestion that he could close his eyes if he wished failed to produce the effect. Although I had guessed that he wanted control over the session, it is possible that, because hypnosis was new for him, he wanted more guidance and structure than I had provided. Therefore, I gave him a *direct* instruction that he close his eyes and relax progressively as he narrowed his attentional focus on my voice as I continued talking.

> Now that you have experienced the trance level you want right now, I'd like you to slowly allow your eyes to close and to allow yourself to relax. And as I continue to talk, please focus more and more on my voice, allowing all other sounds and sensations to gradually fade from your mind. And as I continue to talk, allow your body to relax more and more, all over. As I count from 1 to 10, let yourself become even more relaxed and comfortable.

These suggestions were repeated and varied for the next few minutes. As a result, John's eyes closed, his facial muscles became more flaccid, and his breathing progressively became deeper and slower. From these signs, I concluded that he was in at least a light trance. I then structured the following hypnotic routine around the concepts mentioned earlier. Embedded suggestions are italicized and were vocally stressed.

> Just relax, John, and as you concentrate on the sound of my voice, you can *John allow yourself to become as relaxed* as you wish. You are here (i.e., hear) to learn what I have to say, but your conscious mind is not important, so you can go play soccer (John played soccer in school) till later, and your unconscious mind will hear (i.e., here) what I say ... Growing up well is important for you, isn't it ("Yes-set"); learning and unlearning; things, *John, change* as you, *John change.* When my daughter was an infant, she was often angry, but did not know how to express that anger. As she grew older, she learned its appropriate expression and these expressions changed. So too: in growing up, relationships, *John, develop:*
> How you have heard your father talk about his family.
> How you share and don't share with Joe.
> How you, *John, love your mother* and father *differently.*
> As a child you hugged and loved one way, but now as you cross to being a man, John, your love will grow like you; how your love will, *John, change.*
> When you were a small child, walking seemed so difficult, but you learned; when you were a child, the alphabet seemed so difficult, but you learned; as you begin to drive a car, it seems so difficult, but you will learn. Now, as you are ready to, *John, be a man,* I know you really want to *hold* your head high, *John,* and you can, *John, change the ways of childhood.*
> But we are not here (i.e., hear) to hear (i.e., here) me tell you what you already know, but how to learn and accomplish much more besides within yourself. So, I'll speak to both your conscious and unconscious at different states. And your conscious and unconscious minds will hear (here) what they want to hear, need to hear, and will be able to use all that they want to use in the way that they want to use it. And you will be able to use those things that are valuable for you in a very special way sometime soon. And you can allow yourself to be surprised at the changes you are able to make.

I then brought John out of hypnosis in this fashion:

> And now I'm going to count backwards from 10 to 1. When I reach 1, you'll come out of the trance feeling relaxed and refreshed, able to remember whatever you want to remember.

I explicitly suggested that he might or not might not remember what was said so that the trance could be ratified either way, thus potentially reducing resistance. At first, he claimed that he had not been hypnotized because he remembered everything. When I asked him what he remembered, however, he was actually able to recall very little. He was quite surprised and impressed by this, and I told him that it indicated he had been hypnotized.

I saw John privately for the next two sessions as well. We spent about half of each session working in hypnosis and the remainder of the time exploring his motivation and strategies for overcoming his enuresis and the results thus far. The hypnosis routines followed that presented earlier, with some additions. Because he liked fishing with his father, I structured a fish metaphor around the repetitive use of the terms, "catch and hold," a metaphor for both fishing and urine retention. The routine went like this, after induction of hypnosis:

> I'd like you to imagine that you are fishing with your father. You know, don't you, that you must first *catch* the fish, then *hold* the fish. Either one without the other is useless, isn't it! So, imagine yourself catching the fish and holding the fish, *catching and holding, catching and holding,* catching and holding. After a while, it becomes automatic, doesn't it! Catch and hold, *catch and hold.* And the more you think about it, the more you can apply that to other parts of your life, so that you can catch and hold other things as well.

I also included a routine designed to encourage John to practice and not to become discouraged if success seemed slow at first. This routine was as follows:

> As you learn new and interesting things, you will sometimes stumble. But the more you practice, the more you will succeed. And the more you succeed, the easier it will be to succeed next time. It's like learning to ride a bicycle (a skill learned by all boys), isn't it! At first you are conscious of every movement, feeling very awkward and clumsy, but later you do it so well and so unconsciously that one day you look back and wonder why you ever found it difficult at all! So, success leads to more success and more good feelings about yourself, which leads to more success and more good feelings; so, the better you feel about yourself, the more success you will have, but the more success you have, the better you feel about yourself. So, as you learn, each success builds on other successes. It's just a matter of beginning, isn't it!

In addition, I continued to use the growing and developing metaphor, as follows:

> As you are learning new ways of growing, new ways of being close in different ways, different but deeper feelings as you continue to grow and develop in different ways, feeling good about the changes you are making, wondering with interest and excitement where it all will lead. And feeling comfortable with your own internal growth processes, knowing that they will lead to new opportunities and new possibilities. So that you can relate to others not only differently, but better as well.

The discussions with John were revealing as well. He had some negative feelings towards his father because of the latter's expressions of anger about his enuresis. John also continued drinking fluids just before bedtime, despite (or because of) his knowledge that this contributed to his enuresis. He did reveal once, however, that he had told himself one night not to urinate and had not. He also told me that he felt much closer to his mother than to his father. Although this is not unusual in a young adolescent boy, the feelings in this case seemed to be expressed in an unhealthy fashion. There thus appeared to be a strong secondary gain in John's enuresis, perhaps as a way of achieving more closeness to his mother and expressing covert anger towards a distant and powerful father. Therefore, John would likely have ambivalent feelings about eliminating his enuresis.

Data that I asked Mr. and Mrs. Smith to keep on the incidents of bed-wetting appeared to confirm this ambivalence. The following record is typical of the first few weeks in therapy.

Tuesday—dry
Wednesday—very little, damp only
Thursday—damp
Friday—damp
Saturday—medium wet
Sunday—dry
Monday—dry
Tuesday—wet

Furthermore, he had drunk liquids during the evenings prior to the nights in which he had been enuretic. Thus, the pattern seemed clear. Whereas this was progress of sorts, it was not an outcome that John, his parents, or I would likely accept as the best that could be achieved. However, Mrs. Smith spontaneously reported to me an important additional outcome. After the first hypnosis session, John never again joined her in bed after an enuretic episode. In addition, both parents reported that he seemed to have become more thoughtful, less impulsive, and more mature since he had entered therapy. Although one cannot trace this outcome directly to the hypnotic routine, in fact it was reflected in the content of the routine. Needless to say, I had not disclosed the content of the hypnosis sessions to Mr. and Mrs. Smith.

It appeared that therapy with John alone was likely to produce an ambiguous result, not unlike John's motivation. Therefore, I decided to intervene directly in the family structure, with what I perceived as underlying family relationship issues. I should point out that it is not unusual for hypnotic interventions to be used in conjunction with other interventions; indeed, the hypnotic intervention is often the lesser component. Nevertheless, it can make a significant contribution to the ultimate outcome.

FAMILY TREATMENT

Although the first five sessions had resulted in partial gains, it was clear that family relationship issues still needed to be addressed if John's enuretic problem were to be resolved. Therefore, I attempted a paradigm shift (Calof, 1982). I asked to see Mr. and Mrs. Smith alone for a few sessions so that I could address the following issues.

1. The secondary gain that John received from his enuresis. This was apparent from the fact that John knowingly drank liquids just prior to bedtime.
2. The unusually strong bond between John and Mrs. Smith and the weaker bond between Mr. and Mrs. Smith. This was demonstrated by the fact that the latter slept in separate rooms on separate floors and by John's coming to his mother's bed after an enuretic episode.
3. Mrs. Smith's "rescuing tendencies" with John. This was demonstrated by her supplying John with sweets and drink before bed and by washing John's sheets after an enuretic night.

After explaining to Mr. and Mrs. Smith that a problem such as adolescent enuresis is often partially a result of family interaction, I instructed them to carry out the following tasks for one week and to observe the results. They were then to report to me the following week.

1. They were not to comment to John about his enuresis or to let him know they were either monitoring, or concerned about, his progress. They were to act as if it were his concern alone and to respond minimally if he mentioned it.
2. The television in John and Joe's room was to be turned off at 10:00 p.m. and both boys were to be in bed. Heretofore, the boys had been allowed to watch TV indefinitely, thus possibly contributing to John's deep slumber and consequent inability to awaken before wetting the bed. In addition, this resolved a source of some contention between the parents, as Mr. Smith had insisted the TV be turned off early, whereas Mrs. Smith had covertly allowed it to stay on. Because Mr. Smith was often gone, she was able to do this.
3. I strongly suggested that Mr. and Mrs. Smith sleep together. Mr. Smith was not particularly happy about this, as he preferred the waterbed. However, because most of my suggestions were directed at Mrs. Smith, I thought it important that Mr. Smith make some changes, too. I told them that this change would help John to understand that his parents were a unit acting in concert.

4. I instructed Mrs. Smith to no longer change and wash John's sheets and not to make his bed after an enuretic night. She was to require him to change and wash them himself. She was not to comment about either a wet *or* a dry bed.
5. I instructed both Mr. and Mrs. Smith no longer to stock ice cream, chocolate, or soda in the house, without comment.

Both parents agreed to these instructions, and I asked them to keep a covert record of John's enuretic nights for my information.

In the next two sessions with Mr. and Mrs. Smith together, we discussed Mrs. Smith's rescuing tendencies. She stated that she did not feel particularly powerful vis-a-vis her husband or her sons and saw her boys as needing protection from their father. The following interchange took place, which has been condensed for this presentation:

Therapist (to Mrs. Smith):   Tell me how you relate to John and Joe.

Mrs. Smith: Well, I'm concerned that they fight too much. I always seem to be stopping their fights, or acting as a referee. I think sometimes that John, although he's older, needs protection from Joe.

Therapist: How does your husband fit in to this?

Mrs. Smith: He's gone quite a lot and I'm left trying to figure out what to do with the boys. I sometimes think he's too hard on them, gets too angry, and I guess I try to make it easier for them. I know sometimes I do things that Mark (Mr. Smith) doesn't like, but I don't know what else to do.

Therapist: Is that why you let them stay up late watching TV and let them have soda and cookies at night?

Mrs. Smith: I guess so. It just seems easier to give in than to get into a big fight about it. Mark doesn't really know what goes on around here when he's gone; all he hears about are the problems!

Therapist: Are you angry with Mark for not being available to you?

Mrs. Smith: Well, I suppose a little. Actually, sometimes I feel that all he does is criticize what I do without really understanding why I do it.

Therapist: It sounds like you don't feel particularly powerful at home.

Mrs. Smith: Yeah, that's it! Mark is gone a lot and doesn't really know what's going on. Sometimes I think he doesn't really care. I'm left having to deal with everything. Be-

	sides, he talks so much better than I do, but I have to do it!
Mr. Smith:	I'm surprised to hear you say that. I thought that I've always supported you in dealing with the boys; offering ideas, setting rules. You just don't follow them!
Therapist:	June (Mrs. Smith), can you tell Mark exactly what it is you would like that you aren't getting?
Mrs. Smith:	I think I'd like to discuss things more with you, being able to talk about how I should handle the boys, even having *you* talk to them. All you do is tell me what *I* should do, without helping me in *how* to do it. Then, when I don't do it correctly, you get angry at them and me.
Therapist:	Do you feel that you have to protect John and Joe from Mark?
Mrs. Smith:	I guess so. He gets angry so easily and I don't know what to do with it.
Mr. Smith:	I suppose I *do* get angry a lot. *I* don't feel powerful either. When I'm gone, I can't do anything about what happens here; you can do whatever you want, even though I set rules.
Therapist:	Mark, would you like to work with June together to set and enforce household rules?
Mr. Smith:	Yeah, I really *want* to support her and I thought I was. I can understand now why she might feel that way. I guess I didn't realize how I was coming across. (To Mrs. Smith): Why didn't you tell me earlier how you felt?
Mrs. Smith:	I guess I didn't think you'd listen. Actually, I'm a little surprised to hear you say it now.
Therapist:	Let's work towards setting up guidelines and rules that you both can develop and enforce. I think it's important that you work together on this and agree on what needs to be done.
Mrs. Smith:	I think I needed to hear these things. I'd like to discuss together what the household rules should be and how to enforce them. I think I need to become a little more assertive, too.
Mr. Smith:	I'd like to work together too. And, I don't think you need to rescue the boys from me!
Mrs. Smith:	No, I guess I don't.

Mr. and Mrs. Smith were able to implement together the guidelines we had developed and they continued to keep a log of "wet nights." The pattern of wet–dry nights continued roughly the same as before. However, John had not questioned the new rules and had immediately begun changing and washing his own bedclothes. No explanations were asked for and none were given.

In a subsequent session with John alone, he indicated that he was pleased with his progress, but doubted that he could eliminate wetting completely. He was aware of the connection between drinking fluids late at night and subsequent enuresis, but could not explain this seemingly perverse action. Suspecting a certain lack of motivation along with a need to control the progression of events towards the elimination of his enuresis, I thought it might be important for John to "do it his way" (Erickson, 1980). Therefore, I asked John if he was willing to be hypnotized one more time. He agreed and I conducted the following hypnotic routine, after induction:

> You have had a certain success in overcoming your problem and you can feel good about it. At the same time, however, you can realize that you are giving up something important, something useful. It's like giving up an important part of yourself, isn't it. Yet, growing and developing always means giving up some things while getting other, better, things. Doing things, accomplishing things, in your own way, at your own speed, is also important, isn't it. You know when you are ready to put aside childish things and move on to adult things, don't you. Sometimes you just have to decide, don't you, when you are ready to change. And you can decide soon, if you wish, when you are ready to change. During the next week, you can decide when you would like to eliminate your problem. It might be in a week, it might be in two weeks, or even as long as a month. And you can find your own way to accomplish this, at your own speed, can't you. You know what you have to do, don't you; you just have to decide to do it. So, whenever you are ready, you can *John stop and John change.*

This basic routine was repeated several times, with variations. After trance was terminated, I asked John when it might be reasonable for him to stop wetting his bed. He replied that three to four weeks might be reasonable. I stressed that he was ultimately in control of his problem. He replied, "Do you mean that I can stop whenever I want?" I said that indeed it was so and John left, remarking that this had been the most helpful session of all.

OUTCOME

I saw Mr. and Mrs. Smith for two more sessions, which were devoted to a discussion of John's progress, their implementation of my earlier instructions, and their own progress in working together as a team. They reported that John had suddenly ceased to wet his bed, except for a rare damp night. They had continued carrying out my instructions and were discussing things more openly between themselves.

A telephone follow-up a year and a half later indicated that John's enuresis had not returned. Only occasionally, when he had eaten ice cream or drunk fluids late at night, or when he was angry with his parents about something, did the problem recur and then only slightly. In addition, the parents described John as having matured greatly in the intervening time, both emotionally and physically. Specifically, he had become more thoughtful and considerate of others, less impulsive, and more able to express his feelings openly. He had also spontaneously taken on greater responsibility in the family and his grades had improved. Enuresis was no longer a topic in household discussions.

CONCLUSION

This case illustrates several aspects of successful hypnotherapy. First, it is important to note that hypnosis was integrated into an overall treatment plan, much of which did not involve hypnosis. Indeed, the initial attempt to treat the problem strictly by hypnosis resulted in only limited gains. Thus, this case emphasizes the maxim that hypnotherapy is an adjunctive treatment only, not a therapy itself.

Second, it is important that any secondary gain of symptoms be addressed, especially if the problem is embedded within the family structure and is an expression of aspects of that structure. Too often, psychological problems are still treated in isolation from the client's social context. Although it may be an overstatement to say that all problems are contextual in origin, nevertheless, context is an important feature of many difficulties, particularly conduct disorders. Even where context is less important, ambivalence about change is likely to be still present and should be addressed.

Third, this case illustrates the uneven progress that often occurs in the conduct of psychotherapy. Often, the therapist must use a trial-and-error approach to determine what interventions will have the greatest impact. Therefore, it is important to collect outcome data along the way, in order to determine which techniques are most effective.

Fourth, maturation alone was likely responsible for some of the gains experienced by John, especially at follow-up. Although increasing maturity is important at any age, it is especially a factor during the rapid growth stage of adolescence. Although it is possible that changes in areas of John's life other than enuresis that were noted at termination and at follow-up were due to a treatment "ripple effect," it is also possible that they would have occurred in any event. It is also possible that the enuresis itself might have disappeared spontaneously because of John's increasing maturity, although it would have happened, if at all, more slowly.

One persistent question that is often addressed in the literature on hypnosis was not resolved by this case—that is, the relative contribution of hypnosis and other psychological interventions towards ultimate outcome. Would hypnosis alone eventually have eliminated John's enuresis? Would the family interventions alone have done so? Would the same "ripple effect" have occurred if either had been used alone?

The effect of the actual hypnotic routines is also unclear. Wadden and Anderton (1982) have presented evidence indicating that the effect of hypnosis itself cannot clearly be implicated in treatment success unless the client possesses good hypnotic ability (or susceptibility). In addition, they concluded that hypnosis alone likely could not account for treatment gains in habit disorders. No formal assessment of John's hypnotic ability was undertaken and it appeared from the physical signs he exhibited and the lack of indications of a moderate or deep trance that John was in a light trance only during the hypnosis sessions. Therefore, it is unclear if the hypnotic routines functioned as a placebo or had "real" impact.

Future research should be conducted to determine the contribution made by behavioral and hypnotic interventions in the treatment of adolescent enuresis, perhaps by single-treatment comparisons conducted on matched samples. In addition, the effect of hypnosis itself should be compared with clients high and low on hypnotic susceptibility. If hypnosis can be successfully used only with a minority of "hypnotic virtuosi," then its ultimate utility will be severely limited.

This case demonstrates the multifaceted and multicausal nature of entrenched habit disorders such as enuresis. These problems are often part of the client's social context and provide the individual with a source of gratification not otherwise perceived as obtainable. Treatment programs should therefore be multifaceted as well.

REFERENCES

Calof, D. L. (1982). Shiften's therapeutic paradigms: A case report of adolescent primary enuresis. In J. K. Zeig (Ed.), *Ericksonian approaches to hypnosis and psychotherapy* (pp. 239–254). New York: Brunner/Mazel.

Erickson, M. H. (1980). Utilizing the patient's own personality and ideas: "Doing it his way." In E. L. Rossi (Ed.), *The collected papers of Milton Erickson* (Vol. 4, pp. 233–234). New York: Irvington.

Gibbons, D. E. (1979). *Applied hypnosis and hyperempiria.* New York: Plenum Press.

Gordon, D. (1978). *Therapeutic metaphors.* Cupertino, CA: META Publications.

Kroger, W. S. (1977). *Clinical and experimental hypnosis in medicine, dentistry, and psychology.* Philadelphia: Lippincott.

Kroger, W. S., & Fetzler, W. D. (1976). *Hypnosis and behavior modification: Imagery conditioning.* Philadelphia: Lippincott.

Wadden, T. A., & Anderton, C. H. (1982). The clinical use of hypnosis. *Psychological Bulletin, 91,* 215–243.

IV

A CLINICAL CASE
CONFERENCE: ELLEN

INTRODUCTION

STEVEN JAY LYNN

There are at least as many ways of incorporating hypnosis into psychotherapy as there are different schools of psychotherapy. If you consider that there are in excess of 300 different psychotherapeutic approaches (Lynn & Garske, in press), it is obvious that it is beyond the scope of any book to adequately describe the ways in which hypnosis can play a role in the panorama of contemporary psychotherapies. So what the contributors have done in this section is to narrow the field of discussion by illustrating how experts who represent very different yet popular traditions of clinical hypnotherapy conceptualize and treat a person with problems in living. This section presents the "Case of Ellen," followed by the commentaries of well-known clinicians who represent psychoanalytic psychotherapy, rational–emotive behavior therapy (REBT), multimodal therapy, and Ericksonian hypnosis.

Since Sigmund Freud's work more than a century ago, no other therapy has equaled the influence of psychoanalysis (Baker, 1985). Freud was so impressed by the apparent submissiveness of certain hypnotized subjects that he likened hypnosis to being in love. Of course, Freud was mistaken in his idea that hypnosis fosters an erotic or sexual relationship between the therapist and patient. More contemporary psychoanalytic theorists, including Baker, Gill, Brenman, Fromm, and Nash, have instead relied on concepts allied to ego psychology (e.g., regression in the service of the ego,

ego receptivity, and primary process thinking) to account for the thera-peutic potential of hypnosis (Lynn, Rhue, & Spanos, 1994).

Michael Nash's chapter (chapter 15) presents a modern psychoana-lytically informed approach to the case of Ellen. It reminds us just how far psychoanalysis has come from the early days of long-term, intense, essen-tially open-ended treatment. Instead, Nash's therapy is relatively brief, problem-focused, supportive, and mastery-oriented. For Nash, hypnosis can be used to augment treatment by targeting symptoms, modulating disrup-tive affect, enhancing adaptive defensive and coping strategies, and foster-ing feelings of self-efficacy. The reader will note that Nash is not deterred from directly suggesting coping strategies to the client and using behavioral techniques such as desensitization, if deemed appropriate. This represents a trend toward technical eclecticism, evident in a variety of insight ther-apies (Norcross & Wogan, 1983), which emphasizes pragmatism, clinical utility, and function, and minimizes theoretical orthodoxy and rigid rules and guidelines (Lynn & Garske, in press).

This trend toward eclecticism is certainly not limited to insight ther-apies. To the contrary, it is exemplified by many cognitive–behavioral approaches. Cognitive–behavioral psychotherapies integrate diverse ap-proaches and have gained widespread acceptance in the past two decades or so (see Meichenbaum, in press). Two distinct yet related cognitive ther-apies are presented in the chapters by Albert Ellis (chapter 16) and by Irving Kirsch and William Coe (chapter 17).

Ellis is one of the pioneers of cognitive therapy, and his work has been recognized as influential in the development of cognitive–behavioral approaches (Meichenbaum, in press). He has long promoted the idea that many if not all emotional difficulties are caused by the irrational or mal-adaptive beliefs people hold. More recently, his writings have described how cognitive and behavioral techniques can be integrated. His analysis and treatment of the case of Ellen provides a clear illustration of how rational–emotive behavior therapy encompasses procedures designed to modify both thoughts and behaviors. These techniques include disputing irrational ideas, developing coping statements, modeling and role playing thoughts and behaviors, skill training, reinforcement, and in vivo desen-sitization.

One of the premises of the cognitive–behavioral perspective is that whatever can be done with hypnosis can be done without it (Kirsch, 1993). However, Ellis is very clear about the situations in which hypnosis is in-dicated versus contraindicated in the context of REBT. For instance, if cli-ents resist using usual REBT methods or do not respond positively to such methods and are particularly motivated to experience hypnosis, hypnotic procedures might be indicated.

The trend toward technical eclecticism and the use of cognitive–behavioral techniques is nicely exemplified by the multimodal treatment of Ellen advocated by Kirsch and Coe. Their treatment approach is based on the work of Arnold Lazarus, an innovator in cognitive–behavioral psychotherapy. Kirsch and Coe detail a step-by-step treatment in which seven important modalities of functioning are comprehensively assessed (BASIC ID: behavior, affect, sensation, imagery, cognitions, interpersonal, and drugs [physiology]) and serve as a treatment template. Systematic consideration of each of these modalities, independently and in interaction with one another, distinguishes it from other cognitive–behavioral approaches. Yet Kirsch and Coe's approach is consistent with other cognitive–behavioral treatments in its focus on relaxation, imagery, behavioral practice, successive approximation to goals, and cognitive restructuring (see Kirsch, 1993). For these authors, hypnosis is used with clients with positive attitudes toward hypnosis and for whom the use of hypnosis makes therapy more credible.

The treatments described so far represent schools of psychotherapy that incorporated hypnotic techniques at various stages in their evolution, yet were largely independent of innovations in the practice of hypnosis and hypnotherapy. This is decidedly not true in the case of the immensely popular Ericksonian hypnotherapy. In fact, Erickson (1901–1980) is widely recognized as a master hypnotist who pioneered creative techniques of brief psychotherapy based on his experiences with hypnotic interventions. Erickson was a master of the use of paradox, surprise, humor, metaphor, and the nuances and subtleties of language and communication. Unlike classical psychoanalysts, Erickson did not believe it was necessary that the unconscious be made conscious, or that insight be achieved. Nor did Erickson believe that it was necessary to analyze the client's personality or mental mechanisms. Rather, hypnosis could be used to create new meanings, attitudes, and beliefs by accessing the client's inherent skills and potential (see Matthews, Lankton, and Lankton, 1993).

It is in this tradition that Matthews, Lankton, and Lankton formulate their treatment of the case of Ellen. Unlike REBT, and many other applications of hypnosis that use authoritatively worded suggestions, Matthews and his colleagues' approach relies on the use of analogy, metaphor, and associative learning rather than on suggestions that specifically direct actions. Their therapy is goal-oriented and future-oriented. Helping the client to achieve greater flexibility, more elastic social roles, new and more adaptive perspectives or "frames" on current life situations, and increased access to personal resources are important treatment goals.

The case that provides the springboard for commentary was based on an actual case treated by Steven Lynn, with a nonhypnotic eclectic approach. The case description is altered in certain respects to preserve the anonymity of the client. The commentators were not provided with an elaborate description of Ellen and her background. Instead, they were given a succinct description of Ellen intended to convey enough information to constitute a *Grund* for discussion while leaving ample opportunity for interpretation and amplification of her situation to highlight conceptual and technical similarities and differences among commentators.

INFORMATION PROVIDED TO THE COMMENTATORS

The information that was provided to the authors is presented below. The case description will help the reader to place the commentaries in perspective by describing Ellen's current marital and family situation, her presenting problem, family history, history of the problem, prior treatment, and the results of psychological assessment. In their commentaries, authors were asked to address the following questions:

1. What is your conception of this case? What are the psychological and behavioral dynamics pertinent to the treatment of this client?
2. What, if any, questions remain, and how would you go about answering them?
3. What is your treatment plan? More specifically, what strategies, techniques, and methods would you implement?
4. What role would hypnosis play in treating this client? What is the process whereby the decision to use hypnosis is made? Generally, what are the indications and contraindications for using hypnosis in psychotherapy? What are its strengths and limitations?
5. What concluding comments do you have?

THE CASE OF ELLEN

Ellen is a 49-year-old woman with two children and a devoted husband who is 15 years her senior. She is employed as a physician, and her husband is also a physician. They work at the same hospital, she in obstetrics, he in radiology. Her children are both college graduates. Her son is in medical school, and her daughter is in law school.

Ellen presents as a very sophisticated woman. She is witty and articulate, yet very shy. She describes herself as "methodical, thorough, careful, stubborn, insecure, and competitive, particularly with women." Ellen's problem is that she cannot use public bathrooms or bathrooms in which there is any possibility that someone can hear her flush the toilet or hear her urinate or defecate. This anxiety response has been a longstanding problem for her, and it has caused her considerable discomfort. For example, at parties, she has waited up to five hours before using the toilet, stating that her "bladder almost bursts" in these situations. She also has avoided traveling to conventions with female friends and colleagues who invite her to accompany them, because she has been unwilling to share a room with her friends who might "hear her."

Ellen states that, "If anything, over the years, the problem has become more debilitating; it hasn't improved at all." She is particularly discouraged because she recently was invited to participate in an all expenses paid scientific exchange to the People's Republic of China, but is balking at this opportunity. She has a month to decide whether she will accept this invitation for the trip, which is scheduled to occur 9 months after her first appointment with you. Her quandary about whether to accept this invitation or to decline is what prompted her to consult with you.

Ellen's only other contact with a helping professional was during medical school, after her mother died. She was treated at this time for depression at the Student Health Center. Her treatment was brief (2 months) and consisted of supportive therapy and antidepressant medication. During this difficult period in her life, Ellen reported that she felt suicidal, and even engaged in a few episodes of self-mutilation, although at the time she thought "this is crazy." She had a difficult time understanding why she was so depressed after her mother died because she stated that she had never felt close to her mother. In fact, in certain respects, her mother appeared to be a negative role model. She was described by Ellen as a crude person who often embarrassed her by her poor hygiene and her tendency to "walk around the house naked." Ellen described herself as trying very hard to get her father's attention and was aware of being his "favorite child." She noted that her primary motivation to pursue a medical career was to please her father.

Other aspects of Ellen's history are notable. Although Ellen enjoys a warm, affectionate relationship with both of her children, she has a less than satisfactory sexual relationship with her husband. To be more specific, she has little sexual drive and views sex as a chore rather than a pleasant activity. She also is very concerned about cleanliness and admits that despite her "knowing better," she still cannot shake the idea that sex is somehow "dirty." Nevertheless, she still participates in sexual relations with her husband "about once a week or once every other week." Finally, despite her high level of career achievement, she still feels that she is not "good enough" and should "try harder" to be a better doctor.

A summary of test findings, based on the MMPI and Rorschach tests, indicated obsessive–compulsive and somatization tendencies, guardedness and interpersonal sensitivity, generalized anxiety, and feelings of low self-worth.

REFERENCES

Baker, E. (1985). Psychoanalysis and psychoanalytic psychotherapies. In S. J. Lynn & J. P. Garske (Eds.), *Contemporary psychotherapies: Models and methods* (pp. 19–68). Pacific Grove, CA: Brooks/Cole.

Kirsch, I. (1993). Cognitive–behavioral hypnotherapy. In J. W. Rhue, S. J. Lynn, & I. Kirsch (Eds.), *Handbook of clinical hypnosis* (pp. 151–171). Washington, DC: American Psychological Association.

Lynn, S. J., & Garske, J. P. (in press). *Contemporary psychotherapies: Models and methods* (2nd ed.). Pacific Grove, CA: Brooks/Cole.

Lynn, S. J., Rhue, J. W., & Spanos, N. P. (1994). Hypnosis. *Encyclopedia of Human Behavior, 2,* 555–566.

Matthews, W., Lankton, S., & Lankton, C. (1993). An Ericksonian model of hypnotherapy. In J. W. Rhue, S. J. Lynn, & I. Kirsch (Eds.), *Handbook of clinical hypnosis* (pp. 187–214). Washington, DC: American Psychological Association.

Meichenbaum, D. (in press). Cognitive–behavioral psychotherapies. In S. J. Lynn & J. P. Garske *Contemporary psychotherapies: Models and methods* (2nd ed.). Pacific Grove, CA: Brooks/Cole.

Norcross, J. C., & Wogan, M. (1983). American psychologists of diverse persuasions: Characteristics, theories, practices, and clients. *Professional Psychology: Research and Practice, 14,* 529–539.

15

A PSYCHOANALYTICALLY INFORMED APPROACH IN THE CASE OF ELLEN

MICHAEL R. NASH

It is of course necessary for a clinician to approach such case material with an appropriate sense of humility. A formulation and treatment plan for most insight-oriented therapies involves careful attention to the unique thematic associations patients produce to memories, fantasy or dream elements, and affect-laden experience as related during the evaluation phase of intervention. Although the case material on Ellen is interesting and rich, what I offer is still only one construction of what "might be" based on what we know about Ellen. This kind of clinical venture is similar to what literary historians do when faced with the enigma of Shakespeare's life and personality: With precious little solid biographical evidence, they weave stories of "what might have been." Needless to say, there are almost as many "Shakespeares" as there are literary historians. And I suspect that there will be almost as many Ellens as there are commentators.

The advantage we clinicians have in the real world is that our work, or that of our supervisees, is in vivo: Our speculations, then, are more like hypotheses that can be tested, confirmed, disconfirmed, modified, or scrapped based on the ongoing exchange with the patient. I offer here a formulation in the spirit of hypothesis—something to be tested by subsequent patient contact. Further, I sculpt my formulation as closely and faithfully as possible to the contours of the data presented. The formulation is as concise as it is propositional, thus avoiding the kinds of facile, highly speculative "field theories" for which psychoanalysis has been deservedly criticized. My hope is that even if this crude formulation is incorrect, it will serve to instruct the reader on how careful case conceptualization can inform technique (both hypnotic and otherwise). It is my belief that grave clinical errors are made if the therapist's technical reach exceeds his or her conceptual grasp. This may be especially true for hypnosis.

There are elements in the protocol that argue for a formulation based on introjective themes: that Ellen is suffering from an introjective depression, replete with subthemes of anger, power, competition, guilt, and associated self-punitiveness. From this point of view, Ellen's preoccupation with bodily elimination is derivative of inhibited emotional expression in general, and especially in regard to anger. An oedipally determined wish to destroy the same-sex parent leads to unbearable guilt and ambivalence in connection with that parent. There is then secondary identification with the lost (in this case, destroyed) object, and a tendency for the patient to "turn the anger inward." This is a perfectly plausible argument, but one that I find unsatisfying, for as I read the protocol, I believe the core underlying psychic process to be that of shame and not guilt. When in the bathroom, the patient does not experience herself as *doing* something unacceptable, she experiences herself as *being* unacceptable.

Here we encounter the difference between guilt and shame. Guilt is a function of the superego: An unacceptable impulse leads to an expectation of harm (Freud would say "castration"). Shame is derivative of the ego-ideal: A failure to measure up leads to an expectation of abandonment. In the former case the fear is of retribution; in the latter case it is of abandonment, of being unlovable. Shame is developmentally more primitive than guilt. There is a harsh, raw, and global aspect to shame that shapes the patient's experience of herself as essentially unlovable, and this experience is fundamentally body-based.

Thus I would render a tentative formulation based on anaclitic rather than introjective themes. For some reason, early interaction with the mother rendered the patient prone to profound fears of abandonment. Primitive conflict around loss, passive dependent yearnings, and emotional supply arose as the mother failed to provide the good-enough mothering that would enable the patient to internalize a stable sense of safety, and go on to the subsequent tasks of separation and autonomy. It is no surprise then that this developmental failure in the original dyadic relationship with the mother has resulted in an exceedingly tenuous grasp of what it means to be female, what it means to have a female body, and what it means to be passively gratified. To share visceral experience, either sexual or eliminative, is to be found unlovable. The self-mutilation associated with the mother's death is then less a matter of self-punitiveness, and more a matter of desperately attempting a primitive fusion or reconciliation with the mother via a violent, humiliating, and dramatic gesture of need. In a sense, then, bleeding, urinating, and defecating represent a horribly tortured plea for maternal supply.

For Ellen, relationships became the arena in which to prove that she is worthy of love after all. In part this explains the overideation, the wit, the ambition, and above all the competitiveness with women. It seems quite possible that fairly early the patient turned to her father for affirmation that she was lovable, in spite of her deeply rooted shame. Fortunately, her father appears to have been responsive, enabling Ellen to fashion a reasonably functional core of self-esteem, less in terms of who she is, than by what she achieves. But the structural problems with shame repeat themselves in Ellen's relationship with her husband, a substantially older man. I would guess that in many respects this relationship is affirming personally and even in some sense emotionally. But the structural deficit around identity compromises Ellen's ability to participate fully in physical intimacy. Sex is a "duty," and it is shameful and dirty precisely because everything about her body (especially its feminine parts) is associated with danger. It is, after all, not a penis that Ellen seeks, but a breast. Her father could not give this to her, and neither can her husband.

TREATMENT PLAN AND CLINICAL CONSIDERATIONS

It is here that the critical question of therapeutic aim must be addressed with the patient. First the patient should be broadly advised as to the therapist's formulation of the problem. Here the therapist might gently suggest that the bathroom problem is really part of a more general tendency for the patient. She consciously yearns to be loved for who she is, but ends up feeling desperately isolated and unhappy, especially about her body. The clinician might even introduce the concept of shame, to see if, and how, the patient can work productively with such emotionally loaded material. What the therapist must listen for is the patient's ability to construe the problem as essentially interpersonal.

The therapist then eventually says something like this:

We must now decide how to approach this problem. I believe that there is a good chance that with proper treatment spanning over several months, you can gain a reasonable amount of confidence and composure in regard to using the bathroom, enough to take your trip to China. We might use hypnosis or other treatment strategies to very specifically target this single problem area for you. On the other hand, we can approach your unhappiness and distress more systemically in a therapy that will undoubtedly extend beyond your trip to China—attempting to sort out how and why you sometimes end up feeling so desperately bad about *who* you are, and *how* you are with other people. This type of therapy is of course more ambitious, because we attempt to get at root causes. I believe there is a good chance that we can succeed with this broader objective, and that the payoff will be a more broadly satisfying life. The "down side" is that it takes longer, it costs more, and it will probably "stir you up" quite a bit at times. As I see it, the prognosis is reasonably good either way. Let's talk about how we want to proceed. . . .

The therapist and patient can then spend the time necessary to settle on a treatment plan. Sometimes patients ask whether they can "do both": first get rid of the symptom, and then work on insight. My stance on this is fairly straightforward: A brief, supportive problem-focused therapy such as we are discussing is really quite incompatible with a more traditional, uncovering therapy that rigorously and relentlessly focuses on the transferential–countertransferential mix, a focus that requires careful attention to neutrality. If the patient wishes to address the symptom alone now, but later (a year later) finds that he or she wishes a more aggressively uncovering therapy, I might be amenable to taking the case, but I would generally prefer the patient do such work with another therapist.

As the purpose of this casebook is primarily the explication of hypnotic technique, I am going to assume that the treatment selected is a relatively brief, problem-focused, supportive therapy. Although hypnosis certainly can play an important role in long-term psychoanalytic therapy (Fromm & Nash, 1996), it is only one of several uncovering techniques, not all of which fall within the purview of the present book. Therefore, from this point on I will assume that the aim of this therapy is symptom relief, and the duration of the therapy relatively brief—let us say 3–4 months.

A supportive, problem-focused intervention involves using hypnosis to modulate disruptive affect; reinforce syntonic, adaptive, and defensive coping strategies; and encourage feelings of self-efficacy. Further, the intervention is designed to resolve clearly delimited and circumscribed symptom clusters rather than broad maladaptive ways of relating to the self and others. Here there is an emphasis on support of ego-boundaries, reinforcement of body integrity, and exploitation of the positive transference to instill hope and remoralization. To some extent with this patient we might also expect there to be some discharge of disruptive emotion, especially that associated with sadness: here the challenge is to support affect regulation and containment via use of the patient's most typical and over-used defenses. Specific hypnotic technique then targets enhanced self-efficacy, tension reduction, and rehearsal of future adaptive coping. These interventions are fashioned from content emergent during hypnosis. With this patient in particular, training in self-hypnosis is indicated to further reinforce the importance of autonomy, self-reliance, and achievement that she so reveres.

All of this supportive work is not to say that powerful and important transference and countertransference will be absent in the therapy. To the contrary, one can expect that as the therapy progresses, Ellen may be inclined to project her own self-contempt onto the therapist from time to time (a kind of repetition of her relationship with her mother). This could lead to a very tense and tenuous working alliance. In a long-term uncovering therapy, these feelings would be patiently, but persistently, interpreted in service of insight. In a psychoanalytically informed, supportive, short-term intervention the aim is different: The therapist must find some way to mobilize the powerful positive affiliative yearnings that Ellen associates with her father, so as to neutralize or blunt the sharp edge of Ellen's darkly destructive, bad, internalized mother.

GENERAL APPROACH TO TREATMENT

A short-term, psychoanalytically informed, and supportive approach to Ellen's difficulties strives to employ hypnosis as per above. With an eye to Ellen's generally positive relationship with her father and his emphasis on achievement, the therapist might conduct him or herself as a kind of coach: someone who will teach Ellen the skills necessary to become more completely autonomous and in charge of her body. I would envision four stages of the therapy. First, an introduction to hypnosis with clinical assessment of hypnotizability; second, a period of exploration during which some elaboration of affect-laden themes related to the bathroom is encouraged and during which extant coping strategies (with associated images and memories) are identified; third, the coping strategies (in this case self-soothing strategies) are then further refined by teaching the patient self-hypnosis and instructing her to practice it daily; fourth, autonomy and self-efficacy are consolidated by employing desensitization and age-progression techniques.

An Introduction to Hypnosis With Clinical Assessment of Hypnotizability

After the patient and therapist agree on the treatment plan, an appointment is made for the patient's first experience with hypnosis. Ellen should be told that the initial session with hypnosis will involve no work with her bathroom inhibitions, but is instead simply a way of familiarizing her with hypnosis, and a means by which the therapist can assess how she responds to hypnosis. Above all else, Ellen must be told early and often that hypnosis is to be used as a means of gaining enhanced self-control and as a way to discover ways of increasing security and mastery. What follows is an induction, derived from Fromm & Nash (1996), with annotated process notes on the right.

The Eye Fixation/Relaxation Technique

Now I would like you to find a spot or an object on the wall or the ceiling, any spot will do. Perhaps it will be a spot on one of the paintings or perhaps a spot on the wall or an area where the sun strikes the wall or the ceiling in some particularly interesting manner.	Permissive attitude.
I would like you to find a spot and focus your eyes on that spot. I am going to call that spot the target. I would like you to focus your eyes on the target and listen to my words	Facilitating ego receptivity via focusing of attention and absorption.
By doing so you will find out what it is like to experience hypnosis.	Expectant attitude, language of discovery.
I assure you that no matter how deeply hypnotized you become you will remain in complete control. Hypnosis is really something that you and I do together.	Discouragement of passivity. Emphasis on interactive and relational features.
Eyes comfortable and heavy, focus on the target, continue focusing your eyes on the target and listening to my words.	Repetition.
There is nothing particularly mysterious or other worldly about hypnosis. It really is a quite natural ability that almost everyone has to some extent. In a way hypnosis is like being absorbed in a movie that you are watching and forgetting that you are part of the audience but instead you become part of the story, or perhaps you are one of those people who enjoys listening to music and can be transported by that music so that	Absorption. Passive voice.

everything else fades into the background and the music becomes center stage.

Continue to focus on the target. If your eyes should wander away from the target, that's fine but just bring them back to the target. You may notice that the target moves about or again changes color and if that should happen you can let it take place. Just concentrate on the target and listen to my words, allowing yourself to relax more and more. As you relax more and more you become aware of a certain kind of drowsiness, a relaxation coming across your entire body. Pretty soon you will notice that the object that you are staring at is changing a bit, perhaps it is becoming nebulous or perhaps changing colors . . . you find that the eyelids are beginning to get heavier and heavier and you are looking forward to finding out what it is like for your eyelids to grow heavy and close in this way . . . what it is like to go into hypnosis.

It is a strain to look at a single object for so long and it would be so nice to relax completely. *Allow* yourself to relax completely. As your eyelids become heavier and heavier you may notice that your eyes become wet from straining . . . so tired and wet from straining. Your eyes may soon close themselves and when they do you can let that happen . . . and drift into a comfortable state of relaxation because you will gradually, and at your own pace, be drifting into hypnosis.

Attention to resistance. Imagery and language of sensation. Expectant attitude.

Paced/graded suggestions. Repetition. Passive voice and language of discovery.

Repetition. Passive voice. Language of sensation. Making causal attributions. Paced/graded suggestions.

Soon your eyes will close themselves and when they do, you can really allow yourself to relax completely. As your *eyes* become heavier and your *body* becomes more and more limp and relaxed. Your eyes and your body drifting together into hypnosis. Your eyelids become heavier, blinking, blinking, [patient closes eyes].

Condensation and displacement. Repetition.

That's right, your eyes are closed now and they will remain closed for the duration of our work together but if you would wish to open your eyes while remaining deeply hypnotized, you could do so, but you would do so only for a moment and then close them again. But most likely your eyes will remain comfortably closed as you continue to listen effortlessly to my voice.

Permissive attitude. Attention to resistance. Passive voice. Monitoring and adjusting patient response.

Now that your eyes are closed you can really settle into a deep state of relaxation and hypnosis. In a moment I'm going to touch the very top of your head with my hand and when I do, I would like you to notice these warm waves of relaxation that begin to emanate from the very top of your head and pass through your entire body. In a little while I will touch the top of your head and when I do you will notice these wonderfully warm waves of relaxation that pass from the top of your head through your entire body. And you will become even more comfortably hypnotized. I am touching your head now. [therapist touches head for 2 seconds].

Utilization of positive transference via touching. Language of sensation.

Allow those warm waves of relaxation to radiate down, down through your entire body. Where do you feel these waves of relaxation right now? [patient responds "at the top of my head"]. Good, I am going to count from 1 to 20 and as I do you will become more and more relaxed and continue to enter a comfortable state of hypnosis in which you can experience many different things.

Language of sensation. Repetition. Nonconscious involvement. Expectant attitude.

1. . . . Allowing those warm comfortably warm waves of relaxation to pass down through the top of your head, across your facial muscles so that the muscles of your forehead, your eyes, your face become limp and relaxed, limp and relaxed . . .

Language of sensation. Repetition. Nonconscious involvement. Expectant attitude.

2. Allowing these warm waves of relaxation to pass down through the back of your head and into your neck, you know how tense your neck can become during the day but as these warm waves of relaxation pass through it, your neck becomes limp and relaxed, limp and relaxed.

3, 4. Allowing these warm waves of relaxation now to pass down through your shoulders, your shoulders now dropping limp and relaxed, limp and relaxed as you effortlessly listen to my voice and allow yourself to drift into a comfortable state of relaxation and hypnosis . . . 5, 6. Allowing these warm waves of relaxation to pass down through your shoulders and into your arms, down toward your elbows and down toward your wrists, your arms are now limp and relaxed as these warm waves of relaxation pass down through your hands pushing any excess

Passive voice. Nonconscious involvement.

energy in your arms and hands out through the ends of your finger tips.

7, 8. Now letting these warm waves of relaxation pass down through your chest and your upper back and you can be aware, perhaps not for the first time, that your breathing is becoming more and more slow and regular, slow and regular as these warm waves of relaxation pass down through your chest, down your back, limp and relaxed, beginning to become more and more sleepy and drowsy as your breathing becomes more and more slow and regular . . . 9, 10, Letting these warm waves of relaxation pass through your stomach muscles and your lower back. How good it feels to be so completely relaxed, how good it feels to feel the support of the couch and these wonderful waves of relaxation that transform the relationship between your body and your mind because you are comfortably drifting into hypnosis at your own pace.

Passive voice. Nonconscious involvement. Language of sensation. Utilization of positive transference. Making causal attributions.

11, 12. And you can be aware of how these warm waves of relaxation passed down through and beyond your waist, down your legs towards your knees and your thighs . . . relaxed, legs comfortably relaxed, allowing these warm waves of relaxation to continue to pass through your legs, over and through your legs . . . 13, 14. Down beyond your knees . . . 15. Down towards your ankles and pushing any excess energy out through the ends of your toes.

Imagery. Language of sensation. Passive voice.

16. More and more sleepy and drowsy, drifting alone, sleepier and drowsier, and as you listen to my voice, you can be aware that no matter how deeply hypnotized you become, you will always be able to hear my voice, you will always be able to hear my voice no matter how deeply hypnotized you become.

Discourage passivity. Elicitation of interactive features.

17. And you are now becoming more and more aware of how really relaxed and sleepy and dreamy you have become. More and more relaxed and as you are aware of how these warm waves of relaxation continue to permeate through your entire body, you can continue to listen effortlessly to my voice going deeper and deeper into hypnosis.

Language of discovery. Expectant attitude. Language of sensation.

18. More and more deeply relaxed, more and more sleepy, more and more drowsy. You are curious about how your mind and body work together in this hypnotic state . . . it is so comfortable, so pleasurable to be so deeply hypnotized and relaxed as your are now, with each breath it seems that you go deeper, more and more sleepy, more and more drowsy, yet listening effortlessly to my voice. We are working together to find out more about what hypnosis is like for you.

Repetition. Language of discovery. Discouragement of passivity. Elicitation of interactive and relational features.

19. It feels good to be drowsy, to be hypnotized . . . as we find out what hypnosis is like for you. 20. Deeply relaxed and deeply hypnotized.

Labeling patient's response. Language of discovery. Elicitation of interactive and relational features.

Deepening techniques can include a number of fairly common images and approaches. The following somato-attentional technique might be particularly well-suited for the work with Ellen because it gently targets what is for Ellen an area of importance—the relationship she has with her body and its sensations. Again a brief example of such a protocol is included below:

Now that you are relaxed and deeply hypnotized, I would like you to be aware of your breathing for a moment. One way to go more deeply into hypnosis is to pay attention to your breathing for awhile.	Expectant but permissive attitude. Absorption and focusing of attention.
Notice, as you breathe slowly and normally, how good it feels to exhale . . . inhale and exhale [the therapist may time the words "inhale" and "exhale" to the patient's actual breathing pattern] and as you continue to feel all these sensations the way your muscles move quite naturally and effortlessly to facilitate your slow and normal breathing, you become more and more relaxed with each passing breath. More and more hypnotized.	Repetition. Monitoring and adjusting to patient response. Labeling patient responses and making causal attributions.
It's as though every time you exhale, you purge your body of the stress and tension of the day. Every time you exhale, while you are hypnotized, every time you exhale, without even thinking about it, you will become as deeply and comfortably hypnotized as you wish.	Passive voice and facilitation of nonconscious involvement. Paced and graded suggestions.
Now I am going to count from 1 to 25 . . . and as I do, you will go more deeply and comfortably into hypnosis . . . because every time you exhale, your body will become more and more limp and relaxed . . . your mind will become more and more clear, and you will find yourself curious about how your mind and your body work together in this relaxed and interesting state	Language of sensation. Passive voice and facilitation of nonconscious involvement. Language of discovery. Discouragement of passivity.

[the therapist might choose to
time the counts with the
patient's breathing]. 1. More and
more relaxed, 2, 3, etc.

A series of suggestions designed to assess the patient's hypnotizability can then be administered. Some suggestions might be hand lowering, hands together, hypnotic dream, and suggestions for hand warmth. Hypnosis is then terminated and sufficient time is reserved for a thorough posthypnotic interview. Assuming the patient's experience with hypnosis is positive, the therapy then moves on to the second phase of the treatment, exploration. If the patient is rendered overly anxious by hypnosis, or is low hypnotizable, nonhypnotic alternatives to treatment might be considered.

Period of Exploration

The second phase of the treatment involves the search for effective methods for containing disruptive affect associated with the bathroom symptoms. Typically in this phase of short-term work, the patient's ability to enter hypnosis easily is further refined, deepening is increased, the duration of inductions is decreased, and the patient is introduced to some carefully modulated uncovering techniques, with an emphasis on mastery and self-efficacy. Induction time can be decreased quite easily for good hypnotic subjects with something like the following procedure:

As you remain deeply hypnotized I will now help you to learn how to enter hypnosis easily and quickly. Whenever you are in this room, and in your chair, and whenever we want to use hypnosis in our work together, all you need do is to close your eyes and listen to me count from one to five . . . and when we do this together you will find that by the count of "five" you will be as deeply relaxed and hypnotized as you are now . . . perhaps even more so. When I reach the count of "five" you will be deeply relaxed, finding yourself walking down the spiral staircase that you liked so much today. Whenever we are in this room together, and we wish to use hypnosis in our work together, all you need do is close your eyes and listen comfortably to me count from one to five. And by the time I reach the count of "five" you will be deeply relaxed and hypnotized . . . walking down that very special spiral staircase.

More time can then be devoted to exploring with Ellen images, metaphors, words, sensations, or memories that are associated with self-efficacy and safety. These techniques include hypnotic dream, affect bridge, age regression, theater metaphor, clouds technique, or any number of other generally expressive techniques delineated in Fromm and Nash (1996). The point of these techniques is to allow Ellen as much latitude as possible to define her own solution to the problem. The affect bridge technique involves making suggestions for the relevant affect to emerge with great force in hypnosis. When the patient appears to be fully involved with this feeling, the suggestion is made that "you will now go back in time to an important moment when you first felt this way." The theater metaphor technique involves suggesting that the patient is in a theater audience about to watch the curtain go up on a one-act play that has something to do with his or her problem. The cloud technique invites the patient to imagine clouds floating by overhead. The patient is then asked to describe what these clouds look like. What follow are examples of two other uncovering techniques which might be used initially with Ellen: The first gently encourages emotional expression; the second facilitates mastery.

The Dream

> In a little while I am going to stop talking, and when I do I would like you to have a dream . . . a real dream . . . just the kind you might have if you were asleep at night. But this will be a special dream . . . this will be a dream regarding what your feeling concerning bathrooms is all about . . . you're going to have a dream . . . a dream about what this bathroom business is all about . . . whatever you dream will help us understand how to solve this problem . . . Now I am going to stop talking for a little while. When I do, you will sleep and have a dream . . . a dream about what this bathroom problem is all about . . . a dream that will help us in our work together . . . when I speak again you will remember everything about your dream, and you will be able to tell me all about it. . . .

Haven From Shame and Fear

> Now that we know from your dream (or other source) how important fear and shame are in your bathroom problems, I would like you to now listen very carefully to what I have to say. In a little while I will begin counting from 1 to 10 . . . and by the time I reach the count of 10 you will find yourself in a wonderful place feeling perfectly safe, good about yourself and your body, and just feeling wonderful. Now this might be a place or situation that you remember, or one that you have read about, or maybe even one that will happen in the future . . . or perhaps something else. But when I reach the count of 10 you will be there . . . and there will be utterly no room for shame or fear . . . you will be feeling so completely, so solidly safe and good about yourself. . . there will be no room for anything else . . . 1, soon you will be there in this wonderful place, maybe doing something or maybe

just doing nothing, but feeling good and safe. 2, 3, more and more completely there . . . 4, 5, 6, soon you will be there . . . no room for anything strained or stressful . . . 7, 8, 9 and you will be able to tell me all about it . . . 10 . . . Where are you?

Over the course of 5–8 sessions, these types of techniques are used to first identify and then refine personally relevant coping mechanisms. I would anticipate that Ellen would settle on one of two broad classes of self-affirming scenarios: either a transparently narcissistic and active scenario involving victory, achievement, and successful competition (winning an athletic event, celebrating academic achievement, defeating an evil enemy), or a more primitive and passive scenario involving simply "being" with some benevolent object or in some wonderfully durable safe place (e.g., being in a special chair all curled-up; embracing an early favored object like a teddy bear; quietly contemplating a stream, a beach, or the mountains; being with a special friend but doing nothing). I will assume that Ellen surprises the therapist by demonstrating some tolerance for her passive–dependent yearnings, and finds imagery associated with her childhood teddy bear to be dramatically evocative of safety and acceptance.

Self-hypnosis and Further Refinement

The next phase involves teaching Ellen self-hypnosis. A general protocol for teaching such patients is as follows:

Now that you are deeply relaxed and hypnotized, once again with your teddy where no discomfort of any sort can reach you, listen to my words carefully. Whenever you wish to go into hypnosis, whenever you wish to take control of the sensations you have in this way, all you need to do is to find a reasonably comfortable place to be, shut your eyes, and count slowly to yourself from one to five. As you count you will note that your breathing changes, the way your body feels changes, and you become transported once again into that wonderful chair with your teddy bear. So that by the time you reach the count of "five" you will always be deeply hypnotized, and in the wonderfully relaxed state you are now in, with your teddy . . . utterly at peace with yourself and your teddy. you will feel the texture of his fur . . . and know that things are good and safe. You may find that you actually go even more completely and deeply into hypnosis with practice.

Whenever you wish to go into hypnosis, all you need do is find a comfortable place, close your eyes, and count silently to yourself from one to five. You will find that your mind and body are effortlessly transformed back into this peaceful state of hypnosis. A state in which you have a different and better kind of control over your sensations. At the count of 5 you will always be right there with your teddy, calm, tranquil, free of all undue discomfort. Once you are thus hypnotized, once you are once again with teddy, you can stay for as long as you like. You need only stay there one or two minutes to obtain the benefit of hypnosis, or you may choose to stay longer. But whenever you wish to bring yourself out of self-hypnosis, all you need to do is take a deep breath in, and open your eyes, and you will be wide awake . . . refreshed . . . alert . . . and completely comfortable. You can be surprised how far this refreshed, comfortable, and alert feeling will extend in the remainder of the day. You will practice self-hypnosis in this way at least twice a day. For now, just remain hypnotized, as you listen to my voice.

[Therapist repeats the general instructions of the second paragraph]

Now, in a little while you will come out of hypnosis. Soon you will take a deep breath . . . open your eyes . . . and you will be wide awake. You will remember everything we did today. You will find you are especially clear on how to do self-hypnosis. After you have a chance to talk a bit about your experience today I will ask you to practice self-hypnosis right here in the office.

After termination of the hypnosis, the patient and therapist discuss the work of the day. The therapist then reminds the patient of the self-hypnosis instructions and asks the patient to practice hypnosis in the consulting room:

Now what I would like you to do is to go ahead and use self-hypnosis right now with me here. [Therapist reminds patient of instructions]. When you are there with teddy, comfortably hypnotized, just say the word "Now", so that I know you are there. When you do, I will speak to you, and help you go even more deeply into hypnosis. Now I will be quiet for awhile . . . go ahead and go into hypnosis . . . just saying "Now" when you are there with teddy again.

When the patient signals that she is hypnotized, the therapist probes for her experience, repeating by-now familiar phrases associated with increased depth. It is once again suggested that Ellen employ self-hypnosis at least twice a day, more if needed. The self-hypnosis sessions need be no more than one or two minutes each, but they can be longer if Ellen so wishes. Ellen is then asked to come out of hypnosis as she would when doing self-hypnosis alone. The therapist then queries Ellen about the self-hypnosis experience, again reiterating the instruction to practice self-hypnosis at least twice a day. The first order of business on the subsequent session is to discuss how Ellen found self-hypnosis to be. For the most part, patients who respond well to traditional heterohypnosis respond well to self-hypnosis. Patients like Ellen, who struggle with conflicts around autonomy, will sometimes actually report that they go deeper into hypnosis when they do it alone. On the other hand, strikingly dependent patients may resist self-hypnosis initially, but this is rarely unmanageable.

The remainder of the refinement and utilization period is devoted to reestablishing Ellen's connection with her own viscera—thereby disentangling desperate wishes to eliminate passive–dependent yearnings from the eliminative processes themselves. Like an anorectic whose wish to not eat is really a counterphobic derivative of profoundly intense yearnings to be fed, Ellen's wish to avoid the eliminative process is derivative of intense yearnings to be changed by a loving and accepting other. In both types of patients, fear and gastrointestinal sensations become quite confused.

Hypnotic suggestions can be given that enhance interoceptive awareness by directing attention to visceral cues in the context of safety and support. The goal is to familiarize the patient with bowel sensations and thereby minimize the chance of gross misperception. For example, after the usual initial experience with hypnosis and following suggestions for relaxation and support, the therapist might suggest to Ellen the following:

> Now pay very close attention to your lower abdomen . . . every sensation you are having right now . . . you are relaxed, comfortable and hypnotized . . . with teddy, and you are able in this state to feel every sensation . . . what is there and what is not there . . . what is your bowels and what is not . . . tell me what you feel right now . . . you can even create feelings in your gut . . . perhaps right now you begin to feel tingling in your bladder . . . go ahead . . . imagine tingling in your bladder . . . now you *really* feel the tingling. . . .

Following some elaboration of this work, the therapist can begin to offer metaphors of voluntary regulation, for instance:

> You are becoming better and better able to know what is happening in your bladder and gut . . . better able to distinguish what has to do with your eliminative process and better able to control every aspect of it. . . . You will become increasingly able to just relax and experience the security that comes with taking more and more control of these processes . . . there is just no room for any interfering feeling . . . and that teddy will be there for you no matter what. Finally now, you are taking control of your body . . . your body will resume its normal functioning . . . like a clock . . . effortless and easy regulation. . . .

Over this phase of therapy, then, typically the therapist begins hypnotic treatment by asking Ellen to use self-hypnosis, and to signal the therapist when she is deeply hypnotized. The therapist then can employ hypnotic suggestions to enable Ellen to experience visceral sensations related to elimination while remaining profoundly relaxed. If the therapist so chooses, this procedure can graduate to something similar to a desensitization procedure during which Ellen imagines remaining poised and competent in a host of bathroom settings.

Consolidation

For several sessions, as symptoms hopefully abate, the therapist can employ procedures which consolidate and support ego-mastery. Prominent among these procedures is age progression in which Ellen might be "moved ahead" in time to her trip to China. Suggestions of support, pride, and achievement can be coupled with ever more flexible use of bathrooms both in vitro and in vivo:

> As I continue to count forward, time moves forward . . . there, now you are in China. You are feeling confident . . . walking anywhere you wish. Where are you now? . . . Yes, you are doing quite well. Your body is really working quite automatically, like a clock, taking care of itself. That is right, you are in complete control of your body. . . . Now what is happening? Where are you? That's right, everything is fine, like clock work . . .

This procedure is then extended across time and situations.

CONCLUSION

One complication of the termination process may be a tendency for Ellen to spoil (or soil) her accomplishment as a way of avoiding the anticipated loss of the therapist, thereby engendering a return to the therapist in shame. If it occurs the therapist must patiently interpret this development not as a failure, but as an understandable response to the sadness of separation. In sum, the proposed therapy integrates psychoanalytic formulation, short-term objectives, and hypnotic technique. But of course the bedrock of this work is careful and thorough formulation from an interpersonal perspective. Hypnotic technique, then, is a natural derivative of the clinical process of uncovering, expression, and ego-mastery.

REFERENCE

Fromm, E., & Nash, M. R. (1996). *Psychoanalysis and Hypnosis.* Madison, CT: International Universities Press.

16

USING HYPNOSIS IN RATIONAL–EMOTIVE BEHAVIOR THERAPY IN THE CASE OF ELLEN

ALBERT ELLIS

I see this client as having, in all probability, a personality disorder, with obsessive–compulsive disorder (OCD) and depressive tendencies. She was born of, as well as in part reared by, a seriously disturbed mother and I would suspect, and probe for, other disturbed people among her mother's and possibly her father's close relatives (Cloninger, Svrakic, & Przylbek, 1993; Ellis, 1994b; Steketee, 1993). Unlike other people with strong depression and OCD tendencies, this client doesn't have serious low frustration tolerance, but has worked hard most of her life to become a physician, an effective mother, and a "good" wife. She has thereby compensated for her underlying deficiencies and her predisposition to panic when others may even slightly disapprove of her. Being bright, witty, and articulate, she has used her high-level assets to achieve *conditional* self-acceptance: That is, she often accepts herself as a "good person" because she functions well as a physician, as a wife, and as a mother. But she has a strong tendency not to accept herself *unconditionally*—just because she is alive and human. Her conditional self-acceptance is underlaid by her ceaselessly spying on herself to make absolutely sure that she doesn't act stupidly or badly and that there is no chance that she is disapproved of by significant others.

When this client does badly in her own eyes and when she thinks (rightly or wrongly) that others despise her, she feels inadequate and insecure as a person and finds it most difficult to forgive herself for her "poor"

335

behavior. Being intelligent and hardworking, however, she works at correcting her "mistakes" and at winning back others' approval, usually succeeds in these respects, and therefore goes back to conditional self-acceptance rather than to unconditional self-acceptance (Ellis, 1972/1990, 1973; Ellis & Velten, 1992; Hauck, 1992; Mills, 1993).

Like most inveterate self-castigators, this woman has a severe secondary symptom: disturbance about her disturbance. Thus, when she makes herself anxious about flushing a toilet or being heard urinating or defecating, she also deprecates herself for feeling anxious—and for having others *know* she is anxious. In terms of rational-emotive behavior therapy (REBT), she begins her vicious cycle of disturbance by taking her sensible preference for doing well and winning others' approval and by making it, or constructing it, into an absolutist *demand*: "At all times and under all circumstances, I *must not* let others know I am doing a 'dirty' act like urinating or defecating because if they discover this and despise me, they're right! I *am* a *no-good, dirty person!*" (Beck & Emery, 1985; Ellis, 1962, 1986; Wachtel, 1994; Walen, DiGiuseppe, & Dryden, 1992: Yankura & Dryden, 1990).

Once she demands that she have complete cleanliness and approval—which, of course, is impossible for her to guarantee—this client makes herself very anxious (and often panicked). But, noting her own "wrong" and "silly" failings, she then (secondarily) demands "I *must not* be anxious! I *have to* hide my panic from others and thereby I *must* get them to like me!" She then feels panicked—and self-deprecating—about her panic and is convinced that she absolutely must avoid it. So she compulsively avoids urinating and defecating (Ellis, 1979).

This client also probably has a tertiary symptom—about her psychotherapy—which she brings on with a third demand: "I *must* use my therapy to effectively help me overcome my anxiety! If I don't improve, I'm really no good for not doing better in therapy—as, of course, I *absolutely must!*"

If my case conception is correct, this inveterate self-downer is defaming herself, first, for being "dirtier" than she should be and for letting people know how "dirty" she is. Second, she is demeaning herself for being so anxious and neurotic. Third, she may well be shaming herself for not improving over the years—and in fact, getting worse—and for not using psychotherapy successfully. She thus has triple-headed self-denigration!

It is possible that this client picked up her horror of being heard urinating and defecating from her disturbed mother, or that because her mother was too open about her body, her daughter is now going to opposite extremes and forcing herself to be too closed. But the question still remains: Why did the client take her mother's behavior so seriously (when her siblings may not have done so)? My answer is, whatever the family or environmental reasons for the client's obsession with cleanliness, she prob-

336   *ALBERT ELLIS*

ably has a natural tendency to take some things too seriously and to obsess about them. Therefore, as a therapist, I had better show her what she *easily* and *naturally* does in these respects, to help her to unconditionally accept herself with these (innate and required) tendencies, and to teach her several cognitive, emotive, and behavioral methods of ameliorating them (Ellis, 1994a, 1994b).

TREATMENT PLAN AND CONSIDERATIONS

My concerns in treating this client would be (a) to show her that she has her presenting symptoms—anxiety and obsessive–compulsive thoughts and behaviors about people finding her "dirty"—but that, just as importantly, she has secondary symptoms of anxiety about anxiety, horror of being anxious and obsessive–compulsive; (b) to show her that both her primary and secondary symptoms stem largely from her *dire need*, rather than her healthy *preference*, for doing well and obtaining approval of others; and (c) to teach her how to use a number of cognitive, emotive, and behavioral methods to unconditionally accept herself as a good person whether or not she performs well in life (or experiences disturbances) and whether or not significant others approve of her behavior and of her.

I would try to achieve a good collaborative relationship with this client by listening to her carefully, giving a tentative hypothesis about her problems, showing her clearly that I unconditionally accept her in spite of her foolish and self-defeating behaviors, and indicating that I have knowledge and competence to help her without taking over and insisting that she do things my way. I would not expect this kind of model, by itself, to enable her to unconditionally accept herself.

In fact, if I merely modeled unconditional positive regard—as Carl Rogers (1961) and some other existentialist therapists might do—I would see this as being risky. For she then could wrongly conclude, "Because Albert Ellis completely accepts me with my flaws and worries, that means I am really a good person." This would be a dangerous conclusion on her part because she would really mean, "Now that my therapist accepts me, I am okay." This is conditional self acceptance, and would tend to enhance her view that when people *outside* of therapy did not unconditionally accept her—which, of course, most of them probably would not—back to being a no-goodnik she would go!

So I would be determined to give her unconditional acceptance and also to teach her how to think about it and be able, with or without my help, to give it to herself. Thus, I would actively and philosophically teach her how to use the two main ways to achieve unconditional self acceptance. REBT practitioners often explain to their clients (a) "I am okay (a 'good' person) just because I am alive and human, whether or not I perform well and whether or not others approve of me"; (b) "I am neither okay nor non-okay. Once I establish goals and values—such as to live happily and to tolerate other people—I am a person who does good things (that is, which enhance my goals) and a person who also does bad things (things that sabotage my values). So I'll only rate, measure, and evaluate what I think, feel, and do and refuse to evaluate my global *self, being, essence,* or *personhood.*"

I believe, perhaps falsely, that if I teach my clients these, and other, methods of unconditional self-acceptance, as well as model it and show them (by my manner, tone, gestures, and verbal reactions) how I fully accept them as persons, that they are much more likely to learn to unqualifiedly accept themselves (but not what they *do*) than if I only accept them or only teach them to accept themselves (Dryden, 1994; Ellis, 1994b; Ellis & Velten, 1992).

In this client's case, I would work long and hard to help her fully accept herself, and thereby stop damning herself for performing "badly," for being disapproved, for being neurotically anxious, and for anything else she did "wrongly." In many ways, I would try to encourage her to have the philosophy of "accepting the sinner but not her (or his) sins."

If this client became too involved with me (as she had been with her father) or was afraid of involvement with me (as she might be with her husband), I would show her how she was overgeneralizing and creating this kind of transference, and how she could realistically view me as a helpful therapist and not as a father-figure or husband-figure.

I would also look at my possible countertransference—meaning how I was prejudiced in favor of a client because of her appearance, status, or other traits, or how I was prejudiced against her for various reasons, such as her antisexuality. If I found such prejudices in myself, I would move to minimalize them and not let them interfere with my therapeutic endeavors (Ellis, 1994b).

SPECIFIC RATIONAL–EMOTIVE BEHAVIOR THERAPY COGNITIVE METHODS

In addition to the treatment methods already outlined, I would use a number of rational-emotive behavior therapy cognitive methods. Thus, I would dispute and show the client how to keep disputing her imperative musts, such as, "I must at all times achieve outstandingly"; "I have to win important peoples' approval"; "I'm no good when I foolishly make myself anxious—as I *must* not!"; "I absolutely must lick my emotional problems and it's awful when I don't" (Ellis, 1991).

I would work out with the client some rational coping statements and have her write them down and work at believing them. For example, "It would be great if I were not anxious and not obsessive–compulsive. But if I am, it's only inconvenient and not the end of the world!" (Ellis & Abrahms, 1994; Ellis & Velten, 1992).

I would encourage her to record her sessions with me and listen to them, review them, and discuss her thoughts about them. I would work out cognitive homework with her, so that she found her *musts* and other beliefs, and practiced changing them to sensible preferences. I would show her how to make a list of the disadvantages of indulging in her compulsive avoidance of urinating and defecating and to go over these disadvantages consciously until she easily kept them in mind. I would encourage her to use the principles of REBT to understand how her relatives, friends, and patients frequently upset themselves and to practice teaching them some of the REBT techniques, so that she could better learn and practice them herself (Bernard, 1991, 1993; Ellis & Abrahms, 1978; Ellis & Velten, 1992).

As I always do when using rational emotive behavior therapy with clients, I would use with this anxious, self-denigrating woman a number of forceful, experiential, emotive methods. For example:

- *Rational emotive therapy*: The patient should vividly imagine a "bad" event—like being caught flushing the toilet by a friend—and let herself feel very anxious and self-downing. Then she should work at changing her feelings to the healthy, appropriate ones of disappointment and frustration, instead of horror (Ellis, 1993a; Maultsby, 1971).
- *Shame-attacking exercises*: Encourage the client to deliberately do a "shameful" or "humiliating" act in public without feeling ashamed or self-denigrating (Ellis, 1969/1987).
- *Forceful coping statements*: Help the client to tell herself very forcefully and vigorously coping statements like, "I'm never a worthless, rotten person, no matter how bad some of my actions are" (Ellis & Abrahms, 1978).
- *Roleplaying*: Let this disturbed client role-play herself in a "dangerous" situation and show her how to handle the situation and how to stop disturbing herself as she is in it.
- *Reverse role playing*: The therapist should rigidly hold one of a client's dysfunctional beliefs while the client forcefully disputes it (Ellis & Abrahms, 1994; Ellis & Velten, 1992).
- *Humor*: Use humorous disputing of the client's self-defeating ideas (Ellis, 1977a, 1977b).

I also use a number of behavioral methods and would use several with this client, such as:

- *In vivo desensitization or exposure*: Encourage the client to take risks she always avoids, such as flushing the toilet when someone could easily hear it (Ellis & Velten, 1992).
- *Encouragement to stay in uncomfortable situations*: Help the client to stay in "bad" situations—with, for example, a very critical acquaintance—until she reduces her horror about it, and only then choose to leave it (Ellis & Dryden, 1996).
- *Reinforcement*: Have the client reinforce herself with some enjoyable act only contingent upon her doing some difficult homework she has agreed to do.
- *Penalization*: Encourage the client to penalize herself by performing some obnoxious activity when she fails to carry out a difficult homework assignment (Ellis & Abrahms, 1978).
- *Skill training*: Help the client acquire useful skills, such as communication, assertion, or sex skills (Ellis & Abrahms, 1994; Ellis & Velten, 1992).

THE ROLE OF HYPNOSIS IN TREATMENT

Would I use hypnosis in the treatment of this client? Usually not, because I only occasionally use hypnosis with REBT, as hypnosis tends to stress suggestion and autosuggestion, or the displacement of irrational beliefs with more rational coping statements. Even when this works—which it sometimes does—it is an inelegant solution to the problem of disturbance. Thus, if I suggest to this client, when I have hypnotized her, that she tell herself, "I can shamelessly let others know that I urinate and defecate," she may accept this suggestion and temporarily follow it, but even so, she may still basically believe, "But if people hear me flushing the toilet and think I am no good for using it, they are right. I really *am* no good!" (Ellis, 1984, 1985, 1993b).

I would rather, instead, help this client clearly see her irrational belief and actively and forcefully dispute it in several ways, until she really convinces herself that this belief is invalid. If she mainly, under hypnosis, accepts *my* view that flushing the toilet is all right, she may only weakly and conditionally believe this. But if she keeps proving to herself that it is not shameful, as I can probably teach her to do without hypnotic suggestion, she is more solidly in control of her own emotional destiny.

Secondly, I am probably more likely, without hypnosis and with general REBT philosophic discussion, to show this client that many acts (like theft, murder, and foolish behavior are "wrong" or "stupid" but that *nothing*—yes, nothing—is unforgivable and shameful in the sense that one is a *bad* person for doing this act. Under hypnosis, where the client mainly listens and hardly discusses the problem with the therapist, profound philosophical discussions and dialogues are not too likely to occur or to be useful.

I would tend to use hypnosis with this client (and with other clients) under these kinds of conditions:

1. If a client resists using the usual REBT cognitive, emotive, and behavioral methods and seems to require some special technique, such as hypnosis, that might add something new or different to these methods.
2. If a client is enthusiastically in favor of hypnosis, and resists working at therapy unless it is included.
3. If the client seems to be very suggestible and not too capable of or inclined to think or to work for herself.
4. If the client (wrongly) thinks that hypnosis is magical, will not change easily, and when her low frustration tolerance requires such "magic" and "ease" to help her work at improvement.
5. If the client rigidly holds some antitherapeutic idea, such as, "I'll never be able to change! I've tried everything and nothing works so far and never will!"
6. If the client has used REBT and other normally effective methods and seems to be getting worse instead of improving.
7. If the client seems to be blocked in finding traumatic activating events, in being in touch with her disturbed feelings, or in finding her self-defeating beliefs, and if she might be able to unblock and unrepress herself under hypnosis.
8. If the client is discovering and understanding her dysfunctional, irrational beliefs, but is only lightly and occasionally disputing them and still strongly promulgates them and even enhances them.

STRATEGIES AND TECHNIQUES OF HYPNOSIS

I would first, as I mention above, use regular REBT with the client we are considering and use it without hypnosis. If for any of the above reasons it was not working too well after several weeks or months, I might then suggest (or accept her suggestion) that we use hypnosis. On agreeing to do so, I would attempt to put her in a light hypnotic trance or a state of profound relaxation by employing the usual direct techniques of suggestion that many therapists use, and that even Milton Erickson frequently employed (Haley, 1973).

Thus, I would suggest that she relax her muscles, from her toes to her head, and do her best to go—because she really wants to go—into a deep state of relaxation or hypnosis (Jacobson, 1938). I would try to induce her to listen carefully to everything I was suggesting to her, to heed what I was telling her, and to follow up on my instructions posthypnotically. I would be strongly authoritative—though not authoritarian—in my hypnotic and in my therapeutic suggestions to her, as I have indicated in detail in previous descriptions of my particular hypnotic technique (Ellis, 1986, 1993b).

Once I believed that the client was in a fully relaxed or hypnotic state, I would give her REBT instructions, such as the following.

> As I have been showing you with rational-emotive behavior therapy, you seem to have both a primary disturbance (panic about being discovered urinating, defecating, and even flushing the toilet) and a secondary symptom about your primary symptom, namely, a horror of being panicked or phobic. So I want you to resolve and work on the secondary symptom first—to give up your horror and panic about being panicked.
>
> To do this, you look for the irrational beliefs that you are holding to create your anxiety about your anxiety. Forget, for the moment, your original panic and phobia about being discovered urinating or defecating. We'll deal with that later. But first, after you come out of this hypnotic state and go back to year real life, I want you to remember (yes, remember!) posthypnotically that you have this panic about panicking and that in many ways it makes your original panic worse and blocks you from giving it up. For if you keep thinking, as you often do, "I *must not* be panicked! I *have to*, I've *got to*, I *must* overcome it," will your demands actually work? Of course not! As far as I can see, this is one of the main reasons you are getting phobic.
>
> So look at your absolutist *musts* and *demands*, question them, challenge them, dispute them, as we have previously discussed in REBT. Ask yourself, "Why *must* I not be panicked? Where is it written that I have to lose my phobia? In what way am I a weak, inadequate person if I never overcome my horror of being overheard flushing the toilet? Why is it *awful* and *terrible* to continue to have my silly avoidance of urinating and defecating?
>
> Think about these questions. Answer them! Show yourself— really prove to yourself—that there is *no* reason you *must* not be panicked, though it would be highly preferable if you no longer were. Conclude that it is only written in your head (and nowhere else!) that you *have to* lose your phobia. Figure out that in no way are you a weak, inadequate person, if you never overcome your horror of being overheard flushing a toilet. No, you would then only be a person who at times acts weakly and inadequately. Clearly see that it is definitely not awful and terrible, but only a damned inconvenience, for you to continue to have your silly avoidance of urinating and defecating.
>
> That's right—think about the self-defeating beliefs that are mainly creating your anxiety about your anxiety, your irrational fear of

your irrational fear. Think and think about your dysfunctional beliefs until you give them up—or at least have significantly reduced them. Work at your thinking—yes, work at rethinking!

I would very vigorously and repetitively go over these REBT instructions and urge this client to implement them over and over when she is in her regular posthypnotic state. I would also, while she is still hypnotized, instruct her to use some of the emotive–evocative and behavioral REBT techniques to help her minimize her anxiety and her anxiety about her anxiety. Thus, I would probably encourage her to do shame-attacking exercises whenever she risked doing some "shameful" act—such as acting foolishly in public—and to learn not to denigrate herself if people laughed at her for doing it. And I might show her how to use rational–emotive imagery (Maultsby, 1971; Ellis 1993a). I would encourage her to imagine some of the worst things that might happen to her, such as being scorned for defecating in a friend's bathroom, to let herself feel very anxious and depressed about this imagined "horror," and then to work at making herself feel, instead, only appropriately sorry and disappointed.

Behaviorally, if I had several hypnotherapy sessions with this client, I would encourage her to do in vivo desensitization posthypnotically: such as, to risk talking about her phobias to some people, and then actually use a friend's toilet and loudly flush the toilet several times, knowing that the friend would hear her do so. I would give this client several cognitive, emotive, and behavioral techniques to use posthypnotically. Occasionally, I would give her an exercise, such as rational–emotive imagery, while she was actually under hypnosis. Usually, however, especially for her first hypnotic session, I would do all the talking while she merely listened and didn't interrupt me; and I would tell her exactly how to do rational–emotive imagery and other homework exercises, but not necessarily get her to do them yet. I would also give her handouts, books, and cassettes to read and listen to that would instruct her to do various exercises posthypnotically (Ellis, 1994b; Ellis & Dryden, 1996, Ellis & Velten, 1992).

I would record my hypnotic sessions for the client and give her a copy of the recording to listen to for several more days in a row. In using this recording, she might tend to go into a deeper relaxation hypnotic state than she did at first; she might hear my instructions more clearly after several repetitions; and, hopefully, she would become more suggestible and cooperative in following out the posthypnotic assignments.

Because of the use of tapes, I might only have one or two hypnotic sessions with the client, although I might previously and subsequently have a greater number of REBT nonhypnotic sessions. If our first hypnotic session worked well in regard to, let us say, alleviating the client's anxiety about her anxiety, other sessions might mainly be about her original anxiety and phobia—or about any other phobias that she brought up in the course of our sessions. If the hypnotic sessions did not work well, they might be repeated; or, after a while, they might be replaced with regular nonhypnotic REBT.

After the hypnotic sessions, the client would be checked to see if she had actually done the posthypnotic homework; and if not, what irrational beliefs she held to block herself from doing it. If she had actually done the homework, I would discover how well it worked, when and why it did not work, and how it could be improved in subsequent hypnotic or nonhypnotic REBT sessions.

Supplementary aspects and methods of REBT might also be recommended for this client. She might be encouraged to join one of my regular therapy groups, to participate in an REBT marathon event or group, to take in an REBT nine-hour one-day intensive, or to participate in other programs that we hold at the psychological clinic of the Institute for Rational–Emotive Therapy in New York. She might attend, for example, our lectures, our four-hour workshops on specific psychotherapeutic topics, and my regular Friday Night Workshop, where I interview individual volunteers in public, show them how to use REBT with their problems, and then throw the workshop open to active questioning, discussing, and disputing by other members of the audience. Usually, therefore, clients with whom I use hypnosis I encourage to use regular REBT and other rational–emotive behavioral procedures in addition to their hypnotic sessions (Bernard, 1991, 1993; Bernard & Wolfe, 1993; Dryden, 1994; Dryden & Hill, 1993; Ellis, 1994b; Ellis & Abrahms, 1994; Ellis & Dryden, 1996; Ellis & Velten, 1992; Walen, DiGiuseppe, & Dryden, 1992; Yankura & Dryden, 1990).

CONCLUSION

I see the client in this case as a woman with a severe phobia and obsession, with extreme anxiety and anxiety about her anxiety, and as probably having a personality disorder, such as an avoidant personality. I would especially work with her on her panic about her panic, and then on her original panic. Above all, I would try to help her with her self-denigration and her dire need for others' approval.

Because of her intelligence, natural competence, and some degree of high frustration tolerance, I would think that the prognosis for distinct improvement, though hardly for a thoroughgoing cure, is good. I might well never use hypnosis with her but, if I did, I would probably use it only a few times, would give her clearcut posthypnotic instructions, would record her sessions, and would give her the recordings to audit a number of times. I would use hypnosis along with regular individual sessions of REBT and would likely encourage her to participate in some other kinds of REBT procedures and processes.

Preferably, the kind of hypnotic sessions that I use with clients like this one should be compared in research studies with groups of clients using only regular nonhypnotic REBT sessions and those using hypnosis, to see if hypnosis significantly adds effectiveness to the REBT usage. My guess is that it sometimes does and often does not.

My method of combining rational–emotive behavior therapy with hypnosis differs somewhat from that of other clinicians who have combined the two modalities. Thus, Golden, Dowd, and Friendberg (1987) are closer to regular cognitive–behavior therapy in their approach and do relatively little to find the client's core musturbatory beliefs and to actively dispute them. Stanton (1977, 1989) uses REBT with hypnosis, but mainly teaches clients, when they are in a hypnotic state, rational coping statements.

Tosi and his associates (Tosi, 1974; Tosi & Baisden, 1984; Tosi, Fuller, & Gwynne, 1980; Tosi, Judah, & Murphy, 1989; Tosi & Marzella, 1977; Tosi & Rearden, 1976) use REBT with a number of emotive–evocative methods and find that this combination, if used with hypnosis, is effective. Studies comparing REBT by itself and REBT combined with hypnosis have yet to be done. They could well prove to be illuminating.

REFERENCES

Beck, A. T., & Emery, G. (1985). *Anxiety disorders and phobias*. New York: Basic Books.

Bernard, M. E. (Ed.). (1991). *Using rational–emotive therapy effectively: A practitioner's guide*. New York: Plenum.

Bernard, M. E. (1993). *Staying rational in an irrational world*. New York: Carol Publishing.

Bernard, M. E., & Wolfe, J. L. (1993). *The RET resource book for practitioners*. New York: Institute for Rational–Emotive Therapy.

Cloninger, C. R., Svrakic, D. M., & Przybek, T. R. (1993). A psychological model of temperament and character. *Archives of General Psychiatry, 50*(12), 975–990.

Dryden, W. (1994). *Progress in rational–emotive behavior therapy*. London: Whurr.

Dryden, W., & Hill, L. K. (Eds.). (1993). *Innovations in rational-emotive therapy*. Newbury Park, CA: Sage.

Ellis, A. (1962). *Reason and emotion in psychotherapy*. Secaucus, NJ: Citadel.

Ellis, A. (1973). *Humanistic psychotherapy: The rational–emotive approach*. New York: McGraw Hill.

Ellis, A. (1977a). Fun as psychotherapy. *Rational Living, 12*(1), 2–6.

Ellis, A. (Speaker). (1977b). *A garland of rational humorous songs* (Cassette recording and song book). New York: Institute for Rational–Emotive Therapy.

Ellis, A. (1979). A note on the treatment of agoraphobia with cognitive modification versus prolonged exposure. *Behavior Research and Therapy, 17*, 162–164.

Ellis, A. (1984). The use of hypnosis with rational–emotive therapy. *International Journal of Eclectic Psychotherapy, 3*(2), 15–22.

Ellis, A. (1985). *Overcoming resistance.* New York: Springer.

Ellis, A. (1986). Anxiety about anxiety: The use of hypnosis with rational–emotive therapy. In E. T. Dowd & J. M. Healy (Eds.), *Case studies in hypnotherapy* (pp. 3–11). New York: Guilford Press.

Ellis, A. (1987). A weekend of rational encounter. In A. Ellis & W. Dryden (Eds.), *The practice of rational–emotive therapy* (pp. 180–191). New York: Springer. (Original work published 1969)

Ellis, A. (1990). *Psychotherapy and the value of a human being.* In A. Ellis & W. Dryden (Eds.), *The essential Albert Ellis* (pp. 77–93). New York: Springer. (Original work published 1972)

Ellis, A. (1991). The revised ABCs of rational–emotive therapy. *Journal of Rational–Emotive and Cognitive Behavior Therapy, 9*, 139–172.

Ellis, A. (1993a). Rational–emotive imagery: RET version. In M. E. Bernard & J. L. Wolfe (Eds.), *The RET source book for practitioners* (pp. II-8–II-10). New York: The Institute for Rational–Emotive Therapy.

Ellis, A. (1993b). Rational–emotive therapy and hypnosis. In J. W. Rhue, S. J. Lynn, & I. Kirsch (Eds.), *Handbook of clinical hypnosis* (pp. 173–186). Washington, DC: American Psychological Association.

Ellis, A. (1994a). *Reason and emotion in psychotherapy revised.* Secaucus, NJ: Citadel.

Ellis, A. (1994b). The treatment of borderline personalities with rational–emotive behavior therapy. In C. R. Cloninger (Ed.), *The treatment of personality disorders.* Washington, DC: Psychiatric Press.

Ellis, A., & Abrahms, E. (1978). *Brief psychotherapy in medical and health practice.* New York: Springer.

Ellis, A., & Abrahms, M. (1994). *How to cope with fatal disease.* New York: Barricade Books.

Ellis, A., & Dryden, W. (1996). *The practice of rational–emotive behavior therapy.* New York: Springer.

Ellis, A., & Velten, E. (1992). *When AA doesn't work: Rational steps for quitting alcohol.* New York: Barricade Books.

Golden, W. L., Dowd, E. T., & Friedberg, F. (1987). *Hypnotherapy: A modern approach.* New York: Pergamon.

Haley, J. (1973). *Uncommon therapy: The psychiatric techniques of Milton H. Erickson.* New York: Norton.

Hauck, P. A. (1992). *Overcoming the rating game: Beyond self-love-beyond-self-esteem.* Louisville, KY: Westminster/John Knox.

Jacobson, E. (1938). *You must relax.* New York: McGraw-Hill.

Maultsby, M. C., Jr. (1971). Rational–emotive imagery. *Rational Living, 6*(1), 24–27.

Mills, D. (1993). *Overcoming self-esteem*. New York: Institute for Rational-Emotive Therapy.

Rogers, C. R. (1961). *On becoming a person*. Boston: Houghton Mifflin.

Stanton, H. (1977). The utilization of suggestions derived from rational-emotive therapy. *International Journal of Clinical and Experimental Hypnosis, 25*, 18–26.

Stanton, H. (1989). Hypnosis and rational–emotive therapy: A destroying combination. *International Journal of Experimental and Clinical Hypnosis, 37*, 95–99.

Steketee, G. S. (1993). *Treatment of obsessive compulsion disorders*. New York: Guilford Press.

Tosi, D. J. (1974). *Youth: Toward personal growth, a rational–emotive approach*. Columbus, OH: Merrill.

Tosi, D. J., & Baisden, B. S. (1984). Cognitive experiential therapy and hypnosis. In W. Wester & H. Smith (Eds.), *Clinical hypnosis* (pp. 155–178). Philadelphia: Lippincott.

Tosi, D., Fuller, J., & Gwynne, P. (1980, June). *The treatment of hyperactivity and learning disabilities through RSDH*. Paper presented at the Third Annual Conference in Rational–Emotive Therapy, New York.

Tosi, D., Judah, S. M., & Murphy, M. M. (1989). The effects of a cognitive–experiential therapy utilizing hypnosis. *Journal of Cognitive Psychotherapy, 3*, 273–290.

Tosi, D., & Marzella, J. N. (1977). The treatment of guilt through rational stage directed therapy. In J. L. Wolfe & E. Brand (Eds.), *Twenty years of rational therapy* (pp. 234–240). New York: Institute for Rational–Emotive Therapy.

Tosi, D., & Reardon, J. P. (1976). The treatment of guilt through rational stage directed therapy. *Rational Living, 11*(1), 8–11.

Wachtel, P. L. (1994). Cyclical processes in personality and psychopathology. *Journal of Abnormal Psychology, 103* 52–54.

Walen, S., Di Giuseppe, R., & Dryden, W. (1992). *A practitioner's guide to rational–emotive therapy*. New York: Oxford University Press.

Yankura, J. & Dryden, W. (1990). *Doing RET: Albert Ellis in action*. New York: Springer.

17

MULTIMODAL TREATMENT IN THE CASE OF ELLEN

IRVING KIRSCH and WILLIAM C. COE

When we get a flat tire driving down the road, we sometimes wonder what caused it. If it was produced by a puncture, what caused the puncture? Was there a nail or some glass in the road? One way to find out might be to search the road for objects that might have caused the flat tire, but we rarely do this. We certainly don't spend much time doing it. The search may or may not be successful, but in either case, it does not help solve our problem. We are much more interested in fixing the flat tire than we are in finding its cause. So we change the tire and take it to a garage, where it can either be repaired or replaced. A good mechanic is more interested in current causes than past causes. What is keeping the tire from holding air right now and how can it be repaired?

Clients often want to know the causes of their problems. "Why am I like this?" they wonder. "How did I get to be this way?" Part of their motivation for asking these questions may stem from natural curiosity and a desire to know themselves better. Another motive may be based on the misconception that insight into the distant roots of a problem is the key to solving it. But, according to a behavioral view, just as in the case of the flat tire, initial causal factors lying hidden near the beginning of life's road may have little relevance to solving current problems. In contrast, the current, maintaining factors are likely to be most critical. Therefore, we

349

will take note of some of the obvious dynamic factors for Ellen, but we will ignore the temptation to focus, for example, on the possible, unresolved Oedipal longings, with their attendant hostility toward mother, which could lead to unconscious guilt when mother died. Instead, we will file them away as hypotheses to be turned to should treatment based on more parsimonious hypotheses fail.

After our initial salutation and listening to Ellen's problem, we would want to do two things before formalizing a therapeutic plan. First, we would like to reduce any need for urgency in obtaining results. If we or Ellen are anxious about getting results in a hurry, therapy may be hindered by our rushing or her lack of honesty about improving. Therefore, we would evaluate with her just how important it is that she go on the trip. Is it life or death? How disappointed would she be? How depressed? How much would her life change, and so forth? It would probably turn out to be something that she would like to do, but after all, life will go on and there will probably be other opportunities. The really important thing is to work on her problems and to make steady gains. In the same vein, what if she accepted the invitation, and then had to back out 8 months later? What would be the worst consequences? If the consequences turn out not to be so bad, then we both can stop worrying about the immediate issue. She can go ahead and accept a place on the trip and still have 8 months before she makes a final decision.

Next, we would use Lazarus' (1981) multimodal therapy approach to obtain a more complete evaluation and to determine a treatment plan. Lazarus offers his BASIC-ID as an acronym for seven, important modalities of her functioning: behavior, affect, sensation, imagery, cognitions, interpersonal, and drugs (physiological). The BASIC-ID is used as an evaluation guide, which ensures completeness of the evaluation, and at the same time, problems in a specific modality point to specific treatment techniques that should be effective for such problems. For example, if the client shows a deficit in the "behavior" modality, reinforcement treatments based on operant conditioning may be indicated to decrease the deficit. Similarly, problems in "affect," "sensation," and so forth indicate behavioral techniques developed to deal with such difficulties. Despite the need for more information on each of these dimensions, we can establish the following problem areas and possible solutions from the information currently available.

Behavior: Inhibition and avoidance of elimination in bathrooms where she may be heard. Operant shaping procedures (successive approximation) to decrease inhibition and increase performance can be applied.

Affect: Anxiety and sadness. Both of these unpleasant emotions seem to be a product of negative thinking and interpersonal sensitivity. Thus, desensitization and cognitive restructuring techniques may be helpful.

Sensation: Although, we do not yet have information about specific sensations, muscle tension and tightening seem likely. If this is the case, the use of muscle relaxation training, combined with both imagery and in vivo practice is indicated.

Imagery: We do not yet know what images she experiences in connection with her problem. Does she picture herself as a "nasty" person? Does she imagine people laughing or scowling? Does she have images of her father expressing disappointment in her? Knowing her spontaneous imagery would affect our use of imagery in desensitization procedures.

Cognitions: She thinks of elimination and sex as "dirty" or "bad," even though she "knows" better. She has the belief that she will not be able to eliminate. She has thoughts about what people will think if they hear her eliminating, although the exact content of those thoughts are not yet clear. She may be catastrophizing and thinking of her inhibitions as "awful," and she almost certainly has the thought, "I am not good enough!" Such thoughts can be changed with a combination of the "stop" technique[1], rational discussion, and the development of counteracting, positive thoughts.

Interpersonal: The presence of others increases Ellen's problems of elimination. She has a warm and affectionate relationship with her children, but her relationship with her husband is marred by her sexual dissatisfaction. Her concern about the presence of others and her negative attitudes about sex should be incorporated into the desensitization and cognitive restructuring techniques used to change her beliefs and thoughts (cognitions).

Drugs and physiology: No known drug or physiological defects relating to her problems were reported. However, we do not know whether she has seen a urologist or a gynecologist. If not, the possibility of a contributing physiological problem should be explored.

THE THERAPEUTIC RATIONALE

We now have a number of possible approaches to Ellen's difficulties. We are also aware of lacking some information that may be important to

---

[1]The "stop" technique (Lazarus, 1981) is meant to deal with compulsive-like, troublesome thoughts. The patient is asked to focus purposely on the particular thought. For example, Ellen may be asked to close her eyes and to concentrate on thinking that "she cannot urinate." She is asked to raise her finger when she becomes involved in the thought, whereupon, the therapist shouts "Stop!" She would probably startle, open her eyes, and look at the therapist in a puzzled way (or perhaps angrily). The therapist then asks if she in fact had stopped thinking about not urinating. She would very likely agree. Then, it would be explained that she can do the same thing. She would be asked to again become involved in the thought and to shout "stop" herself, then focus her attention on something in the room and describe it aloud. If successful, she would then be told to do it again, but this time to just think the word "stop." Again, she would redirect her attention to some neutral object, or perhaps an important, therapeutic alternative, like "urinating is natural, pleasant, and simple." The point is to demonstrate to her that she can control what she thinks and even learn a more positive way of thinking.

therapy (as indicated above), and were this not a response to a printed case, we would have the option of more interviewing before finalizing a plan. Based on what we do know, however, at this point we might share the following multimodal conceptualization of Ellen's presenting problem with her. In an actual session, the message would be presented in an interactive dialogue with Ellen, not as a monologue. Each component and rationale of our case conceptualization would be checked against her phenomenal experience and modified to fit it. Similarly, her language would be used throughout. If she referred to a problem as "peeing," that is the word we would use; if she said "urinate," we would use that word instead. Because Ellen is a highly educated individual, technical terms like "conditioned inhibition" and "overgeneralization" can probably be used without too much explanation. With other clients, we would omit these terms entirely.

> You might be surprised at how many people, women and men, feel uncomfortable about urinating and defecating in public places. The problem starts with toilet training. We are taught to inhibit our natural biological functions. What our bodies must learn is to draw a pretty fine line of inhibiting in most circumstances and releasing in certain others. So it's not surprising that some of us overlearn and others underlearn. When that happens, we need to relearn. In your case, the task is to loosen the inhibitions, without loosening them too much.
>
> Urinating and defecating are natural functions, but the organs through which they are done are close to our genitals, and sex often has "dirty" connotations in our society. Simple words for sexual organs and sexual activities are called "dirty words," and we are taught as little children not to use them. We are often told that words for urination and defecation are dirty, as well. So we are not to say "piss" or "shit." All of this sets the stage for over-inhibition later in life, and the problem can be aggravated even more if we are told things during toilet training that reinforce the idea that natural, physiological functions are dirty.
>
> A negative role model, like your mother, whose poor hygienic habits and open nudity upset you, can aggravate the problem. You may fear that you also will become a "crude" person like your mother, although it seems clear that you never could. But to be certain, your body has found a way to make it impossible for you to be thought of as crude or vulgar by restricting your eliminative and sexual functions. Your body is not as intelligent as you are, and it has therefore found an unnecessarily rigid way of protecting you from being "crude."
>
> The important thing is to understand how your past experiences are affecting you *now*, and even more importantly, to figure out what kinds of new learning experiences are needed to break these uncomfortable habits. A few different, but interrelated factors are likely to be involved. One is a simple behavioral-conditioning process. You were earlier reinforced for holding in your urine and feces when you were toilet

trained. But now, holding in has overgeneralized to situations in which it is not appropriate. You now need to learn when to let go appropriately. We'll use both imagery and real-life practice to reverse such conditioned inhibition.

Part of what makes your problem difficult is the anxiety you experience in situations related to eliminative and sexual functioning. When you are anxious, you tighten up physically, as well as emotionally. To let go, you have to be able to relax. So I'll be teaching you some relaxation skills, possibly with the aid of hypnosis, as a way of reducing your anxiety.

Your anxiety, however, is not mindless. Instead, it's connected to some of the thoughts you have about urinating and defecating. For example, it's clear from what you've told me that you have come to think of both sex and elimination as "dirty," and I am sure that plays a role in the difficulty you are having. At the same time, you say that you "know better." That's very important because it will make our work much easier! You have what I call a "head–heart split." What you "know" to be true is different from what you "feel" to be true. We will need to do some work on allowing your mind to convince your body of what it knows to be true.

There is another thought you are having which might be causing you trouble. When you go into a bathroom where you might be heard, you think in advance that you won't be able to urinate or defecate. Believing that you won't be able to urinate is part of what makes it difficult, and trying doesn't help. It's like wanting to go to sleep, but thinking that you won't be able to—you become so caught up in thinking that you won't fall asleep that it becomes impossible for you not to interfere with falling asleep. Our task will be to break the vicious circle.

INTRODUCING HYPNOSIS

In deciding whether or not to use hypnosis, the client's attitudes are of utmost importance. When the possibility of using hypnosis was introduced earlier, Ellen might have reacted in a way that indicated acceptance or apprehension. If she had reservations or misconceptions about hypnosis, they must be addressed and corrected. Research has indicated that patients can benefit by the addition of hypnosis to cognitive–behavioral treatment, even when they initially hold some moderately negative attitudes toward hypnosis (Schoenberger, 1993). However, if Ellen had strong negative feelings about hypnosis, it could be omitted altogether. Changes in terminology to the conventional words of cognitive–behavior therapy would be necessary, but few differences in procedure would occur. For example, the "induction" can be called "relaxation training," "self-hypnosis" can be called "self-relaxation and imagery," and "suggestion" and "self-suggestion" can be called "automatic-thoughts" and "self-statements." The only difference between these common hypnotic procedures and their even more common nonhypnotic counterparts is the use of the word *hypnosis*. Nevertheless, this minor difference in terminology has been shown to produce substantial differences in therapeutic outcome for clients with positive attitudes and expectations toward hypnosis (Kirsch, Montgomery, & Sapirstein, 1995; Lazarus, 1973; Schoenberger, 1993). Furthermore, the hypnotic context can be useful in enhancing the effects of therapeutic suggestions, the client's involvement in imagery, cognitive activities like changing beliefs and attitudes, and for using self-instructions for coping with potential stressful situations or persons.

Assuming that Ellen is not strongly opposed to hypnosis, any of her initial apprehensions might be put to rest as follows:

Therapist: I mentioned hypnosis earlier, and I wonder what your reaction is to using hypnosis as part of our work together.

Ellen: Well, I really don't know much about hypnosis, but the idea of going into some kind of trance is a little frightening. I like to be in control of myself, and I want to know what's going on.

Therapist: Well, if hypnosis is too uncomfortable for you, we can use nonhypnotic procedures. But my guess is that most of what you are afraid of is based on myths from the popular media. Hypnosis isn't very mysterious at all. When we use the term *trance*, all we mean is that you are absorbed and involved in your ongoing experiences. In fact, many of us don't like the terms "trance" or "state" at all because they are so misleading. You know how you can get very absorbed in a good book, in a movie, or in a fantasy you might have while driving? Well, that's the kind of "trance" we are talking about when we say a "hypnotic trance." It's really that simple. You'll be as much in control of yourself as you are when reading, watching a movie, or driving. In fact, all hypnosis is really "self-hypnosis," meaning that *I* won't be hypnotizing *you*, but instead, I'll be *teaching you* how to hypnotize yourself. Let me give you the opportunity to experience what responding to a suggestion feels like without being hypnotized. O.K.?

Ellen: Sure!

Therapist: I have here a small key hanging on a piece of thread. See? [Therapist holds it up for her to see.]

Ellen: Yes. What are you going to do, hypnotize me by swinging it in front of my eyes?

Therapist: Nothing like that! In fact, I'm going to ask *you* to hold it—maybe you'll hypnotize me. [Chuckle.] Okay! Now rest your elbow on the table right in front of you and hold the thread between your thumb and your forefinger. That's it. [Therapists steadies the key so it's not moving.] Now I'd like you to just focus on the key; forget about anything else. Now, imagine it swinging back and forth, back and forth, back and forth. [It starts going back and forth.] Good! Now imagine it's changing into a circle, a nice round circle, round and round, round and round. [It changes to a circular movement.] Great! Now, I want *you* to imagine it slowing down and beginning to go back and forth again, just use your mind. [Wait until it's going back and forth.] Great! Now, imagine a circle again. [It changes to a circle.] That's it! Wider and wider, wider and wider, imagine a bigger and bigger circle. [It increases in size.]

Ellen: That's amazing!

Therapist: Very good! Excellent! You're not in any kind of trance now, are you? You're wide awake. You know who you are and where you are. You can put the key down now. I want you to notice that you were the one who made it move, not I. You could have ignored my suggestions entirely. I could have suggested it move in one direction, and you could have made it move in another direction. It was all up to you. And there was nothing magic about it, no matter how uncanny it seemed. Obviously, your thoughts caused your finger muscles to move ever so slightly. You're not aware of it because you're so focused on the key. The length of the thread exaggerates the small movements and the key swings. Well, that is very much what responding to a hypnotic suggestion is like. I don't make the suggestions happen; you do. If I suggest something and you don't want to experience it, you can just ignore it, and it won't happen. All that hypnosis does is make it easier to experience something that you would like to experience. It doesn't make the experience happen. You have to do that. Have you ever practiced relaxation exercises, or meditation, or anything like that?

Ellen: Well I once took a yoga class and we used to meditate at the beginning and end of it.

Therapist: What was that experience like?

Ellen: It was very relaxing, although sometimes it got boring.

Therapist: Uhuh! Well, hypnosis might not feel much different than meditation, although I hope you won't find it boring. Most people find it very relaxing and enjoyable. But the point is that you will be in as much control during hypnosis as you were while meditating. You'll be in no more of a trance than you were then. So, what do you think?

Ellen: Well that makes it sound okay, but I don't know if I'll be very good at it.

Therapist: Hmm. . . . Well some people are more responsive than others, but you responded very well to what we call the Chevreul pendulum illusion, the key on the thread. Are you able to really concentrate and get absorbed in things that you're interested in?

Ellen: Yes! Sometimes I get so lost in a book that my husband has to repeat himself three times before I know that he's talking to me.

Therapist: Good! I'm sure you'll respond well enough to do whatever we will be doing to help your problems.

TEACHING HYPNOSIS AND SELF-HYPNOSIS

Research indicates that in most instances, one type of induction is as good as another, as far as increasing responsiveness to suggestions. Because practicing self-hypnosis outside of the consulting room will be an important part of Ellen's treatment, a relatively simple, straightforward induction, similar to that presented in Kirsch, Lynn, and Rhue (1993) is indicated. Obviously, an induction including relaxation is preferable in this case, because relaxation will be an important part of the therapy. For example, emphasis might eventually be placed on relaxing the stomach and pelvic areas, and on releasing, flowing, and letting go. Induction imagery might focus on a woodland waterfall:

> . . . and you can imagine yourself sitting by a stream in the woods beside a small waterfall . . . and as you sit there comfortably, you can smell the fresh clean scent of the woodland air, clean, water flowing gently down, flowing, rippling, glistening, and gleaming . . . and as you sit there in perfect comfort, relaxing, loosening, letting go, you can be lulled by the gentle sound of the flowing water, soothing you, as you let yourself go deeper and deeper . . .

Indirect therapeutic suggestions like "clean and fresh," "sitting comfortably," "water flowing," and so forth are embedded in this induction and are aimed specifically at Ellen's complaint. They may be obvious to both the reader and to Ellen.

Toward the end of the induction, Ellen is asked to choose a cue word to associate with the comfortable, relaxed feelings she is experiencing. Perhaps she chooses the word *calm*. The therapist then continues as follows, frequently inserting the word *calm* when she exhales:

> ... You can think the word *calm* to yourself each time you exhale, and as you do so ... [client exhales] ... calm ... it becomes more and more strongly associated with the ... calm ... relaxed feelings you are having now ... calm ... So that whenever you think *calm*, you can bring on these calm feelings of relaxation. You will find it easier and easier ... calm ... to feel more and more relaxed, because you know how easy it becomes ... calm ... to do things automatically, once you've learned them well ...

The induction would be taped during the first session, and Ellen would be asked to practice it at home daily. When she becomes sufficiently familiar with it, she should begin practicing without it and merely repeat the induction subvocally. Subsequent hypnosis sessions can begin with the instruction, "Put yourself into hypnosis, and let me know when you are ready by nodding your head or raising your finger." Hypnosis can be ended with the instruction, "... and as soon as you feel ready, bring yourself out of hypnosis and open your eyes."

IDENTIFYING NEGATIVE AND POSITIVE SELF-SUGGESTIONS (COGNITIONS)

Therapist: Do you remember when I gave you a suggestion about the key moving in a certain direction?

Ellen: Uh huh!

Therapist: By imagining along with the suggestion, it moved in the suggested direction, without your even being aware that you were moving. On the hypnosis tape, I gave you suggestions for relaxation and for feeling the pleasure that you might feel by a stream in the woods. You've been able to generate feelings of peace and relaxation with that imagery. Right?

Ellen: Yes!

Therapist: Well sometimes we give ourselves suggestions that lead us to feel and behave in particular ways, and we may not even know that we are giving them to ourselves. Part of what we have to do now is to identify the negative self-suggestions that you have been giving yourself to make you feel uncomfortable. Your major concern seems to be that someone will hear you eliminating. What if someone does hear you? What's wrong with that?

Ellen: Well then they would know that I'm doing what I'm doing.

Therapist:	Yes?
Ellen:	Well it's embarrassing!
Therapist:	Exactly what about it embarrasses you?
Ellen:	Well it feels like it's dirty. I mean, I know it isn't, but it feels like it is. I know that sounds crazy, but that's the way it feels.
Therapist:	Okay! So now we know at least one negative, self-suggestion you give yourself, "Going to the bathroom is dirty." And we also know what's wrong with that suggestion. You know that eliminating isn't dirty, that it is a normal, healthy, human function. That knowledge can be the basis of a positive, self-suggestion with which you can replace the negative, self-suggestion. By the way, is urine dirty?
Ellen:	Well actually, not generally.
Therapist:	Now I'm not an expert, but I understand that it can be used as an antiseptic, is that right?
Ellen:	In a pinch.
Therapist:	What is it composed of?
Ellen:	Mostly water—uric acid, of course.
Therapist:	And also small amounts of sodium, potassium, calcium, magnesium, and phosphorus. Are these substances dirty?
Ellen:	[Laughs] No.

One effective way of identifying negative self-suggestions and potential countering, positive self-suggestions is to use a variation of the Gestalt empty chair technique. The therapist might say to Ellen:

There's a part of you that thinks of elimination as filthy and shameful and doesn't want anyone to know that you do it. And there's another part of you that knows that elimination is a normal, healthy, human function—nothing to be ashamed of at all. I'd like to get those two parts of you talking to each other. I'm going to ask you to sit first in this chair. When you're in this chair, I want you to be the part of you that thinks elimination is filthy or embarrassing or any other negative beliefs that make you not want to be heard. I want you to imagine that the other part of you is sitting in that chair, and I want you to try and explain and convince that part of you of your point of view. Then I'm going to ask you to switch chairs. When you sit over there you will be the part of yourself that understands that there is nothing wrong with elimination or with people overhearing, and your job will be to convince the other part of you of what you know to be true.

The client is instructed to go back and forth from chair to chair, until the maladaptive part has run out of arguments.

Through these processes of Socratic questioning and Gestalt role-playing, positive self-suggestions can be discovered that can counter negative self-suggestions. Ellen is asked to codify these self-suggestions, that is, to come up with short phrases that are codes representing completely thought-out arguments in which she believes. The advantage of codes is that they can be invoked rapidly, like cues or signals, for invoking or canceling a posthypnotic suggestion. Because they are associated with rational arguments that the client has already accepted, their invocation counters the negative self-suggestions (automatic thoughts) that help maintain the problem.

Sometimes negative self-suggestions are so strong they appear to be obsessive, out of the patient's conscious control. In such cases, the "Stop" technique described earlier can be used.

HYPNOTIC AND IN VIVO REHEARSAL

Constructing a Hierarchy

One of the basic principles of behavior therapy is that of successive approximations. To insure success, one begins with easy tasks and progresses to more difficult ones only after the easier ones have been mastered. There are likely to be a number of factors that would affect Ellen's feelings about a situation in which she needs to relieve herself. They might include urinating, defecating, or merely flushing the toilet; the number of people nearby; whether they are friends, relatives, or strangers; the background noise level; how far removed the bathroom is from where people are congregated; the number of people the bathroom is designed to accommodate; and so forth. The effect of each of these factors on Ellen's discomfort should be evaluated, and she should be asked to identify other pertinent situational factors.

Once the factors that affect the severity of her difficulty are identified, various permutations of them are rated on a subjective units of disturbance scale (SUDS; Wolpe & Lazarus, 1966). SUDS ratings may be introduced as follows:

Therapist: I'm going to ask you to rate the degree of discomfort you would feel in various situations on a scale of 0 to 100. Zero represents no discomfort at all. It is what you feel when you are perfectly at ease and relaxed, without a care in the world. You might take a second now to identify a time when you've felt so completely comfortable and relaxed.

Ellen: [After a pause.] I can remember standing on the deck of the Q. E. II just as land is first coming into view. I think that's about as completely relaxed and comfortable as I've ever felt.

Therapist: Good! That would be the situation of zero discomfort, the bottom of the scale. Now, I'd like you to think of the most *uncomfortable* situation you've ever experienced, regardless of whether the feeling was shame or disgust or something else.

Ellen: I've got it, but do I have to tell you what it is?

Therapist: No, you can keep that private if you'd like. The important thing is that you've got an anchor for the number 100, the top of the scale. Now I'd like you to identify a situation that produces a feeling about midway between 0 and 100. [Therapist pauses. Patient nods.] Okay! That's a 50. Now imagine the following: You are at home alone in your bathroom, just about to urinate. What is your discomfort level?

Ellen: Hmm. About a 20. That's no problem for me.

Therapist: Good! Now, let me know at what level urinating or defecating would become difficult?

Ellen: Do you want a situation or a number?

Therapist: Just a number at this point. We'll get back to situations in a moment.

Ellen: Hmm. I guess about a 40 or 45.

Therapist: Okay! Now lets try putting some numbers to some situations. You're in the bathroom at home. Your husband is in the next room . . . rating?

A number of situations are then generated and rated on the SUDS, usually 8 to 12, about 10 to 15 units apart. To facilitate future work, it is useful to concentrate on situations that can be easily arranged for in vivo (real life) practice. An easy way to find a variety of levels of difficulty is to keep most aspects of the situation constant and vary only one or two systematically. For example, one could move from Ellen being alone, to having her husband in the next room, to having a friend in the house, but a few rooms away, etc., the variables being the type of persons and the distance from them to the bathroom. A systematic approach of this sort is especially likely to be well received by Ellen, who sees herself as methodical, thorough, and careful. An example of such a hierarchy will be shown in the next section.

Desensitizing a Voluntary Response

With background work done, a direct confrontation of the presenting problem can begin. Because flushing the toilet is an easily controlled, voluntary behavior, compared to urinating or defecating, it is chosen as the behavior to work on first. From the list generated during hierarchy construction, a relatively easy situation is selected, one with a fairly low SUDS rating. The SUDS rating should be low enough to make it very likely that Ellen will be successful, but it should be high enough to feel like an accomplishment when she does succeed. Also, the situation should be one with as few external constraints as possible, so that subsequent in vivo practice is made easier. For example, because it is more accessible in real life, a restaurant restroom, rather than airplane restroom, might be chosen for imaginary work.

During hypnotic rehearsal, Ellen is asked to imagine being in a situation for the purpose of overcoming her inhibition. As the imagined scene unfolds, the therapist monitors her discomfort by eliciting SUDS ratings. When the SUDS rating exceeds Ellen's discomfort threshold (which she had reported to be around 40 or 45), the therapist asks her to invoke the relaxation cue and the therapeutic self-suggestions formulated earlier. Unlike systematic desensitization, Ellen is instructed to continue imagining being in the uncomfortable situation while utilizing self-hypnotic skills to lower her discomfort and to counteract any negative thoughts with positive ones. Such imaginary experiences provide a close equivalent to the in vivo exposure assignments that will follow. They also provide experiential evidence that treatment can be effective, thereby reducing any negative response expectancies that may be helping to maintain the problem.

> Therapist: In a moment, I am going to ask you to imagine entering a rest room and flushing the toilet. I will want to monitor your level of discomfort. So from time to time, I will say the word *level*. Whenever I say *level*, I'd like you to tell me the number that most closely represents your level of discomfort. Level?
>
> Ellen: 20.
>
> Therapist: Okay! Now place yourself into hypnosis. You can let me know when you're ready by nodding your head.

The therapist waits for the client's head to nod and then continues with some deepening instructions like "relax more and more," "deeper and deeper," "calmer and calmer," and so on, following which, therapeutic imagery is initiated.

> Therapist: You're sitting in the Victorian Lady restaurant, lingering over a cup of coffee. Level?
>
> Ellen: 20.
>
> Therapist: You are getting ready to go into the bathroom to flush the toilet. Level?

Ellen:	30.
Therapist:	You stand up and walk toward the rest room. Level?
Ellen:	40
Therapist:	You open the door, walk in, close and lock the door behind you. Level?
Ellen:	50.
Therapist:	You close your eyes momentarily, take a deep breath [client inhales], and think "calm" as you exhale. You remind yourself that going to the bathroom is clean and natural, clean and natural. ["Clean and natural" is the phrase that Ellen has chosen to represent the adaptive self-suggestions that counter her maladaptive self-suggestions.] You recall that using the bathroom is a very civilized thing to do. It is nothing to be ashamed of . . . [The therapist repeats some of the self-suggestions Ellen had identified during the interview and empty chair role-play.] Level?
Ellen:	45.
Therapist:	Good! You can let your body relax even further. Calm. Clean and natural. [The therapist reminds the client of additional positive self-suggestions represented by the signal "clean and natural."] Level?
Ellen:	30
Therapist:	Very good! Now you prepare to flush the toilet . . .

The scene is continued through some number of toilet flushes, until it fails to elicit a substantial degree of discomfort. A different, more difficult scene is then chosen, and the hypnotic rehearsal is repeated. Before the end of the session, client and therapist agree upon situations in which Ellen will practice between sessions. She will practice in imagination during self-hypnosis sessions in an easy chair at home, and she will practice in vivo by entering a restaurant she frequents often, for example, going into the bathroom, flushing the toilet, and moderating her discomfort with relaxation and positive, self-suggestions.

Desensitizing and Disinhibiting Involuntary Responses

Because Ellen's inhibition of urination and defecation is not voluntary, desensitization and disinhibition of them are slightly more complex than desensitization of voluntary toilet flushing. She cannot intentionally evoke inhibition of elimination for the purpose of in vivo practice. However, her inhibition is connected to the sounds associated with elimination, because the sounds indicate what she is doing. Therefore, it is the sound, rather than the act, to which she needs to be desensitized. To that end, she is asked to make an audiotape recording of herself urinating and defecating. The therapist then repeats the process used to desensitize Ellen to flushing the toilet. Before flushing the toilet, however, Ellen plays the audiotape, first in imagination during hypnosis and self-hypnosis, and then in vivo. During in vivo practice, she is to sit on the toilet, intentionally inhibit the urge to urinate or defecate, and play the audiotape recording, using relaxation and self-suggestions to decrease her discomfort. Although instructed to inhibit elimination, we would not be surprised if she came to feel comfortable enough to spontaneously ignore this instruction and eliminate. However, we do not suggest eliminating because it is a rather large step. Being conservative, we progress one small step at a time and reduce the likelihood that failure will be experienced.

Once desensitization to the sounds of elimination is accomplished, our attention turns to disinhibiting urination and defecation (assuming that this has not already occurred). The first step is to have Ellen practice gaining control over stopping and resuming elimination in a comfortably private situation. Next, after she is confident with on-off control, she is asked to hypnotize herself while sitting on the toilet and then to *imagine* being in a less comfortable situation while intentionally stopping and starting elimination. Once she can control comfortably in more and less difficult imaginative situations, a hierarchy is constructed for in vivo practice. It is critical to begin with a very easy situation, one in which Ellen expresses a high degree of confidence of success. Once sitting on the toilet, she is to hypnotize herself, monitor her discomfort, reduce it if necessary, begin playing the audiotape used in desensitizing toilet flushing, and practice releasing and inhibiting. During her initial trials she is merely to practice tensing and releasing the muscles that control urination and defecation. The actual release of urine and feces is not to be attempted until she feels sufficiently comfortable tensing and releasing in this situation. Although we would not tell her this at first, we would not be surprised if she were to release some urine or feces unintentionally during this in vivo exercise. This, of course, would provide the best possible evidence that she had become sufficiently comfortable.

CONCLUSION

As the presenting problem is overcome, suggestions for generalization may be useful. In particular, what Ellen has learned has implications for her feelings about sex, and these can be noted, along with a permissively worded suggestion indicating that she may notice some of those thoughts and feelings changing, just as her thoughts and feelings about elimination have changed. As we mentioned earlier, more information is needed about her sexual functioning before a reasonable therapeutic program can be developed. Another subgoal of therapy could be to help her to differentiate herself more clearly from her image of her mother and thereby reduce her fear that she will become a "crude person." Cognitive restructuring in the form of generating ways that she is in fact different from her mother might be very useful.

A complete therapy for Ellen might be much more detailed, including various aspects of her life where inhibition interferes and where self-doubts reduce her joy of living. For now, we have presented a plan for limited problems based on cognitive–behavioral concepts and techniques. We would expect positive gains within 1 month with perhaps two sessions per week. In 9 months, sessions should be no more than one or two per month, primarily for evaluating the permanence of outcome and dealing with any unforeseen problems that may arise.

REFERENCES

Kirsch, I., Lynn, S. J., & Rhue, J. W. (1993). Introduction to clinical hypnosis. In J. W. Rhue, S. J. Lynn, & I. Kirsch (Eds.), *Handbook of clinical hypnosis* (pp. 3–22). Washington, DC: American Psychological Association.

Kirsch, I., Montgomery, G., & Sapirstein, G. (1995). Hypnosis as an adjunct to cognitive behavioral psychotherapy: A meta-analysis. *Journal of Consulting and Clinical Psychology, 63,* 214–220.

Lazarus, A. A. (1973). "Hypnosis" as a facilitator in behavior therapy. *International Journal of Clinical and Experimental Hypnosis, 21,* 25–31.

Lazarus, A. A. (1981). *The practice of multimodal therapy.* New York: McGraw-Hill.

Schoenberger, N. E. (1993). *Effectiveness of a cognitive behavioral hypnotherapy for public speaking anxiety.* Unpublished doctoral dissertation, University of Connecticut, Storrs.

Wolpe, J., & Lazarus, A. A. (1966). *Behavior therapy techniques.* Oxford: Pergamon.

18

THE USE OF ERICKSONIAN HYPNOTHERAPY IN THE CASE OF ELLEN

WILLIAM J. MATTHEWS, STEPHEN LANKTON, and
CAROL LANKTON

Questions, questions, and more questions come to mind when meeting a client for the first time and in each session thereafter. Ellen presents an interesting profile and, in our view, because of her considerable strengths, a positive prognosis. In assessing a client, we are looking for or constructing information, depending on one's epistemological viewpoint, that makes a difference relative to therapeutic change. For us, information is either useful or not useful, as opposed to correct or incorrect. In our work with clients, interview management is an important and necessary aspect of an effective clinical approach. Thus, in some instances, depending on the client's presentation, assessment may necessarily be preceded by the pragmatic activities of establishing rapport, determining how to communicate with the client in a way that we can understand, reducing the immediacy of a crisis if necessary, and recognizing the client's motivation for therapy.

In our assessment process we attempt to consider four areas: (a) the presenting problem, (b) background information about the problem itself, (c) the current family or social system organization, and (d) information about the family of origin of each spouse or partner (Lankton & Lankton, 1986, 1989; Lankton, Lankton, & Matthews, 1991). Let us briefly discuss each of these four areas within the context of the specifics of Ellen's case.

THE PRESENTING PROBLEM AND BACKGROUND

What is the presenting problem as defined by the client? In this instance, Ellen complains of her inability to use public bathrooms in which there is a possibility of anyone hearing her urinate or defecate. We might then ask a series of questions such as: How is this a problem? Given that this has been a long-term issue, what brings her into therapy now? What outcome would she want in therapy relative to the problem? What would happen if no change occurred? Questions such as these define or contextualize the problem (i.e., the when, where, and how issues). Asking Ellen what is her desired therapeutic outcome can be potentially quite significant, as her response may offer valuable insights for us about her beliefs, attitudes, and worldview that may unnecessarily constrain her sense of agency.

Continuing our focus on the presenting issue we might then ask such questions as: When is this behavior not a problem? What is that situation like? When is it most a problem? How does she manage this issue in her daily life? Perhaps most interestingly we would ask, given that Ellen has reported to have had this presenting issue over a long time, what brings her into therapy now rather than last year or the year before? In asking these questions not only are we seeking to define the specifics of the problem behavior but, perhaps more importantly, when Ellen experiences herself as not having a problem or at least less of a problem. Questions of this nature become interventions as they either directly or indirectly suggest client control where she had not previously perceived it. A key element in the process of change is helping the client to shift behavior previously thought to be involuntary to voluntary control (Haley, 1978). Ellen may never have thought about when her bathroom behavior is not a problem and what she does that is different from when it is a problem. Implicit in this view is that the desired change is not only possible but perhaps already occurring.

With any change, no matter how positive, there are consequences. For example, I (Matthews) once saw a client who sought release from his writer's block. When asked what would happen when he became unblocked, he stated his expectations to write the "great American novel." In this instance, I suggested he hold on to his writer's block a bit longer perhaps to secure the transition from unpublished author to one of fame and fortune. In this instance, the writer's block may have served a purpose of protecting the client from a greater disappointment of unfulfilled expectations than the annoyance associated with the block itself. In this case, therefore, we would ask Ellen what would be the upside of making the desired change and, relatedly, what is the downside of making the desired change? Ellen may have never considered the positive value of her problem behavior or the consequences of changing it. Therapeutic intervention would then seek to respect and utilize the useful aspect of her behavior while eliminating that which is no longer useful.

Finally, as part of the problem focus it would most likely be useful to have Ellen's understanding of when this bathroom experience became problematic. Was this always a problem even in her childhood or did this develop later in life? Is there a specific traumatic or unpleasant experience from which she developed her behavior? What meaning did her mother's crude behavior (i.e., poor hygiene and walking around the house naked) have for her? At the conscious level, these reports suggest that Ellen was perhaps traumatized as a child seeing her mother dirty and naked. Although what is meant by the mother's hygiene is not fully reported, it does not seem unreasonable to speculate that perhaps as a child Ellen witnessed some aspect of menstruation by the mother. Her alarm and shock at this event may translate into her symptoms concerning bathroom activities. Implicit in these types of questions is information of a time when the use of the bathroom was not problematic. Such a time frame may be useful for later hypnotic age regression, in which Ellen may be given the opportunity to reexperience pleasant anxiety-free bathroom behavior.

Within our perspective of Ericksonian work, these types of questions about the presenting problem seek to contextualize the behavior within a frame that will create the possibility for a later intervention. Questions of this nature may reveal the meaning Ellen attributes to the problem, where her problem management skills are strongest, and what value or use the problem may have in her present life. For us, these types of questions provide a direct or indirect way to place limits on the problem relative to the client's life and to suggest or emphasize assets or strengths Ellen may have overlooked. For example, Ellen indicated that her bathroom problem is most intense when she is certain that someone can hear her, and conversely least problematic when she assumes no one can hear her. We might use this frame for a hypnotic intervention of negative hallucination in which she is trained during hypnosis to not notice certain external stimuli (e.g., the presence of others). Thus the act of being in the bathroom could become a posthypnotic suggestion to negatively hallucinate (i.e., not notice) external stimuli.

Nuclear and Family of Origin Assessment

Symptom removal, although important, is not necessarily the primary focus of our work. We try to consider the client within a life span developmental perspective. Where is the client now in his or her development and where might he or she be expected to go? As stated elsewhere (Lankton, Lankton, & Matthews, 1991), we set assessment goals that will facilitate our understanding of the client from this developmental perspective on at least four arbitrary levels of functioning: (a) the family organization and its constraints on the social roles of its members, (b) the constraints of social roles upon behavior and affective expression, (c) the constraints of behavioral and affective expression on beliefs and cognitions, and (d) the constraints of beliefs and cognitions upon the availability of conscious or unconscious resources.

In our assessment of Ellen, we would look at the various roles being played and listen for the type of role-defining transactions, which have no doubt occurred numerous times in a multitude of ways, that define her present constraints. What was the range and type of behavior (i.e., social role taking) allowed and not allowed in Ellen's family of origin? For example, maybe her brother was expected to show assertive, aggressive, and competitive behavior whereas Ellen, being female, was expected not to express this type of behavior.

To the extent that Ellen's social role became limited in expressing anger, assertiveness, and tenderness, her ability to respond to current situations with those resources is dramatically limited. The type of communications and behavior available to Ellen would be congruent with the limitation of her learned social role. Her self-image becomes consolidated as a result of this prior learning and continues to be reinforced in her current interactions. For example, in asking Ellen what she says to herself in various situations such as in the bathroom, bedroom, and office we would expect her to engage in a fair amount of negative self-talk ("I'm a failure," "sex is dirty," "no matter what I've done, it's not good enough," etc.). This negative self-talk serves to reinforce her self-image and limit the availability of resources that could mediate, in a more useful way, these everyday experiences.

As part of our assessment it would be important for us to know who else is part of Ellen's family of origin. Who was connected to, closest with, and most distant from whom? What is and was each family member's view of their mother's behavior? How did each deal with this situation? What was different and what was similar? Why? Does anybody else have anxiety associated with the bathroom or anything else? If not, what is Ellen's understanding of how other family members have negotiated their family experience? Here again we are seeking to make meaning of Ellen's experience within her family of origin. Questions like these place Ellen's behavior in a wider context than she may have considered and may indirectly suggest that her current behavior may have been a legitimate response to a difficult childhood experience. This aspect of the assessment process seeks to obtain useful information while depathologizing her current behavior.

Important in our assessment of Ellen is the perspective of her present family, particularly her husband, as her own children are launched. Presumably, Ellen sought out treatment for herself. However, because her husband is in the present family system, he is, by definition, connected to the problem and most likely will need to be part of the solution. What is his view of Ellen's bathroom anxieties? What is his view toward change or continuance of the problem? How does he understand the issues? How does he deal with her bathroom and sexual behavior? Is he as committed to change as she? What would happen if she does not change? What would happen if she does change?

Given that their children are fully grown, we might inquire as to their availability for a consultation. What is their view of the situation? Interestingly, how were Ellen's children raised in relation to various bathroom behaviors? If none of her children have anxiety associated with the bathroom activity, we would ask how did she teach them to be without anxiety? For example, we could suggest the therapeutic bind in asking, "What did you do with your children in teaching them to use the bathroom without anxiety that perhaps you did not even know you knew?" If Ellen knows the answer to this question then we might use her response as part of an intervention. If she does not know, then there is an implication of knowing at the unconscious level. Even if no one from her present family were available to come to a session, we could ask Ellen to consider these questions from the perspective of each family member, indirectly suggesting alternative perspectives. These types of questions may serve to create multiple realities as opposed to the fixed and unhappy one of Ellen. Multiple perspectives may allow us a wider range of intervention possibilities. In asking a particular question, she may respond by saying, "Oh, I never thought of it that way before." The possibility of developing new associations and learnings will have begun.

A key element in the Ericksonian approach is recognizing the strengths and resources (e.g., abilities, skills, adaptability) of the client. Ellen's strengths seem obvious and abundant. She has a long-term marriage, children, success (even if she does not fully recognize it as such), and financial security. In her self-description as "methodical, thorough, careful, stubborn, insecure, and competitive, particularly with women," we might indirectly challenge her self-view with a more positive consideration. A simple humorous offering such as "I like methodical doctors. They're less likely to leave clamps in you after an operation" may present further diagnostic information. Does she laugh, smile, or otherwise respond to the statement?

Ellen could have come into therapy at any time because the things that lie ahead of her are important. Although the fact of the upcoming China trip has significance, we would speculate that there has always been some significant upcoming event that is important. Her choice to enter therapy at this time may have as much to do with the impending retirement of her husband and what that developmental shift may bring as the upcoming trip to China. This would bring to mind the possibility of enjoying life; questions about the meaning of life, and the meaning and associated issues of being intimate; and the possibility of what they have worked for all these years bringing satisfaction.

Without her children as a possible buffer between Ellen and her husband, a future filled with demands for intimacy may seem particularly anxiety provoking. This approaching developmental transition brings to mind other developmental transitions that we would speculate have not gone as well as one might have hoped. We might speculate that in every stage of development having to do with independence and pleasure, Ellen learned to respond with compulsiveness and discipline. As mentioned earlier, the obvious problems associated with her mother's problematic behavior at a critical time in Ellen's development most likely contributed to her symptomatology. Continuing this line of reasoning, perhaps each developmental stage brought her some degree of shame and difficulty. In a positive frame, her discipline allowed her to become a physician. However, we would speculate that she has not learned to assert her own needs or develop a useful notion of joy, intimacy, or self-pride.

Treatment Formulation

Because of Ellen's obviously intelligent conscious mind and its associated limitations to consider other possibly adaptive frames of reference, hypnotherapy may be an optimal strategy to create new learnings, reframe old experiences, and suggest new behaviors. Using the above speculation as a basis for our treatment formulation, we have an initial three-part plan involving the use of hypnosis: (a) dissociation[1] from her trauma in connection to (b) a reexperiencing of earlier developmental stages with the positive attributes that any child might be expected to have, followed by (c) the development and association of resources needed to better enjoy her present life stage (e.g., independence and sexual intimacy with her husband). We are aiming at her ability to understand that she is not the same as her mother, even though they are the same anatomically, and that her own ability to decide and judge things can come from her own integrated life and her intelligence both as a doctor and as an adult woman.

Following our initial hypothesis, we would seek to replace her fear of the menstrual and excretory process with feelings of compassion and love initially directed toward herself and her own needs, while negating the apparent neglect and insensitivity she may have experienced from her mother. We would then focus on developing the forgiving attitude and cognitive changes previously mentioned that are necessary for her next stage of development. It is important for us to make associations to joy,

---

[1]In this instance we are using the concept of dissociation to suggest to the client that while experiencing hypnosis she can review a previously difficult or painful childhood scene or scenes from a different perspective than she did as a child, without reexperiencing the associated anxiety.

self-respect, and tolerance toward her own mistakes, as well as successes she has had over time. Therefore, we will offer her the opportunity, with hypnosis, to "redo" her toilet training experience with the proper love, attention, and support, as opposed to whatever she did or did not receive from her mother.

As mentioned earlier, the third stage in our treatment would be to assist in generalizing the joy, respect, tolerance, and compassion of her earlier development, now relearned in the hypnotic experience, to her own current developmental needs—specifically, to the legitimate social role that encompasses assertiveness, aggressiveness, tenderness, and sexual behavior. We would then design a therapy scenario around each of the following areas: hypnotic induction, retrieval of the needed resources, the dissociation from the trauma, the association of the positive resources to the current life situation, and finally generalizing into the future. Specifically, posthypnotic suggestions would be offered about such upcoming events as the trip to China, her husband's retirement, and their time together with their children out of the home. Our approach is predicated on the notion that her symptomatic complaint is not complicated by any competing overt or covert agenda on the part of her husband or her family. The inclusion of her family in our assessment is designed to manage such possibilities.

A cautionary note to the reader is worthy of mention at this point. Our assessment, choice of interventions, and overall treatment plan are coconstructed *with* the client, as opposed to being pronouncements from the expert(s) to the client. It is not our wish to impose our view (i.e., goals, etc.) on or force the client to acquiesce to our treatment plan. In this case, if Ellen were to respond to our questions or initial hypnotic experience in a way not initially anticipated, we would change our intervention and behavior in accordance with the needs of the client. For us, the assessment–intervention process is a recursive loop between the client and therapist in which each simultaneously influences and is influenced by the other (Matthews, 1985).

THE HYPNOTIC WORK

Based on the previous discussion, the following is a verbatim transcript, as we would construct it, of hypnotherapy with Ellen.

> Ellen, after talking this over, I think you and I are in agreement that here and now is a valuable opportunity to learn self-hypnosis from the standpoint that you may experience immediate relief or a great deal of amelioration from the distress you have discussed, and you would rather, as in that old saying, learn to fish than just be given a fish. Of course we are not after fish here. We are using that simply as an analogy to say that there are experiences of *confidence* and *ease of living*, and

there are those experiences of *well being that you are seeking* and that I feel very confident we will be able to facilitate, and in facilitating, help you experience on a regular and more frequent basis through the course of your daily life.

I want to begin by doing two things at once. First of all, I need to underscore and emphasize that the only person I really know how to hypnotize is myself and likewise, the only person that can *hypnotize you* is *Ellen*. So all hypnosis is self-hypnosis. Hypnosis is a state of heightened awareness for subtle internal events: memories, thoughts, ideas, beliefs, impulses, feelings, and so on. Let me give you an illustration of that right off, and I believe that you will understand from both an intellectual and experiential position.

If you would position your arms in the following way so that your hands are floating four inches above your lap, about a half inch apart with your fingers open lightly and, if possible, position yourself so that your wrists and your elbows do not touch your lap or your side. This is not the only way a person can *use self-hypnosis* but I often teach it because it will immediately illustrate the definition of hypnosis in *your own experience* and help demystify and *bring a better understanding about your degree of self-control and your ease and comfort in using self-hypnosis*.

So, get yourself in that position now, with your eyes opened or closed, either one, that's right. Pose yourself a proposition in the form of speaking to yourself, along the following lines: If my unconscious is prepared to help me *increase my sense of ease, well-being, and confidence*, then my fingers will come together and I'll *go into a trance*. Now, you change my words so that they *suit you as a person*, and in future settings, change the words so that they suit your immediate purpose of going into trance as far as you can understand at that time.

In this initial phase of the hypnotic experience, we are creating a foundation and positive expectancy for the change to come. In appreciation of Ellen's desire for self-control, we are emphasizing the idea of self-hypnosis. This is to underscore the notion that she will be in control, not the therapist. Woven throughout our hypnotic communication is the use of indirect suggestions, in contrast to suggestions which specifically direct her actions. The idea is to create maximum flexibility for Ellen to develop her unique hypnotic experience. Our intention is to circumvent Ellen's self-critical cognitions (e.g., "this isn't working," "I'm not doing it right," etc.) and create a context where whatever she does will be considered as successful. The italicized words indicate a voice tone shift (i.e., for increased emphasis) for embedded suggestions within the hypnotic induction:

Now, a very interesting thing *will begin to happen* when you hold your hands in this way and your conscious mind may wish to spend a few moments reflecting on the proposition that you made with your unconscious mind. For starters, you've given some guidelines so your own associations and sense of working on this problem will stay within the boundaries and the limits of your guidelines. Isn't it nice to know *you have that control* or maybe you didn't know you knew it. It's rather like waking up and thinking: *I'm going to have a good day today.* And even though you have that in the back of your mind and *you don't think about it again*, it continues to be a part of your framework and *push toward a good day each day*. Another analogy is that it is rather like getting in your car, starting the engine, and saying: I think I'll drive to work today at this moment. And you don't need to continually remind yourself that you're on your way to work, do you? You go to work, because, while your thoughts can wander and think about other things, they are all in the framework of that original self-direction. That's right.

The use of statements that by definition are essentially true create a positive response set for the hypnotic process and future therapeutic work (Erickson & Rossi, 1979). Additionally, by emphasizing the everyday way in which the unconscious mind, as distinguished from the conscious mind, works, we are laying the foundation for other therapeutic ways in which Ellen's unconscious mind can push toward a good day, good feeling, and so forth.

So, recapping, you hold your hands in just the way you have them. That's very good. And now you can see that your fingers are beginning to gradually jiggle and begin to move together. At this point we don't have a common vocabulary for this experience you may have in your fingers. I want to use the word "magnetic" feeling because it does nicely describe the experience, doesn't it? Do you feel a kind of magnetic feeling in your fingertips pulling them together? As your fingers touch, *let your eyes close.* It's not a true magnetic feeling. It's not a magnetic feeling at all. I rather think it's like the sensation of blood pulsing in the fingers that's there all the time and which we seldom notice in our busy day. Now *let that pulsating feeling*, sort of a numbness or tingliness, come into the forefront of your mind and *enjoy the experience as you have it.* It's a different and novel experience, and without realizing it, you might have overlooked the fact that it is kind of a *pleasant, safe, alive feeling* that you have in those fingers.

Now let those pleasant feelings come up past your first knuckle and use your conscious mind to try to anticipate feeling that very subtle feeling all the way to the middle knuckle of each finger on both hands. And gradually anticipate its movement toward that middle knuckle. And as you do that with your conscious mind, your unconscious will *sensitize or stimulate the ability of your feeling* cortex to sense that experience in the foreground and let the other feelings that the customary sense of your fingers used to bring fade into the background. And then just let that continue on up towards the base of your fingers where they meet the back of your hand and discover in which ways you can help that feeling move through the palm of your hand or the back of your hand most easily and let it spread over the palm and back and around your thumbs as I count backwards from 20 to 1 so that by the time I reach 1, you can have gradually and systematically moved it all the way up your arms, around your neck, and so on.

In this instance, we are offering the doctor a different way of learning about and attending to her feelings, which she understands physiologically, but perhaps not as yet psychologically.

And I want to take a moment as you do that, 20, *and 19*, gradually anticipating its slight movement across the back of your hand, toward your thumb, 18, until finally, 17, it comes near the base of your thumb, 16. And then continue again to anticipate it moving through your thumb, 15, until it passes through the tip of your thumb into your other thumb, 14. And many people at this point can feel it sort of pulsating around almost like a little cyclotron of élan vital through the fingers and thumb, holding them in midair *effortlessly, weightlessly, 13, 12*. And a very nice thing about this as *you do self-hypnosis, Ellen*, is that it emphasizes what hypnosis is. It is a heightened awareness for internal experience, thoughts, and memories, and so on as I mentioned before. A very natural set of *internal experiences* like this one that *you're feeling* have often gone unnoticed until now while you have a heightened sense, *10, 9*. Now begin to let it move up your wrists and up your forearm until it goes around your elbow, up your upper arm. You can do this at your own speed as I continue to count.

And just let your breathing fall into your abdomen, 8, 7 and at this point you notice that *relaxation is beginning to replace* those spots of tension in your neck, cheeks, 7, and that *relaxation will continue* to replace the tension that falls from the top of your head, down your neck, around your jaw. And as it does, you may *feel a sense* of that élan vital pulsation you originally experienced as it takes a slightly different form and moves all the way up your shoulders and around your neck. And now you could probably recognize the original cycle that had gone from your fingers to your thumbs, 6, is now able to be noticed going from your fingers all the way up to your arms and around your shoulders and neck and back down your arm to your fingers. And in just a moment you will be able to move it quite easily all the way down your torso, *relaxing* your back, your stomach, your hips, all the way down past your pelvis, legs and knees, down to your lower legs, feet and toes, 5, 4.

And if you can't do it yet, you'll soon be able to feel that same experience you originally noticed in your fingers, with a slightly different sensation owing to the fact that you're dealing with elongated muscles, being the predominant experience over your whole body, almost like you're wrapped in a protective cocoon of your own making. A world of your own design that is your concentration and heightened awareness on one or two of your unconscious resources.

We are expending some effort here to help Ellen attend to feelings and sensations related to relaxation, comfort, and security. The purpose is twofold: (a) to develop the hypnotic experience so that (b) these sensations can be the basis for creating a positive self-image in dealing with the presenting issues of the bathroom behaviors and sexual and intimacy concerns at a later time in therapy.

And as you listen to the things I say, be certain that you follow my original recommendation of only *taking those suggestions from me that apply and fit for you as a person*. Only accept those suggestions that you hear from me that are *relevant to your goals and your growth* and modify all the others from me so that *they fit for you* as a person with your own goals and your growth as a person in mind. And if anything I say happens to be irrelevant or cannot be easily modified, then discard it or ignore it. *Follow your own thinking*. So, I might mention that a person remembered smelling a lilac bush and you remembered smelling wisteria. Modify what I say so that it fits for you as a person. And that way, with your sense of heightened awareness, you bring to your mind and revivify your own experiential memories, which are *helpful to your purposes and your original goals*.

And it may seem ironic that I would say you have a heightened sense of internal experience, and yet you know that sometimes *people have amnesia for hypnosis*. And that's because, while you're listening, 4, 3, to the things that I say, you'll begin to think about those things that apply to you as a person and are relevant to your own history. And you'll remember some part down memory lane, 3, and 2, till you have a sense of taking those tours down memory lane, possibly thinking about times that you enjoyed a pleasant walk in a park, perhaps passing under a weeping willow tree or smelling the fragrance of lilac. And then all of a sudden you realize that I've been speaking about something and you don't remember what I was speaking about because you were interested in what was important to you as a person. You heard me and yet you didn't hear me in a way. Then, perhaps wondering what the continuity of things said really was, you remember that you hadn't been listening closely enough because you had been thinking about your own internal memories, 1, that nice state of *protective, safe cocoon, alive, excited* about the *well-functioning of your own person*. And *it's nice to absorb yourself in that feeling*.

And if that's all that you do with your self-hypnosis with your conscious mind, *notice that resource in a pleasant way*. You can trust that your unconscious mind will continue along the original path of your consciously stated intent, modified only slightly to include aspects of additional resources of well-being that are needed to accomplish the goal you set out with yourself, for yourself in the beginning. And you may only know about the pleasant experience you had sitting with your eyes closed as time passed. And remembering that, you don't know fully what the direction of my speech had been because you had been thinking about your own interesting memory of something that you can believe you'll be able to put your finger on if you just think about it for a moment and then realize that you forgot what you were thinking about.

You forgot what I was saying. It was relevant at the time and you had a great deal of awareness for it. And hypnosis is a state of heightened awareness for internal events and memories and experiences, and while you had that heightened awareness for internal events and experiences and awareness, ironically *you have amnesia for what you were thinking and for what I was saying. And that is not an uncommon experience.*

Ellen is reminded to use what is offered if it fits and discard what does not. Again, reinforcing that she has control. The suggestion for amnesia is offered because forgetting is a common occurrence in the hypnotic process that can then be utilized to ratify Ellen's specific experience. Additionally, by forgetting some of the suggestions and experiences suggested in the present, she may be more likely to own those feelings when they are stimulated in the future, rather than attributing them exclusively to suggestions by the therapist.

And while you're there, deeply absorbed as you are, I would like to suggest that you consider some ways of helping yourself further facilitate the accomplishment of your goals. The first thing I'd like to suggest is, to the extent that you feel comfortable and pleasant sitting there now on the couch, that you recognize the ease with which *you can develop the feeling of pride* in many, many accomplishments that you have. And as you do that, your conscious mind could simply think through all the times in your adult life when you have, as a doctor, succeeded in small and significant ways. You could develop an understanding about how hypnosis can be a tool you comfortably use to enhance and magnify your feelings of pride in the thousands and hundreds of thousands of accomplishments that *you have earned over the years.*

For example, a child seldom takes the time to record in a diary a strong sense of pleasure that she may feel due to the accomplishment of learning to tie her own shoelaces. Children usually gurgle with glee at the recognition that they have learned to button their own buttons for the first time. A competitive child will realize that she finally has learned to ride her bicycle around the block and her feeling of independence has been greatly amplified by her mastery of a simple task of pushing down a bicycle pedal with one foot while keeping your balance on the seat, holding the hand grip to steady the front wheel while you push down with the other foot. And repeating the process again and again with as much energy as possible, zooming with wind in your face. How magnificent the motor skills and accomplishments the child has developed that now enable you to transport yourself from place to place with such a small degree of effort covering such a large expanse of ground.

And other children are fascinated by their ability to polish their shoes *just to their own satisfaction* or still others will be simply astounded at how skillfully they have colored within the lines the first time they learn to use crayons *to their satisfaction*. Even the child's ability to build a sand castle or to identify what kind of bird is going into a bird house are also opportunities that present themselves over the years, and *your mind is able to learn a feeling of confidence and pride, which we seldom have an opportunity to amply express. But they are there, waiting for you to think them through, to reflect on them, to feel them, to have them again, and to know as you come to experience them that they are yours and they can be used as a foundation for greater learnings*, like the ability to write the letters of the alphabet, to compose a letter and address an envelope to a friend, even the ability to watch your handwriting develop and the complex inner relationship between all the various roots of pride and mastery that go into bringing home those report cards of which you can be proud.

And sometimes, when we think about the B we got as a grade in some class, at the time we are so sorry we didn't get an A. But as we look back on it years later we realize in the larger context it was really of little consequence, especially now being a doctor, and you realize that you did get the grades that you needed to get into medical school. *You have accomplished a great deal that you never realized you would accomplish as a child.*

At this point we are seeking to establish the legitimacy of feeling a sense of accomplishment and pride in success as an adult and a professional. Ellen is reminded of a range of likely experiences she probably had as a child that form the basis of taking pride in her accomplishments as an adult. We also offer in this section the notion that being competitive is legitimate and useful in one's development. Here we also shift our use of pronouns, often within the same sentence, between "she" and "you" to further increase her identification with, in this instance, the childhood experiences being described.

And if your conscious mind thinks on these things while your unconscious keeps that experience of well-being constant, *you'll have a further feeling of enrichment and well-being and pride as a foundation* for your own self-hypnosis. However, if you let your conscious mind pay attention to the feeling of well-being that you have in the chair, and just let your unconscious mind put together those ideas about which I spoke with your own memories, then *you'll have a strong feeling of security, pride, and mastery* to enhance that feeling of well-being that you have in the chair. And you may not even fully pay attention to what I'm saying because some of those feelings are so important that you can let them develop in your mind as your own personal place to go during your self-hypnosis.

And the next thing I'd like to suggest is that with all the adventures you've had in the past, hold that *feeling and those resources which you're having now* in the chair constantly in mind, or let your unconscious hold them, let your conscious mind drift ahead to the ideas of going to China so that you can make a connection in anticipation of the small things of packing your bag, unpacking your bag, brushing your teeth, looking out from the hotel room, of walking in the streets and smelling the new smells, hearing the new sounds. All of those antici-pations of what you'll encounter in China can be linked by means of your own posthypnotic suggestions to these *feelings of pride, security, joy, and accomplishment.* Take just a few moments to hold onto those feelings and resources that you've put together and enhanced your *feeling of well-being* with, and link them to your conscious mind's an-ticipation of the various sights and sounds you'll encounter on your way to China and your return back and the people you'll share it with once you're home in the states, having a successful trip. I always make it a point to think about the places I'll go when I *have these feelings of well-being,* so that, on the trips, my brain wonders what to be thinking about now, and in the background there will be the answer: *Have these feelings of well-being at that time.* And there will be a connection that was created by my anticipation and deliberate linking of the good feelings I felt unconsciously to those things that I thought about con-sciously, or perhaps the things that I was consciously feeling good about while my unconscious took the time to link those anticipated events of things such as the trip to China. You can't be sure just how *you will experience those feelings of well-being.*

Our intention is that the upcoming events for Ellen, such as the visit to China, would begin to be associated with those feelings of pride, mastery, and accomplishment that we have attempted to access in this session. This is not to say, however, that simply because we have made these associations that she will be able to stimulate those feelings for herself. In fact, it seems reasonable, based on our assumptions about her family interactions, to view her general style of competitiveness as having created an attitude or belief system that continually inhibits the very associations we are hoping to help her establish in that preceding work. Assuming we are in good rapport with Ellen, that her presentation (i.e. facial gestures, body movements, etc.) are congruent with the therapeutic process to this point[2], the follow-ing portions of the hypnotic process are offered to address the issue of Ellen's previous learnings:

> You know, Ellen, there are a lot of years of experience that a person gains as they grow into adulthood *as you have,* and it would be a shame to overlook the possibility of *weaving together the continuity of years of*

---

[2]If, however, Ellen were showing or reporting signs of distress, discomfort, or anxiety, we would need to respond accordingly, adjust our intervention, and reassess what is needed in the moment.

hope and anticipation. Because by connecting together those threads of your life over time, one strengthens your own understanding of who you have become and who you are. And the more you strengthen those understandings, the weaker the grip of earlier doubts become, which may have inadvertently become the foundation for some of the developing personality.

So think back in time to the young girl that you once were. Maybe you can imagine seeing photographs of her or maybe you can just remember what she would have looked like. I'm not suggesting that you see the world through her eyes, but rather see her in her world through your eyes from the future, with compassion. You spoke to me about some distance that little girl had from the loving care of a mother for a variety of reasons. In seeing her and reaching back, give me a head nod when you can begin to imagine seeing her there in front of you. You can then modify that scene somewhat so that little girl and her attention is something that you can attract, and speak to her and gain a head nod from that little girl such that she hears you and you can share that head nod with me. There's a sense of communication with that historical past. Now that you've accomplished that to some degree, you'll realize that further thinking about it will further strengthen your ability to use your imagination in this way. And whether or not it is just your conscious mind imagining that you're making such a link or whether or not your unconscious mind is being used to make such a link with your imagination really doesn't matter.

Assuming that we have established a place of comfort and security for the adult Ellen, we are going to ask her to use these positive feelings to support herself as a little girl in ways and instances, according to our hypothesis, that her mother did not. We ask for a simple head nod in order to confirm that Ellen is able to create this imagery and follow our suggestions. If she were unable to achieve this imagery, we would adjust our response accordingly and approach the issue in a different manner. Also, as part of our hypnotic approach, we employ a high number of indirect or permissive suggestions that allow for a wide latitude of responses by Ellen.

What might be much more important is to imagine telling that little girl you once were that you're the woman from her future and that *she will have accomplished a great deal that she can be proud* of over the years and that you are living proof of that. And tell her that you wanted to come back and reassure her and *reach out a loving hand to her* from a woman that she can respect and be proud of and tell her in your own way that she is a little girl who didn't learn much about anticipating the joys of new things. Maybe she didn't learn much about anticipating the joy of growing into a woman but you learned a great deal about that and that you would like, by returning from the future to speak to her, to extend some of this positive energy and these resources you are feeling to her so that she can have a sense of continuity with a woman who *she can look up to and be proud of.*

And tell her, in your own way, that it's really of great importance to you now that she have a model of a woman she can *look up to and be proud of* and that you would love to offer that to her, that you would like very much for her to rely upon you as a model that she can use over the years to aspire, as many children will, to a model to which she can be proud and really excited. And *tell her of all the things she has done in the past that bring a smile of joy to your face,* knowing that she contributes so much to the world by having the aspirations that she does of growing into a wonderful woman that she will someday become. And *really hold her attention* and talk to her heart to heart and person to person about all *the wonderful accomplishments that she will have* and the joy of becoming a woman *who is mature, such a good citizen, confident, feels the feeling of well-being that you feel.* And continue to nod your head to me from time to time that she is communicating with you, listening, and by communicating, understanding deeply inside, so that in your own way you are helping connect those historical roots of the person you once were with the understandings you've formed over the years of your own value.

The essence of our work is to associate, or reassociate, these resources (pride, contentment, confidence, etc.) with Ellen's self-image such that she can experience and anticipate, as in the China trip, herself experiencing life in a positive manner. In creating a scene of the adult Ellen comforting, teaching, and communicating with the childhood Ellen, our intention is to introduce a number of suggestions about the natural use of her own resources and associations. The notion being, that however unpleasant the childhood, a valuable, positive person about whom the child could feel hope and pride emerged. The strength of Ellen has been such that she has developed confidence and pride over the years but lacked a parental model that would have organized this for her as a woman of whom she could have been proud. This deficiency in her childhood experience may have made it easier for her to deride her achievements rather than to feel enhanced by them.

As such, we have attempted to provide a substitute mother figure for the little girl in a framework that says: As your substitute mother, you have the image of an admirable, respectable woman simultaneously being paired in her mind with the memories of childhood. This could be expected to introduce the idea of pride in being a woman, with the implication that becoming a woman is marked by the special activity of the young girl's bodily functions, such as menstruation or other private activities done in bathroom grooming.

We do know from her history that she was disposed in a negative way to her mother's grooming habits. By helping her make associations in the manner offered, we hoped to have strengthened her self-image and the coping mechanisms she will draw upon in her adult life. Our intention is that Ellen will begin to associate the concepts of being a woman and becoming a woman, with all of its ramifications, while simultaneously thinking about the needs of small girls. We might speculate that perhaps this is the first time these associations have been identified and paired in this manner for Ellen. As such, we might expect that she is creating new coping skills and ways of interacting in her environment based on our goal of enhancing her body and overall self-image. These connections and associations will not be left to chance, but will be stimulated and guided by future therapy and hypnotic work. This session is designed to lay the foundation to which we will return in future sessions.

Finally, we might expect a strengthening of her self-image resulting from recognizing that she never acted on any childhood aggressive rages directed toward her mother.[3] We remind her repeatedly that she has developed into a fine woman despite whatever urges she once had toward her mother. These strengthened cognitions, secondary thinking, and reality testing provide for a therapeutic enhancement of Ellen's self-image that would have been expected to have occurred with kind and loving parental support. However, because she did not have that parental support, enhancing them now can simultaneously strengthen these resources in the adult while the imagery and ideas of the little girl who did not have these experiences and resources are stimulated.

Thus, those impulses, urges, and ideas that may have resulted in denial and self hatred as defense mechanisms when she was a child are once again stimulated by the magnitude of the revivification of that child in her mind. However, as she revivifies aspects of the child's experience in the session, she is simultaneously processing data that indicate that her childhood coping mechanisms did not result in any catastrophic behavior. She did not harm her mother and ruin her life. Instead, she developed into a fine citizen, a person about whom she can be proud. By having retrieved and strengthened those resources prior to the revivification of childhood, they become the major frame and lens through which that child's behavior can be examined, thereby allowing a strengthening of the reality testing and secondary processes.

The need for more archaic defense mechanisms can be diminished in concert with the symptoms to which the breakdown of those mechanisms gave rise. This change would include her somewhat shy attitude as a result of self-criticism and the anxiety that she has about performance, especially performance related to those things closely associated with her body (i.e., the various tasks of cleanliness, urination, and menstruation).

---

[3]Our assumption here is that because of her mother's non-mothering behavior, Ellen may have had a number of aggressive and negative thoughts directed toward her mother, about which she may have felt guilty. Her guilt feelings would be expected to further contribute to her negative self-image.

CONDUCTING FUTURE WORK

As this explanation and transcription is a demonstration of what we might do with each major piece of therapy, it might be wise to remind the reader that we do not see this as a single session, even though it may read as such. In fact, what we have accomplished to this point would probably be a matter of several sessions depending on how easily Ellen communicated with us and to what extent our working hypotheses were confirmed. With that in mind, at any given time, the treatment intervention presented here would be altered to respond to the unique individual we have in the office. The client–therapist feedback loop provides the process that informs our action. Assuming we are going in a useful direction, we proceed now into what might be the sixth to seventh session.

Assessment and Evaluation

To the extent that Ellen has responded as we might expect at this stage in our work, we would now proceed with an extensive self-image thinking focus in the next session. The goal of a well integrated brief therapy encounter is that each part of the therapy overlaps with the next and that seeds for the termination are planted in the beginning. As such, we have been working towards this more complex goal since the initial assessment hypothesis had been formulated. If Ellen had responded differently at any point in the therapy, we would of course adapt to her responses and rework our assessment and interventions. However, we believe our work in the earlier stages was general enough to set the stage for a more focused use of self-image thinking intervention.

Self-Image Thinking

> Self-images are maps of the world and symbols of the self. They elaborate the associations a person expects to experience in various situations. They may be simple residual images of people and events from childhood, objective images of equipment and machines with motor programs attached, or they may be thoughtfully organized scenarios ("I could do that," or "I should have said that", or "Next time I'll do it that way") with associated emotional, postural, and verbal expectations conditioned to occur. (Lankton & Lankton, 1983, p. 312)

Self-image thinking is how the individual constructs meaning about him- or herself based on memories of previous and anticipated future experiences (e.g., "I failed at that in the past and will do so in the future").

The goal of self-image intervention is to facilitate a change in cognitions, attitudes, beliefs, and feelings that the individual holds about him- or herself. With respect to the person's remembered past, self-image thinking seeks to engage in a form of therapeutic revisionism. With respect to the individual's future, self-image thinking seeks to create a set of positive anticipatory expectancies for accomplishment. For us, hypnotherapy creates a process wherein a person can make cognitive and perceptual changes as well as changes in visceral and emotional experiences.

One might consider self-image thinking hypnotherapy as a parallel[4] to the socialization process of individual development. Our goal, then, in the present case is to help stimulate, via hypnosis, Ellen's thinking and framing of her successes in such a way that helps those resources she already has to be available in her ongoing development. Ellen needs to see, hear, feel, and experience herself in a more positive manner than she has in the past. As she acts in a competent, confident manner as a doctor, mother, and spouse she needs to have a set of beliefs and congruent visceral feelings that coincide with and reinforce in her these daily actions.

Owing to our belief in the movement each individual has toward growth, we are led to conclude, supported by our clinical experience, that, given the proper context and guidance for putting together this constellation of attitudes, body images, perceptions, and emotions, clients will, in fact, rally those experiences needed to make changes in their experiential life. Self-image thinking used in this manner may at least provide a skeletal means whereby further growth is possible with the ongoing reinforcement of the environment. It is our intention that the process of self-image thinking help provide the individual with an internal reinforcement contingency created by his or her own sense of value and attitude developed by adjustments made in hypnotherapy.

With Ellen, if our hypothesis has been borne out to this point, we would expect her to be interested in becoming a person who enjoys her body, who enjoys being a woman, and who enjoys bringing joy to others. Self-image thinking provides that structure by which to address these issues. In our conversations with Ellen as therapy progressed, we would expect to hear her report new behaviors, feelings, and attitudes. We would always want to attribute change to her efforts, as opposed to crediting ourselves, and ask her such questions as what she noticed first about her changes, who else noticed them, how will she continue these changes, what would happen if she discontinued these changes, and so forth.

This next aspect of our work with Ellen seeks to develop the process of self-image thinking in some detail:

> So, while you sit there with the set of *resources that you are experiencing now* which *you have put together* and amplified in the last several hypnotic sessions over the last several weeks, we want to offer you an idea

---

[4] This is in no way to suggest that self-image thinking is equivalent to or a substitute for the developmental process of childhood. This is an analogous process designed to enhance or further develop resources already existent.

that you might consider useful for helping unravel that part of your own experience that you have found to be particularly problematic in solving over the years. So begin by either letting your conscious mind imagine a grown-up Ellen sitting on the couch while your *unconscious experiences the resources* we have built over the last few weeks, or let your conscious mind *embrace the resources you've built up and feel so proud of* over the last few weeks while your unconscious mind begins to develop a picture of yourself sitting on the couch in your mind's eye. And nod your head when you have accomplished that to your satisfaction.

And you know that the grown woman has a sense of compassion and understanding for others and a great intellectual ability to understand the functioning of the human body, the human anatomy. And with that visual image of the grown-up Ellen in your mind, you might let your conscious mind float out and observe the Ellen on the couch and the Ellen she's observing while your conscious mind takes a stance from some neutral position elsewhere in the room.

We are asking Ellen to develop a dissociated experience at three levels, herself watching herself watching herself as child. At the very least this process is likely to deepen the hypnotic experience. It is also our intention that dissociation in this context will create the opportunity for Ellen to have a different perspective on her life. We would like her to review a scene rather than only experience it. Ultimately, our goal is that the adult will help the child have positive experiences that in turn positively affect the adult. The analogy is to the M. C. Escher painting of one hand drawing the other (Matthews, 1985).

> When you've accomplished that, raise the index finger of your left hand as a signal of yes to me. It would be so much easier than nodding your head because your unconscious can produce a small jerky movement of your index finger as an indication of yes. And once that signal is given, I'd like to ask you to do something else. Having received that signal, I will ask you to maintain that interesting balance you have of seeing yourself sitting on the couch watching the image of the grown-up Ellen with these resources while you're looking from some other perspective and vantage point.
>
> I would like you to watch the Ellen on the couch and the grown-up Ellen she's looking at as they recall a time from your distant past when little Ellen used to interact around members of your family. Perhaps some photograph that you once saw will come to mind or maybe it will be a picture of yourself in an album, but in any event, it will be most interesting for Ellen's conscious mind to observe yourself sitting on the couch picturing all those resources that the Ellen on the couch is seeing in the embodiment of the grown-up Ellen that can respect a person with knowledge, compassion, and sensitivity to others.
>
> And when some image of Ellen as a child comes to her mind, it can be seen by both of the grown-up Ellens that you're watching, let

their index finger raise again as a signal to me that you see those sights and hear the things that she was hearing and *continue to experience just those things* that you're able to notice she sees, hears, sitting on the couch. She can *feel the resources of compassion and sensitivity and intelligence* that she sees embodied in the Ellen that she imagines in front of her. And seeing and hearing only images and sounds and sights from that time past, watch that little girl go through her customary, normal daily experiences. Watch her eating at the table. Perhaps no one ever really did watch with compassion and sensitivity and it *would be nice to compliment her* on how nicely she's doing in this scene. Maybe pointing out to her in your own inner dialogue that you're from her future and that you dropped by to watch her and *to be proud* of how she sits so nicely in her chair and holds her silverware just so, cuts her food appropriately, and takes care to lean over the plate.

I bet there are at least a hundred things that she would like to hear that she did so well, but somehow perhaps failed to get recognition for or maybe doesn't remember or would just like to have reinforced or would like to strengthen her memory about. Just comments from an *older, compassionate, intelligent, respectful, sensitive woman* about how very well she's performing those complex tasks of learning. And switch the scene and see her in some other learning event, the way she opens her closets and selects her clothing for the day. And by observing, you can find out whether she did or didn't receive the sort of praise that she wanted and deserved, needed, for picking out her color schemes, for thoughtfully placing her socks and turning down the tops, even tying her shoes. Many children like to hear how well they do such routine tasks even though they've done them hundreds of times, because it only *strengthens their sense of pride* and ability to hear that other people noticed and could articulate the efforts put forth on such routine tasks. Especially when you remind her that you're from her future and that *you're an articulate, sensitive, intelligent observer* of human anatomy and human conduct.

We are attempting to match the pace at which the client is able to retrieve the memories we are seeking to reaccess. In addition, we are suggesting that she conceive of praise in the very places where she may have experienced deficiencies as a child. We are asking her to make associational links between parts of her mind and her experiential resources for sensitivity, compassion, attentiveness, praise, and self-respect. At the same time, she is remembering and thinking of her past when those resources needed to be attached to her network of psychological experiences. The goal is to develop more adaptive links to coping and creativity than were previously available. Once this foundation has been established, it would be appropriate to move on to such material that is of a potentially more sensitive nature.

At some point, we will request feedback, which could be verbal or ideomotor signaling (finger raising, head nodding, etc.), that she is ready to proceed to a time of her life that may have been of even greater concern. Given the work of this session and the assumed positive response, it seems reasonable now to ask her to remember Ellen as a child in the bathroom needing advice, consolation, and education concerning the bathroom routines that a child has to go through. Depending upon how sensitive she has been to these issues when previously mentioned, the vocabulary selected would be that which allowed her to be comfortable.

As such, the transcript is not tempered with words that are out of the ordinary but reflect the possibility that Ellen did not require any delicate handling with regard to these matters. If our assumption were inaccurate, then far more thoughtful word selection would be generated for Ellen.

> While your conscious mind observes the Ellen sitting on the couch and the Ellen who is compassionate, well-educated, sensitive, aware of anatomical understandings of the human body, let's ask that you watch those two Ellens watch the younger Ellen during some of her bathroom routines at an early age so that the younger Ellen can also *receive the reinforcement and confidence* that comes through the *recognition of her own efforts toward mastery* and sitting on the toilet, having a bowel movement. And with your own wisdom of a doctor, inform her that you're from her future, that you would like to point out that what she just did *was very well done* for the following reasons. Then think of some reasons and let her know what those are: her degree of effort, her degree of muscle control, her degree of concentration, the time frame in which she had the bowel movement, her awareness of herself, her self-respect that she shows by the way she cleaned up her body with toilet paper and other cleaning aids.
>
> And move that young Ellen into the future where she probably would like to go over with such a *wise advisor as you*, just what happens during her menstruation, both prior to and at that time when she first begins. And let her ask you questions she wants to ask and answer them in a forthright manner *without fear and with that confidence of resource, mastery that you have*, and with that *wisdom and compassion that you are watching yourself have*. And when that experience begins raise your index finger. And when that questioning and answering is over, raise your index finger again a second time. And make sure that you *tell her how very glad you are that she is alive* and that if she ever has any confusion she will turn to you and ask you about it.

It is not clear to us just what sorts of questions and answers she might have as a young woman. Therefore, a good deal of time needs to be left for Ellen to listen to the dialogue herself and only be guided in the reminders of responding back with the sort of wisdom and compassion and anatomical knowledge that she has as a physician. We then progress from this young age of beginning menstruation into adolescence and pick some other scene that would be indicative of her developing body image as well, such as development of breasts. Suggestions befitting this stage of development would be offered as was done at the earlier stages.

An entire section of this self-image thinking needs to deal with Ellen's ability and willingness to recognize what great strides she has taken in developing independence. It could very well be that there is some ambivalence between her desire to be taken care of and be dependent upon a woman such as her mother, while at the same time rejecting that mother for the complexity of reasons previously discussed. This would leave her in a state of ambivalence about independence versus dependence. In our view, this theme is reflected in the symptom she presents.

Consistent with our approach would be for us to use the same self-image thinking to ask her for those memories of scenes of beginning independence such as learning to ride a tricycle or bicycle. Asking her to continue to have the Ellen sitting on the couch watch the mature, resourceful, sensitive, compassionate, intelligent Ellen as she watches and remembers times when the younger Ellen first rode her bicycle around the block or two miles down the road to visit her friend. And ask that the grown-up Ellen, who she can respect and admire, remind her that she is from her future, that she is looking back at what a remarkable, good job she did in exercising judgment, in pedaling the bicycle rapidly, in adjusting her heart rate and breathing rate, in using her eyes and ears to protect herself on the trip. Have the grown-up Ellen let her know how very proud she was of this remarkable feat of development and to get an ideomotor yes signal that the child has heard and a yes signal that the child might be interested in hearing more. If these yes signals are given, then we continue to move forward with other incidents of independence, such as going to the prom, having her first kiss, marrying and officially leaving her family of origin to begin her own family.

A very nice segue is available here by asking her then to imagine scenes of going to China and being at the Great Wall and recognizing what a feat of independence this is and how proud of Ellen she is for that accomplishment. We might then ask to watch her keep experiencing those positive feelings of pride, satisfaction, confidence, and mastery when she urinates in public restrooms in China, while she urinates on the airplane, in airports, in restaurants. We might further suggest that at any given time she may somehow realize that while her conscious mind may notice certain sights and sounds in the use of the toilet facilities in these locations, that somehow she is also aware of a good deal of wisdom, confidence, understanding, compassion, and sensitivity in herself that underscores the independence that she has been able to generate.

We would also ask that the observing Ellen remind the younger Ellen at various times that she became a woman like the Ellen who is watching her and did not become a woman like her mother—that this Ellen who is observing is proof that she did, in fact, become that unique individual of whom she can be proud. One might also ask her to imagine other things that she will do even beyond going to China and to imagine them in such anticipated detail that the sights and sounds and feelings and smells of those future events will remind her of what a wonderful job she has done of becoming independent.

We would also remind her of what a wonderful job she has done in understanding the degree of anatomical skill and mastery that she has had as a young woman going into each of the earlier events discussed. The concept of being a young woman in each of these self-image scenarios has made it possible to weave together the sexuality aspect of her development as well as the issue of independence.

The Possibility of Couples Therapy

In addition to this individual hypnotherapy work, there may be a need for couples work as was discussed earlier. This may be easily accomplished in one or two sessions with the husband present in order to investigate whether or not her avoiding sexual contact may be a communication to him about not liking his way of approaching sex. She may or may not like him to initiate it, or want him to initiate it in some way different than he has been.

If this hypothesis is useful, then the prescription of homework having to do with who initiates sex and in what ways may take as little as one or two sessions to help put into motion an entirely new way for them to discuss, candidly and sensitively, their needs about sexual behavior. However, her husband may have significant individual problems concerning sexual intimacy himself. If such were the case, then therapy with him and the couple may be necessary. Assuming the latter not to be the case, the self-image thinking protocol, could be extended into the more specific intimate relations with her husband in the bedroom.

To this bedroom scene, we would suggest that she add experiences of pleasure, excitement, anticipation of joy, and intimacy. Given the success and rapport established in the previous sessions, it might be possible at this point simply to mention those resources as part of the attributes of the Ellen sitting on the couch or the Ellen whom she is watching who is sensitive and mature, well-educated, and articulate to pass on to the Ellen that she observes in the scene with her husband, those features of a positive emotional experience, which include tenderness, sensitivity, joy, and excitement.

Again, we have created in hypnotherapy a context wherein she can simultaneously think about pleasure, excitement, intimacy, openness, and trust while she thinks about sexual contact with her husband. The emphasis is not on her trying to have insight for the previous lack of association to these experiences, but rather on building up the association of those resources simultaneously with her awareness of her need to have them available.

Considering the attitude changes about her body image, maturation as a woman, and independence that she may have gained in the therapy up to this point, we may require only a few more sessions dealing with her sexual adequacy. Given our hypotheses to this point, this intervention would be the logical approach for us to take in this stage of the work with Ellen.

> Since we have previously been speaking about Ellen's historical comfort and skill being enhanced by the wisdom of the grown Ellen, since some of those earlier questions about your body functioning have been answered by the mature part of the grown-up Ellen, and since an awareness that may have been somewhat lacking about your own skill and independence has been strengthened by the way you have been able to let younger parts of yourself listen to these older parts of yourself, you've *learned a great deal* that will make it possible for you to *easily have feelings of enjoyment, excitement, and intimacy* that you wish to have as the mature individual you desire yourself to become when you're in the situation of initiating and concluding sexual relations with your husband.
>
> So take a moment now in the privacy of your own mind to imagine those scenarios where you let the comfortable Ellen on the couch and the mature, wise, compassionate, perceptive Ellen who you are also imagining remind you at every step of the way, as you think through how you would like to have those resources available in the context of your own bedroom with your husband. Take time to stop and consult with yourself *about your needs and your perceptions and your enjoyment, your risk taking and how very well you're doing.* And see that whole scenario of lovemaking with your husband from beginning to end, giving the yes signal when it begins and allowing it to pass through in your mind in a briefer period of time because you can review so much that actually will unfold a great deal more slowly in the real world. And when you've seen it from beginning to end, going just the way you'd like, have Ellen use that positive future memory as a way to remind herself that she *has those resources for intimacy, joy, mastery, independence, and confidence* with her body image. Be delightfully amused with herself and surprised and proud of herself for having those resources available so that after three or four opportunities of practice with her husband these feelings and resources will become automatic and unconscious and give her even more time to enjoy herself in ways that she has merited.

CONCLUSION

This concludes the portion of the transcription that we feel reflects our understanding of and likely approach to this case. In summary, the essence of our work is resource development and associating those resources in ways that allow the individual to experience more wide ranging socially interactive roles. With Ellen, our goal was to create a therapeutic context wherein she could access the resources from her own life, framing them in a way that places them more in the foreground, thereby more available, than she had previously considered. The therapist is simply a catalyst for helping her access, find, or, if necessary, create those resources that she already has within her. We view our role not as expert in Ellen's life, but as having expertise in guiding her to take the control of her own resources, appreciating that these resources are from and of herself, not conferred upon her in the course of therapy.

The emphasis of the therapeutic work is not to develop insight into a problem, but rather to foster the experiential association of her resources to the desired contexts. Therapy becomes goal directed and future oriented and uses an assessment of the past, with a mixture of memory from that past, as a means to strengthen the continuity and integration of her resources. Our overall treatment goals were to help eliminate her shyness and fear of urinating in public restrooms, to help reduce her anxiety about going on such excursions as the upcoming China trip, and to help make some contribution to her enjoyment of sexual conduct with her husband.

Each of the earlier therapeutic goals (use of public bathrooms and independence to travel) intersected with the goal of sexual intimacy by increasingly complex associations of resources in a similar manner that normal socialization process may have done. Barriers to a more adaptive functioning, such as her ambivalence toward her mother and her own attitude about bodily cleanliness, were focused upon in the therapeutic situation. In the last therapy sessions, there was a greater emphasis upon self-image thinking as a mechanism that would help her with the attitudinal, emotional, and visceral changes for those components of sexuality, body image, and independence.

As a byproduct of the repetitive use of self-image thinking, we would expect that Ellen would begin to develop a more ready access to these desired resources whereby she could plan other events in the future with success. Our goal would be that she could think of and experience her resources as she anticipates the events, thus increasing the likelihood of enjoyment and satisfaction in her experiences. Such a response, of course, would be significantly different from what she had done in the past. This will reduce the negative element of doubt that had fed into her anticipation of various activities in the past.

The case of Ellen presents the connection for us between assessment and intervention in relation to the principles of Ericksonian problem solving. In our brief therapy approach, we attempted to weave in the natural use of hypnotherapy to overcome the presenting symptoms that existed for this client.

REFERENCES

Haley, J. (1978). *Problem Solving Therapy*. San Francisco: Jossey-Bass.

Erickson, M., & Rossi, E. (1979). *Hypnotherapy: An exploratory casebook*. New York: Brunner/Mazel.

Lankton, S., & Lankton, C. (1989). *Tales of enchantment: Goal-oriented metaphors for adults and children in therapy*. New York: Brunner/Mazel.

Lankton, S., & Lankton, C. (1986). *Enchantment and intervention in family therapy: Training in Ericksonian approaches*. New York: Brunner/Mazel.

Lankton, S., & Lankton, C. (1983). *The answer within: A clinical framework of Ericksonian therapy*. New York: Brunner/Mazel.

Lankton, S., Lankton, C., & Matthews, W. (1991). Ericksonian family therapy. In A. Gurman & P. Kniskern (Eds.), *Handbook of family therapy, Volume II* (pp. 187--214). New York: Brunner/Mazel.

Matthews, W. (1985). A cybernetic model of Ericksonian hypnotherapy: One hand draws the other. In S. Lankton (Ed.), *The Ericksonian monographs, 1* (pp. 42-60). New York: Brunner/Mazel.

V

CONCLUSION

19

MAXIMIZING TREATMENT GAINS: RECOMMENDATIONS FOR THE PRACTICE OF CLINICAL HYPNOSIS

STEVEN JAY LYNN, IRVING KIRSCH, and JUDITH W. RHUE

The *Casebook* has provided numerous illustrations of how hypnotic procedures can be incorporated into a wide range of theoretical models and treatments. Yet in no instance was hypnosis used as the sole treatment. Rather, it was an integral part of a well-planned, sensibly formulated treatment. In the discussion of the case of Ellen, the degree to which hypnosis was central to treatment ranged from the Ericksonian approach (chapter 18), in which many therapeutic communications were couched in terms of hypnosis, to rational–emotive behavior therapy (chapter 16), in which hypnosis was recommended only as an ancillary treatment if other approaches were "not working too well." In each case, however, the use of hypnosis was predicated on the idea that it would contribute something unique and important to treatment.

In our own clinical practices, we have found this to be the case as well: Hypnotic procedures are powerful experiential techniques that can bolster treatment success. In this chapter, we discuss ways of enhancing the beneficial effects of hypnotic methods while minimizing negative outcomes. In so doing, we recapitulate a number of important themes that have emerged so far, offer recommendations for maximizing treatment gains, and highlight caveats for therapists who wish to minimize untoward reactions in their practice.

THE IMPORTANCE OF ASSESSMENT

At the outset of the *Casebook*, we observed that clinical hypnosis begins with a careful assessment of the client and an evaluation of therapeutic strategies in relation to treatment goals. Assessment, whether arriving at an appropriate diagnosis, observing a person's responsivity to hypnotic procedures, or targeting different thoughts or behaviors to modify, is absolutely essential to hypnotic and nonhypnotic treatment enterprises.

Assessment is most useful when it directly links well-defined and specific treatment interventions to equally well-delineated areas of human functioning. Kirsch and Coe's (chapter 17) multimodal approach is noteworthy in this regard. Multimodal assessment is, by definition, reasonably comprehensive and provides a useful working scheme for conceptualizing a person's difficulties, devising treatment strategies, and formulating a working rationale for treatment that can be shared with the client in the early stages of treatment. As many of the chapter authors note, an important ingredient of effective psychotherapy is arriving at a mutually agreed-upon treatment plan early in treatment, which can be subject to revision as additional information is gleaned about the person and the problem during the course of psychotherapy. Ongoing assessment provides a basis for revising goals and interventions as treatment progresses.

In treating Ellen, Kirsch and Coe crafted hypnotic procedures to calm and soothe her (affect dimension), whereas nonhypnotic methods were used in in vivo practice sessions designed to reduce her behavioral avoidance of bathrooms. This selective use of hypnosis illustrates one of the main goals of assessment: to locate the role of hypnosis with precision in terms of a more encompassing treatment approach. Furthermore, with multimodal assessment, the impact of hypnosis and other treatments can be evaluated on a pre–posttreatment basis across a variety of dimensions of potential interest to the client and therapist. This process militates against an overly simplistic evaluation of treatment success in "either–or" terms and encourages the client to monitor progress and areas in need of continued attention even after the conclusion of treatment.

In chapter 10, Horevitz correctly observes that it is impossible to gauge the robustness and stability of treatment effects unless a rigorous assessment is conducted some time after treatment (follow-up). Horevitz's writings also underscore the value of using psychometrically sound assessment instruments, with care given to selecting measures theoretically and empirically related to the target problems addressed (e.g., dissociation, anxiety disorders). We are well aware of the time constraints of the typical clinical practitioner and the increasing demands and impositions of managed care environments; nevertheless, we believe that assessment is ultimately economical in light of the potential information yield to the clinician and the resultant benefit to the client.

In clinical hypnosis, the dynamics of hypnosis are superimposed on the dynamics of psychotherapy (Lynn & Rhue, 1991). Thus, no assessment of a potential candidate for clinical hypnosis would be truly complete without some evaluation of the client's responsiveness to hypnotic suggestions.

As we pointed out in the introduction, what is needed for practice is some understanding of the kinds of suggestions to which the person responds so that the suggestions can be chosen and crafted for maximum benefit. One person capable of responding to suggestions for taste alterations, for example, might benefit from such suggestions as part of a weight loss treatment. In contrast, the administration of this type of suggestion to a person who does not seem able to alter sensory experiences in this way may be counterproductive. Not only are the suggestions unlikely to work, but the experience of failure could lower the client's therapeutic outcome expectations and thereby attenuate treatment effects.

Information of this sort can be gleaned without a standardized induction. An example of this was given in the introductory chapter with respect to arm levitation. Assessment of sensory experiences can be disguised by suggesting a multifaceted fantasy and obtaining a detailed report of the client's experiences (e.g., sights, sounds, smells, tastes, pleasure, relaxation, comfort, etc.). This can be described accurately to the client as an assessment of how he or she responds, rather than as a test of the degree of response. Nevertheless, it is likely to provide information on degree of responsiveness as well.

Whether to administer more formal, standardized hypnotizability tests has been the subject of considerable controversy. Michael Diamond (1989), for instance, has argued that quantitative measures can, at best, provide only a gross index of general hypnotic ability, rather than mark the specific imaginative, dissociative, and absorptive skills necessary to respond to therapeutic suggestions. At worst, he stated, hypnotizability assessment is risky business and is a potentially "misleading, intrusive, and transference-contaminating obstacle to the therapeutic work ahead" (p. 12). By contrast, Nadon and Laurence (1994) have gone so far as to argue that hypnotizability assessment with standardized scales is worthwhile and that it may be "unethical to withhold a potentially important assessment instrument" (p. 91).

We believe that formal hypnotizability scales have particular merit when the contribution of responsiveness to hypnosis is at issue in accounting for treatment gains, such as when the therapist wishes to publish a case report of a particularly interesting case for the hypnosis literature. Many of Diamond's concerns can be addressed as Nash suggests (chapter 15) by presenting hypnotizability assessment as a way of familiarizing the client with hypnosis. Furthermore, standardized hypnotizability scales can be useful in clinical situations because they tap a broad domain of suggestions and can be customized to include clinically relevant responses.

Of course, because few individuals pass all hypnotic suggestions, the clinician must be careful to emphasize the client's success in responding and reinterpret failures to pass suggestions. Ultimately, however, each clinician will need to evaluate the pros and cons of administering standardized hypnotizability scales versus more informal ways of establishing a person's hypnotic responsiveness.

Recommendations

- Assess each client carefully (pre- and posttreatment) across multiple dimensions relevant to understanding the person and the problems presented, selecting a treatment, and implementing the treatment effectively.
- Although hypnosis is likely to be a relatively minor component of a multifaceted treatment, it is likely to be a helpful adjunct with most clients. Once a thorough assessment has been made, consider presenting hypnosis as a potential treatment component. Let clients know that hypnosis might enhance the effectiveness of the treatment plan, but also let them know that anything that can be done with hypnosis can also be done without it. Educate them about the promise and the limitations of hypnosis, and then let them make the choice.
- Determine what role hypnosis will play in treatment, while retaining a high degree of flexibility and openness to reconceptualize not only the focal problem but also the role of hypnosis in psychotherapy.
- As was described in the introductory chapter, before any assessment of hypnotizability is conducted, be sure to first demystify hypnosis, thoroughly prepare the client for hypnosis, structure expectations so that even small indicators of responsiveness are seen as significant beginnings, and begin with easy tasks (as is the case with standardized tests) that the client is almost certain to accomplish.
- Assess hypnotic responsiveness before treatment and on an ongoing basis. Be sure to test responses that are clinically relevant (e.g., analgesia, amnesia, age regression, hypnotic dreams, ability to relax) and clearly related to treatment goals (e.g., relaxation for reducing anxiety).
- Standardized hypnotizability scales can be customized to include responses of special interest by administering additional test suggestions after the standard test suggestions, or by using scales that can accommodate individualized test items (i.e., Stanford Profile Scales).

- Use the information from the hypnotizability assessment to structure interventions. Remember that even if a person does not respond to difficult hypnotic items such as amnesia or automatic writing, most individuals can respond to straightforward suggestions for relaxation; ego strengthening, mastery enhancing communications; and imaginative rehearsal and anchoring procedures.
- In order to document the relation between hypnosis and treatment outcome, there is no substitute for a formal measure of hypnotizability.

TREATMENT ISSUES AND CAVEATS

Bolstering Positive Expectancies

Expectancies are important determinants of what clients experience and how they behave in hypnotic situations (see Kirsch, 1990, 1994). In fact, expectancy is one of the few stable correlates of hypnotizability (Kirsch & Council, 1992). Like placebos, hypnosis produces therapeutic effects by changing the client's expectancies. But as we indicated in the introduction, unlike placebos, hypnosis does not require deception in order to be effective. Furthermore, honestly informing clients about what has been learned through research about the nature of hypnosis may reduce resistance and increase responsiveness to hypnotic intervention.

Although patients' initial expectancies play an important role in determining the outcome of therapy, it is equally important to monitor and influence changing expectations throughout the course of therapy. This is facilitated by including therapeutic procedures that are likely to provide clients with feedback indicating that treatment is successfully producing therapeutic changes. Exposure treatments for phobic disorders ensure that clients will experience feedback of this sort. Repeated or prolonged exposure to the phobic stimulus produces temporary habituation, which the client interprets as evidence that the treatment is working, an interpretation that converts temporary physiological habituation into lasting therapeutic change.

Expectancies vary along two independent dimensions. One is the degree of certainty that change will occur. The other is the speed and amount of change that is expected. Ensuring that positive feedback will be experienced during treatment is facilitated by certainty that improvement can occur, but also by the expectancy that it will begin with small, gradual changes. This allows small increments, such as those produced by random fluctuations, to be interpreted as signs of therapeutic success, in much the same way as a twitch of a finger is interpreted as the beginning of arm levitation. Similarly, the assignment of easy initial tasks ensures early successes, which bolster the client's confidence in treatment.

Conversely, perceived failure to comply with suggestions may lead to a vicious circle of negative expectancies and failure to respond to subsequent suggestions (Lynn & Hamel, 1995). Clinicians who imply that a certain "depth" of hypnosis must be reached in order to experience hypnosis successfully are setting their clients up for failure.

Clinicians trained in the use of hypnosis habitually monitor and intervene in ways designed to enhance clients' expectations, often without awareness that this is what they are doing. Many of the clinical innovations of Milton Erickson, for example, are aimed at accomplishing this goal. Their ingenuity indicates an intuitive mastery of the art of changing expectations. As some of Erickson's disciples have noted, "the essence of Erickson's approach . . . was to create a context with the client in which an expectancy for change will occur" (Matthews, Lankton, & Lankton, 1993).

Recommendations

- Be permissive. Present and respect choices as therapeutic double binds, so that either choice promotes improvement and minimizes resistance. Define tasks so that failure is impossible.
- Prevent failure by beginning with easy tasks that the client is almost certain to accomplish. Proceed gradually to more and more difficult tasks.
- Be alert to random fluctuations and capitalize on those that occur in a desired direction.
- Prepare clients for setbacks by labeling them in advance as inevitable, temporary, and useful learning opportunities (Kirsch, 1994).

Interpersonal Issues

Interpersonal issues and concerns can dampen clients' response expectancies, elicit counterproductive response sets, and provoke outright resistance to participating fully in treatment. Some clients' histories with parents, authority figures, or helping professionals predispose them to view the hypnotist with mistrust, anger, and fear. Given cultural associations of the hypnotist as having control, power, and authority over the client, the hypnotic situation may accentuate clients' negative reaction tendencies (Fromm, 1980). Not only may the client be reluctant to become involved in hypnosis, but hypnosis may be experienced as an emotionally charged, aversive event. Of course, this is most likely to occur when the hypnotherapy is imbued with connotations of personal dominance and control.

Alternately, clients might develop a highly charged positive, idealized, archaic, or even sexualized transference (Shor, 1979) vis-à-vis the therapist, which can be equally counterproductive.

Although countertransference difficulties occur during and after hypnosis as they do in psychotherapy, Orne (1965) noted that the hypnotist-directive nature of hypnosis may amplify them. Negative reactions in clients may ensue if they sense that their own needs or goals are somehow of secondary importance to the hypnotist.

Recommendations

- Carefully assess clients' expectancies, attitudes, and beliefs about hypnosis. Demystify hypnosis and portray it as a therapeutic tool that can increase a person's sense of personal control.
- Where concerns about being dominated or out of control during hypnosis are salient, consider defining hypnotic procedures as "imagery work," "goal-directed fantasies," or self-hypnosis.
- Work hard to establish a resilient working alliance with the client as a deterrent against negative or idealized transference reactions (Lynn, Martin, & Frauman, in press).
- If the therapist is aware of having particularly strong positive, sexualized, or hostile feelings toward the client or feels a need to control the therapeutic encounter with little regard for the client's well-being, consultation, supervision, or individual psychotherapy are called for.

Direct Suggestions to Relinquish Symptoms

Just as certain interpersonal issues and concerns may dampen positive treatment expectancies, direct suggestions to relinquish symptoms may provoke an equal, if not greater, amount of resistance. Symptoms may represent coping or adaptive mechanisms that are associated with potent yet unconscious secondary gains. Hence, forceful directives to abandon symptoms may engender significant conflict and outright rebellion in the client.

Recommendations

- Assess a person's psychological defenses, coping skills, and any secondary gains or reinforcement contingencies that maintain or exacerbate current symptoms. In this regard, the therapist ought to consider the following questions: What, in the past, has increased and decreased the behavior or problem at issue? How ready is the person to try something new or to make requisite life changes? How would the person's life be changed if the symptom were no longer a part of the clinical picture? What would have to change in the person's life in order to relinquish the symptom?

- In general, avoid direct suggestions to relinquish symptoms in the absence of a foundation of adequate psychological defenses and coping skills (Lynn et al., 1996). Suggestions for symptom reduction may be safer and more effective than suggestions for symptom elimination, and permissive wording can forestall a sense of failure and provide respect for the client's intuitive sense of timing.

A suggestion like the following, for example, might be preferred to a direct suggestion that pain will no longer be felt:

Pain is an important danger signal, and the pain you experienced once served a useful function. But I wonder if you still need the degree of discomfort that you have experienced in the past. As you are learning to pay closer attention to your body's wise signals, your need for intense pain diminishes—getting less and less—until just enough discomfort remains to remind you to treat your back with respect.

Suggestions May Instigate or Reveal Unexpected Affect

Like many psychotherapeutic procedures, hypnotic suggestions may impinge on a person's current concerns or conflicts, trigger painful memories, and provide an avenue for the expression of suppressed or possibly repressed affect (Fromm, 1980). Certain suggestions (e.g., age regression, hypnotic dreams) about particular events or issues imply that access to early life events can be achieved, and that insight into important psychological dynamics can be gained. Given this focus and the demands upon the client, it is not surprising that unexpectedly intense abreactions can ensue following such suggestions.

Recommendations

- The dictum, "never treat anything with hypnosis that you are not trained or equipped to treat in nonhypnotic therapy" is an indispensable hedge against unmanageable reactions (Lynn et al., 1996).
- Of course, abreactions, when managed with skill and sensitivity, can have enormous therapeutic benefit. However, therapists should have specialized and supervised training in using abreactive techniques (with or without hypnosis) before they incorporate such techniques into their clinical practice.

Pseudomemory Risk

Rather than being a playback of a recorded event, remembering has been shown to be a constructive process, in which memories and imaginings are mixed indistinguishably (Belli & Loftus, 1994). As a result, suggestive and leading information can create false memories that are mistaken for historical truth. Because hypnosis involves direct and indirect suggestions, some of which may be leading in nature, and because hypnosis can increase confidence of recalled events with little or no change in the level of accuracy (American Medical Association, 1985), therapists employing hypnosis must be especially vigilant to the problem of false memory creation. Clients' memory reports during age regression, for example, can seem compelling because the reported images and emotions are vivid and intense. However, neither vividness nor emotionality can be taken as scientific evidence of historical veracity. Similarly, misidentification of a current fantasy as a memory can be facilitated by the mistaken belief that hypnosis provides direct access to the unconscious.

Many hypnotherapists avoid doing memory recovery work, given the many pitfalls associated with using hypnosis for this purpose (see Lynn & Nash, 1994). In his chapter on the hypnotic exploration of childhood trauma, Smith (Chapter 6) argues that one should use hypnosis for memory recovery only as a treatment of last resort and that such treatment must be undertaken with considerable caution. He offers many constructive suggestions for therapists contemplating such work and makes the excellent point that serious memory distortions may be a significant risk in hypnotic (and nonhypnotic) contexts. Specifically, Smith notes that "a person may recall being molested by a sibling at age 8 when in fact it was a baby-sitter when the person was 6. In the distorted memory, the sibling could have been substituted for the actual abuser because of threats made about disclosure" (p. 127).

In the case of "Cindy," which Smith successfully treated, an apparent memory emerged in which her neighbors were her childhood abusers. We have no way of knowing whether the abuse incident actually happened, but there can be no doubt that the process lead to a positive therapeutic outcome. However, it is worth considering what might have happened had a "memory" emerged in which the abusers were her parents, rather than neighbors. Following Smith's line of thinking, her neighbors might have made threats about her disclosing the abuse and Cindy might have substituted her parents for her neighbors. If Cindy had mistaken the source of the abuse, then it could have some very negative effects for both Cindy and her family.

Hence, in our view, memory recovery work is a gamble. In the case of Cindy, with luck and a skilled and sensitive therapist, it paid off. With less luck or a less skilled therapist, the outcome might well have been as detrimental as this one was beneficial. We fully agree with Smith that "accusations of abuse based on hypnotically enhanced memories that could be distorted or even totally false can have tragic consequences" (p. 128).

Each therapist must carefully weigh the risks and benefits of using hypnosis to recover memories. Hopefully, this cost–benefit analysis will be made only after the clinician is thoroughly familiar with the literature on the risks of pseudomemories in psychotherapy, and perhaps only after discussing the issues involved in a particular case with a respected colleague. However, we would argue that there are probably very few cases in which the benefits of attempting to access potentially forgotten life experiences outweigh the potential risk of distorted memories ensuing as a result.

Recommendations

- Educate clients about the risk of memory distortion and the inadvisability of acting on what they remember outside of the treatment context (e.g., legal proceedings).
- Warn clients that recalling traumatic events from childhood will not automatically—or even easily—resolve their difficulties.
- Exercise caution regarding the wording and implications of therapeutic suggestions, as Horevitz notes in his chapter on treating dissociative identity disorder (chapter 10), taking special care to monitor carefully their communications for any contamination by suggestive influences.
- The available evidence (Sheehan, Statham, & Jamieson, 1991a, 1991b; Sheehan, Statham, Jamieson, & Ferguson, 1991) justifies particular caution with high- and medium- hypnotizable participants, although even low hypnotizable participants report false memories.
- Remember that false memories are certainly not limited to hypnosis and may be problematic in a variety of situational and therapeutic contexts (see Lynn & Nash, 1994).
- Evaluate the credibility of purportedly repressed memories uncovered during therapy in light of many factors, including the client's suggestibility and the nature of the procedures used to uncover the remembrances.

CONCLUSION

The concerns we have raised should not deter therapists from adding hypnosis to the clinical procedures they use. Its potential for misuse may be no more than the flip-side of its ability to enhance therapeutic gain. In this sense, it may be like a scalpel, which can save lives in the hands of a skilled surgeon, but should not be wielded by an untrained healer.

Although much more needs to be done in the way of evaluation, the available data indicate that hypnosis can enhance the effectiveness of therapy significantly (Kirsch, Montgomery, & Sapirstein, 1995), and there is reason to believe that this can be the case even for clients with relatively little hypnotic talent. It is our hope that this book will contribute to the trained psychotherapists' ability to practice hypnotherapy with skill, sensitivity, and clinical wisdom.

REFERENCES

American Medical Association, Council on Scientific Affairs. (1985). Scientific status of refreshing recollection by the use of hypnosis. *Journal of the American Medical Association, 253*, 1918–1923.

Belli, R. F., & Loftus, E. F. (1994). Recovered memories of childhood abuse: A source monitoring perspective. In S. J. Lynn & J. W. Rhue (Eds.), *Dissociation: Clinical and theoretical perspectives* (pp. 415–433). New York: Guilford Press.

Diamond, M. J. (1989). Is hypnotherapy not a science? *American Journal of Clinical Hypnosis, 32*, 11–12.

Fromm, E. (1980). Values in hypnotherapy. *Psychotherapy: Theory, Research and Practice, 17*, 425–430.

Kirsch, I. (1990). *Changing expectations: A key to effective psychotherapy*. Pacific Grove, CA: Brooks/Cole

Kirsch, I. (1994). Clinical hypnosis as a nondeceptive placebo: Empirically derived techniques. *American Journal of Clinical Hypnosis, 37*, 95–106.

Kirsch, I., & Council, J. (1992). Situational and personality correlates of suggestibility. In E. Fromm & M. Nash (Eds.), *Contemporary hypnosis research* (pp. 267–292). New York: Guilford Press.

Kirsch, I., Montgomery, G., & Sapirstein, G. (1995). Hypnosis as an adjunct to cognitive behavioral psychotherapy: A meta-analysis. *Journal of Consulting and Clinical Psychology, 63*, 214–220.

Lynn, S. J., & Hamel, J. (1995). *Age regression and negative effects*. Unpublished manuscript, Ohio University.

Lynn, S. J., Martin, D., & Frauman, D. C. (1996). Does hypnosis pose special risks for negative effects? *International Journal of Clinical and Experimental Hypnosis, 44*, 7–19.

Lynn, S. J., & Nash, M. R. (1994). Truth in memory: Ramifications for psychotherapy and hypnotherapy. *American Journal of Clinical Hypnosis, 36*, 194–208.

Lynn, S. J., & Rhue, J. W. (1991). Hypnosis theories: Themes and variations. In S. J. Lynn, & J. W. Rhue (Eds.), *Theories of hypnosis*. New York: Guilford Press.

Matthews, W. J., Lankton, S., & Lankton, C. (1993). An Ericksonian model of hypnotherapy. In J. W. Rhue, S. J. Lynn, & I. Kirsch (Eds.), *Handbook of clinical hypnosis* (pp. 187–214). Washington, DC: American Psychological Association.

Nadon, R., & Laurence, J.-R. (1994). Idiographic approaches to hypnosis research: Or how therapeutic practice can inform science. *American Journal of Clinical Hypnosis, 37,* 85–94.

Orne, M. T. (1965). Undesirable effects of hypnosis: The determinants and management. *International Journal of Clinical and Experimental Hypnosis, 13,* 226–237.

Sheehan, P. W., Statham, D., & Jamieson, G. A. (1991a). Pseudomemory effects over time in the hypnotic setting. *Journal of Abnormal Psychology, 100,* 39–44.

Sheehan, P. W., Statham, D., & Jamieson, G. A. (1991b). Pseudomemory effects and their relationship to level of susceptibility to hypnosis and state instructions. *Journal of Personality and Social Psychology, 60,* 130–137.

Sheehan, P. W., Statham, D., Jamieson, G. A., & Ferguson, S. R. (1991). Ambiguity in suggestion and the occurrence of pseudomemory in the hypnotic setting. *Australian Journal of Clinical and Experimental Hypnosis, 19,* 1–18.

Shor, R. E. (1979). A phenomenological method for the measurement of variables important to an understanding of the nature of hypnosis. In E. Fromm & R. E. Shor (Eds.), *Hypnosis: Developments in research and new perspectives* (2nd ed., pp. 105–135). Chicago: Aldine.

AUTHOR INDEX

Numbers in italics refer to listings in the reference sections.

Nadon, R., 18, 28, 29, 141, 147, *150*, 218,
    220, 397, 406
Nagy, L. M., *219*
Nash, M. R., 3, 4, 7, 17, 26, 28, 51, 70,
    71, *72, 73*, 114, *130, 191*, 217,
    220, 320, 322, 403, 404, *405*
National Center on Child Abuse and Ne-
    glect, 251, 269
Nelson, K., *192*
Neufeld, V., 6, 16, 28, 223, 248
Newton, C. J., 277, *291*
Nielsen, J., 273, 290
Nightingale, M. E., 10, *29*
Norcross, J. C., 312, *316*
North, C. S., 193, *221*
Norton, G. R., *221*
Novey, E. S., 273, 289
Noyes, R., 100, *110*

Offord, D. R., 272, *291*
Olmsted, M. P., 51, *72*
Olness, K., 252, 269
Orbach, S., 66, *73*
Orne, M. T., 12, 15, *29*, 193, *221*, 401,
    406

Pastyrnak, S. L., 46, *49*
Paul, G. L., 34, *48*
Peecher, H. K., 164, *170*
Perry, C., 18, *29*, 229, 248
Persinger, M., *221*
Pfiffner, L., *291*
Pillemer, D. B., *192*
Pintar, J., 254, 269
Pope, A. T., 276, *290*
Potter, H. W., 268
Przybek, T. R., 335, *345*
Putman, F. W., 194, 215, *219, 221*

Quill, T. E., 131, *150*

Radojevic, V., 277, *290*
Radtke, H. L., 10, *29*
Raine, D., 194, *219*
Reardon, J. P., 345, *347*
Rhue, J. W., 3, 6, 12, 16, 17, *27, 28, 29*,
    37, *48*, 51, *73*, 223, 248, 252, 261,
    269, 312, *316*, 356, *364, 405*

Ricci, D. A., 193, *221*
Roberts, S. J., *150*
Rockert, W., 51, *72*
Rockwood, C. A., 133, *150*
Rogers, C. R., 337, *347*
Rorschach, H., 215, *221*
Rosen, J. C., 133, *150*
Rosenfeld, P., 277, *291*
Ross, C. A., 194, *221*
Ross, G., *192*
Rossi, E. L., 179, 190, *191*, 373, *391*
Rossiter, R. R., 277, *290*
Rounsaville, B., 194, *222*
Rudolfa, E. R., 3, 4, *27*
Rush, J., *219*
Russell, D., 251, *270*
Russell, D. E. H., 113, *130*
Russo, N., 77
Ryall, J. M., 193, *221*

Sachs, R. G., 200, *219*
Saliba, J., 133, *150*
Salzberg, H. C., *29*
Sanchez, A., 155, *170*
Sandler, S. A., 133, 138, *150*
Sapirstein, G., 4, *27*, 36, *48*, 140, 147,
    148, *149*, 275, *290*, 354, *364, 405*
Sarbin, T. R., 147, *150*, 253, *270*
Sauzier, M., 252, 269
Scagnelli, J., 173, *192*
Scagnelli-Jobsis, J., 178, *192*
Schaap, C., 16, *29*
Schachter, D. L., *221*
Schatzow, E., 113
Schaughency, E. A., 273, *290*
Scheff, T. J., 132, *150*
Scheinbaum, S., 277, *291*
Schlenger, W. E., *110*, 215, *221*
Schoenberger, N. E., 46, 47, *49*, 353, 354,
    364
Schwartz, A., 77, *97*
Schwartz, R., 77, *97*
Segal, D., 11, 28
Segal, L., 77, *97*
Seligman, M., 77, *98*
Semrud-Clikeman, M., 273, 289
Serfontein, G., 274, 288
Shaw, B., *219*
Sheehan, D. V., 278, 287
Sheehan, P. W., 6, 10, *29*, 217, *221*, 404,
    406

Wolpe, J., 359, 364
Wonderlich, S. A., 223, 248
Woo, C., 291
Wood, L. M., 274, 288
Woodall, C., 73

Yankura, J., 336, 344, 347

Yapko, M. D., 70, 73, 75, 77, 78, 80, 96, 98
Young, W. C., 195, 222

Zecker, S., 277, 291
Zelikovsky, N., 251, 252, 270
Zimmerman, A. W., 274, 290

SUBJECT INDEX

Attitude(s)
  client
    toward hypnosis, 35, 45, 47
  in emotional self-regulation, 158
  negative
    of childhood–adolescent sexual
      trauma victim, 125
Autonomy
  in anorexia nervosa, 57, 64–68, 70
  in borderline personality disorder, 177
Awareness, interoceptive, 55–56

BASIC-ID (behavior, affect, sensation,
    imagery, cognitions, interper-
    sonal, drugs) evaluation in
    multimodal therapy, 350–351
Behavior
  in borderline personality disorder,
    173–174
  in multimodal therapy, 350
Behavior modification
  for ADD/ADHD, 271, 275
  limitations of, 271, 275
  in rational-emotive behavior therapy,
    343
Body image, in anorexia nervosa, 51, 52,
    54, 66
Body-self, after sexual trauma, 120, 124
Bonding, in borderline personality disor-
    der, 178, 179
Borderline personality disorder (BPD)
  background of case, 174–176
  conceptualization of, 177–178
  conclusions, 189–191
  description of, 173
  issues in, 177
  problem behaviors in, 173–174
  therapeutic issues in
    borderline pathology, 179, 182–
      183, 185–186, 187–188
    sexual and physical abuse, 176,
      177, 184–185, 187
    techniques used, 190–191
  treatment of, 178–179
    healing scripts in, 178, 185, 189,
      190
    hypnotic renurturing in, 178,
      181–182, 183, 189
    individuation and separation and,
      177, 179, 182–183, 189

memory reshaping in, 184–188
  outcome of, 188–189
  special problems in, 173–174
  transference and countertransfer-
    ence in, 178, 188
Breathing technique
  in self-hypnosis teaching, 234–235
  for tension reduction, 59–60
Buddy system, in smoking cessation, 230

Camptocormia
  background of case
    current assessment, 137–138
    family history, 133–134
    history of problem, 135
    presentation of, 133
    prior treatment and assessment,
      135–136
  conceptualization of, 138–139, 147
  conclusions, 147
  demographics of, 133
  differential diagnosis of, 131–132
  hypnosis for, 132
  treatment of
    distress zone protection and asser-
      tion in, 146
    erect walking, balance, stress re-
      duction in, 144–145
    heaviness–lightness in, 143–144
    hypnotizability and, 147–148
    outcomes of, 146–147
    perfectionism, affect awareness
      and expression learning curve
      in, 145
    rationale for, 139–140, 147
    relaxation in, 141, 142–143
    sample induction in, 142–144
    suitability of, 147
Chevreul pendulum, 17
Child sexual abuse. See Childhood–
    adolescent sexual trauma;
    Posttraumatic stress disorder
    (PTSD)
Childhood physical and sexual abuse
  borderline personality and, 184–185,
    187
  dissociative identification disorder
    and, 208, 209, 212
Childhood–adolescent sexual trauma,
    113–139
  background of case, 114–115

memories in, 201
  recovery and reliving of, 203
model of treatment in, 216
self-destructive tendencies in, 195, 196, 200, 206
techniques in, 216
treatment of
  chronology of, 201–203
  danger of misdirected, 198–199
  distress in, 203–214
  duration of, 199
  family therapy techniques in, 207–208
  goals of, 199, 200
  hypnotherapy in, 199–201
  risks in, 199
Distancing
  in Ericksonian hypnotherapy, 370
  in storytelling therapy, 261
Distortion, in memory recovery, 128, 129, 403, 404
Distress, in dissociative identification disorder, 203–214
Distress zone, in camptocormia patient, 137, 146
Dream, hypnoptic, 329, 330
Drugs and physiology, in multimodal therapy, 351
Dysmenorrhea. *See also* Emotional self-regulation therapy
  emotional self-regulation therapy for versus hypnosis, 156–157
  rationale for, 157–158
  patient assessment in, 156
  symptom assessment in
    after treatment, 167–168
    baseline, 157
    during therapy, 165
Dysmenorrhea and premenstrual distress
  background of case, 155–156
  effect on workplace, 153–154
  patient assessment in, 156
  prevalence of, 153
  symptoms of, 153
    assessment of, 157, 165, 167-168
  treatment of
    emotional self-regulation therapy for, 156–157
    goals in, 163
    rationale for, 157–158

surgical and pharmacologic, 154
techniques in, 154, 163–167
termination and follow-up of, 167–168

Eating disorders. *See* Restrictors with false-self organization
Eclecticism in psychotherapies, 312
Ego state metaphors, 10–11
Ellen phobia case. *See also named therapeutic approach, e.g.,* Psychoanalysis in Ellen phobia case
  background of, 314–315
  clinical case conference
    approaches to, 311–314
    questions for commentators, 314
  conceptualization of, 315
  Ericksonian hypnotherapy in, 313, 365–390
  multimodal treatment of, 312–313, 349–364
  psychoanalytic therapy in, 312, 317–334
  rational-emotive behavior therapy in, 312, 335–345
Emotional pain, in dissociative identification disorder, 209–210
Emotional self-regulation scale, items on, 159–160
Emotional self-regulation therapy
  advantages of, 168
  applications of, 155
  collaboration in, 166, 168–169
  definition of, 155
  for dysmenorrhea and premenstrual distress, 154–169
    follow-up of, 166–167
    fourth and fifth therapy sessions, 166–167
    goals in, 163
    pain control in, 164–165
    psychological tension reduction in, 163–164
    session one, 158–163
    session two, 163–165
    termination of, 166
    third therapy session, 165
  flexibility of, 168–169
  versus hypnosis, 154, 156–157
  phases in, 158–162

of abandonment
in camptocormia patient, 138–139
in Ellen phobia case, 318
in anorexia nervosa, 63–64
of borderline personality patient
of abuser, 176
of loss of father, 187
of not being heard, 184, 185, 186
of separation, 185–186
of camptocormia patient
of abandonment, 138–139
of others' loss of control, 135, 137
hypnotic haven from, 330–331
of incest victim, 184
of separation from therapy, 69
Feelings
abuse-associated, 180–181
in anorexia nervosa, 55
in depression
controllable, 93
redefinition of, 85
Fictitious memory, 127–128, 403, 404
Flexibility
development of, 82, 86, 87, 90, 91–92
in depression therapy, 84–85
of emotional self-regulation therapy, 168–169
Floating
for relaxation, 163–164, 165
in self-hypnosis, 102–103
Fraudulence, feelings of, in anorexia nervosa, 55
Frustration, in depression, low tolerance of, 78–79

Gestalt empty chair technique, 358–359
Group treatment
hypnosis in, 45, 47
for public speaking anxiety, 36–45. See also Cognitive–behavioral hypnotherapy
for smoking cessation. See Smoking cessation
therapeutic relationship in, 45
Guilt
of childhood sexual abuse victim, 103
of childhood–adolescent sexual abuse victim, 115, 122

HALT (hungry, angry, lonely, tired), 61

Healing scripts
in borderline personality disorder therapy, 178, 184–188, 189, 190
in reshaping abuse memories, 184, 185
Heaviness–lightness suggestions, 17–18, 143–144
Homework
in adolescent enuresis case, 301–302
in rational-emotive behavior therapy, 343–344
in smoking cessation, 238–240
Humor, in rational-emotive behavior therapy, 339
Hungry, angry, lonely, tired (HALT), 61
Hypnosis
active, alert in neurotherapy, 278–279
as adjunctive therapy, 305, 306
assessment in
follow-up, 396
of hypnotizability, 15–16, 259, 397–398, 399
importance of, 396–399
instruments for, 396
recommendations for, 398–399
of sensory experiences, 397
bolstering positive expectancies in, 399–400
contraindications to, 36
dangers in, 118
definition of, 4–5
demystification of, 398
description of, 4–7
disinhibition facilitation with, 7–9
ego state metaphors in, 10–11
historical growth of, 3–4
imagery in, 10
interpersonal issues in, 400–401
misuse of, 404–405
patient variables and, 129
for placebo effect, 8–9
posthypnotic suggestions in, 13
pseudomemory risk in, 113–114, 124, 127–128, 180, 403–404
rationale for, 7–13
referral for, 294
role in treatment, 398
stabilization and soothing in, 9–10
for structure and salience, 7
suggestion in

Pain control (*Continued*)
        sub-maximum-effort tourniquet technique, 164
Parts metaphor, in ego states, 62
Passivity, fear of in anorexia nervosa, 63–64
Penalization, in rational-emotive behavior therapy, 340
Phobia, value of in Ericksonian therapy, 366–367
Phobic anxiety
        background of case, 33–34
        cognitive–behavioral hypnotherapy for, 35–48
                cognitive modification in, 39–42
                hypnotic induction and self-hypnosis teaching in, 37–39
                outcome of, 44–45, 46, 47–48
                outline of sessions in, 38
                pre-therapy education for, 37
                rationale for, 35–36
                real-life exposure in, 42–44
        conceptualization of, 34–35
        conclusions from treatment, 46–48
        therapeutic issues in, 45–46
        treatment of
                assessment for, 34
                cognitive modification in, 39–42
                hypnosis induction in, 37–38
                rationale for, 35–36
                real-life exposure in, 42–44
                self-hypnosis teaching in, 38–39
                therapeutic outcome of, 44–45
Physiologic reactions, phobic, 34, 35
Plabeco effect, of hypnosis, 8–9
Posttraumatic stress disorder (PTSD), 99–110
        background of case, 100–101
        in childhood incest victim, 99–110
        conceptualization of, 101–102
        conclusions, 108–110
        mental status examination in, 101
        symptoms of and hypnosis components, 99–100
        treatment of, 102–108
                antidepressant for depression in, 105, 106, 108
                anxiety management in, 107
                follow-up of, 108
                hypnotic dissociation in, 103
                self-hypnosis teaching in, 102–104
                split-screen technique in, 103, 105

transference in, 105, 109
Premenstrual distress. *See* Emotional self-regulation therapy
Pseudomemory risk. *See also* Memory recovery work
        in hypnosis, 113–114, 124, 127–128, 180, 403–404
Psychoanalysis in Ellen phobia case
        conceptualization of problem, 318–319
        hypnosis in
                consolidation of autonomy and self-efficacy in, 334
                dream in, 330
                exploration period in, 329–331
                eye fixation/relaxation introduction in, 322–328
                haven from shame and fear in, 330–331
                hypnotizability assessment for, 321, 329
                metaphors in, 333
                somato-attentional technique in, 327–329
        problem-focused therapy for
                hypnotic techniques in, 319, 320, 322–328, 331–333
                versus long-term therapy, 318–319
                transference and countertransference in, 321
        self-hypnosis in, 331–332
                practice session in, 332–333
        termination of, 334
Psychotherapies, eclectic trend in, 312–313
Public-speaking anxiety. *See* Cognitive–behavioral hypnotherapy

Quantitative electroencephalographic (QEEG) analysis, in ADD/ADHD, 273–274
Quit cards, in smoking cessation, 232–234

Rape and abortion, of college student, 115, 117, 122, 123. *See also* Childhood-adolescent sexual trauma
Rational-emotive behavior therapy (REBT)
        behavioral methods in, 339–340
        cognitive methods in, 338–339

conceptualization of Ellen phobia case, 335–337, 344
description of, 312
experiential methods in, 339
homework in, 343
hypnosis in
    conditions for use of, 341
    REBT instructions in, 342–343
    relaxation in, 341–342
    role of, 340–341
    strategies and techniques in, 341
supplemental methods in, 344
treatment plan in, 337–338
unconditional acceptance in, 337–338
Reality, confusion of symbolic versus actual, 218
Real-life exposure, cognitive modification integration in, 42–44
Reinforcement, in rational-emotive behavior therapy, 340
Rejection, childhood sexual abuse victim and, 104
Relaxation
    in camptocormia patient, 141
    in Ericksonian hypnotherapy, 373
    floating technique for, 163–164, 165
    hammock metaphor for, 143
    in multimodal therapy, 355–356
    in REBT with hypnosis, 341–342
    in self-hypnosis, 46–47, 235–236
    in somatoform disorders, 141, 142–143
Renurturing therapy
    age regression in, 178, 181–182
    in borderline personality disorder, 178–179, 181–182, 183, 189
    ego-building messages in, 181
    of infant self, 178–179, 182
    purpose of, 183
    relaxation messages and, 181
Rescue, maternal, 295, 301, 302
Response generalization, in emotional self-regulation therapy, 162
Restrictors with false-self organization
    background of case, 52–54
    case history of, 52–54
        assessment results in, 54
        family in, 53–54
        patient assessment, 56–57
        problem in, 52
        treatment history in, 52

conceptualization of
    agency in, 56
    self-integration in, 56
    self-regulation in, 55
conclusion, 69–72
description of, 51–52
internalization and integration in, 68–69
treatment of
    affect identification and symptom management in, 60–62
    agency in: autonomy and separation concerns, 64–68
    course of, 57–69
    follow-up in, 69
    hypnosis in, 57–58, 70
    mastery and control of tension states in, 59–60
    self states work in, 62–64
    self-regulation in, 58–62
    theory in, 57
    therapeutic framework in, 58
    therapist role in, 57
    wrapping up, 68–69
Reverse role play, in rational-emotive behavior therapy, 339
Rigidity
    in depression, 84–85
    moral, 116
Ritalin (methylphenidate), for ADD/ADHD, 271, 274–275
Roleplaying, in rational-emotive behavior therapy, 339

Salience, hypnosis for, 7
Secondary gain
    in adolescent enuresis case, 296, 301, 305, 306
    in camptocormia patient, 138
    issues related to, 140
Self
    as controller versus as victim, 85
    redefinition of, 88
Self-acceptance
    in Ellen phobia case
        conditional, 335–336
        unconditional, 337–338
Self-blame, of childhood–adolescent sexual abuse victim, 102, 117
Self-concept, in anorexia nervosa, 55

Self-destruction
    in borderline personality disorder, 173, 174, 175
    tendencies for
        in dissociative identification disorder, 195, 196, 200, 206
Self-hypnosis
    in cognitive–behavioral hypnotherapy, 37–39
    description of, 12–13
    in Ericksonian hypnotherapy, 373–374
    in multimodal therapy, 356–359
    posthypnotic suggestions in, 24–25
    in posttraumatic stress disorder, 102–104
    in psychoanalysis, 331-332
    relaxation in, 46–47
    self-suggestions in, 42
    in smoking cessation, 234–238
    teaching script for, 19–24
        anchoring in, 23
        emerging from, 23–24
        induction in, 20–22
        key phrase in, 23–24
        termination of, 25
Self-image thinking
    definition of, 382
    for future development, 383–384
    goal of intervention in, 382–383
    in recognition of independence versus dependence, 387
Self-integration, in anorexia nervosa, 56
Self-monitoring, in smoking cessation, 238–239
Self-mutilation, in Ellen phobia case, 318–319
Self-regulation
    in anorexia nervosa, 55–56, 58–62
        impaired, 55–56
        treatment of, 58–62
Self-reinforcement, in smoking cessation, 234
Self-statement, stories associated with, 253–254
Self-states, in anorexia nervosa, 62–64
Self-suggestion(s)
    identification of negative and positive Gestalt empty chair technique in, 358–359
    Socratic questioning in, 357–358, 359
    modification of, 41–42
    negative, 40–41
    positive, 45–46, 46–47
    self-hypnosis and, 42
Self-talk, negative in Ellen phobia case, 368
Sensation
    increase in, 59–60
    in multimodal therapy, 351
    warm for pain control, 164–165, 166–167
Sensory recall
    in emotional self-regulation, 157–158
    exercises for, 159–160
Separation and individuation
    in anorexia nervosa, 57, 64–68, 69, 70
    in borderline personality disorder, 177, 182–183
Sex, in Ellen phobia case, 319, 388–389
Sexual expression, camptocormia patient and, 135, 137
Sexually abused child
    background of case, 254–257
        assessment in, 256–257
        mother's anger in, 257, 258
        testing in, 257
        victim's anger in, 255, 256, 257, 258
    child–mother relationship and, 258
        in John's case, 262, 266–267, 268
    conceptualization of case, 257–258
    effects of abuse and, 251–252
    incidence of abuse, 251
    narrative reconstruction and storytelling for, 251–268
        for achievement of mastery, 260–262, 264–265
        advantages of, 259
        for establishment of therapeutic relationship and safe environment, 260, 262–264
        ethical dilemma in, 258–259
        functions of, 253
        history of, 252
        rationale for, 252–253
Shame
    abuse-associated, 180

attack exercises for, 339
versus guilt, 318
hypnotic haven from, 330–331
Skill building versus pathology framework, in depression treatment, 88, 95
Skill training, in rational-emotive behavior therapy, 340
Smoking, as learned habit, 228–229
Smoking cessation, 223–247
    background of case, 224–225
        history in, 224–225
        psychiatric history in, 225
    conceptualization of problem, 225–227
        addiction and, 227
        life successes and accomplishments and, 226
        previous attempts and, 225–226, 227
    goal in, 226, 227
    group treatment approach to, 227–246
    guidelines for reduction, 239
    homework assignments in, 238–240
    hypnotic suggestions in, 240–245
    outcome of treatment, 246–247
    pregancy and, 231–232
    quitting ceremony in, 240
    relapse in, 223
    self-hypnosis in, 234–238
        anchoring in, 236–238
        breathing in, 234–235
        emergence in, 238
        relaxation in, 235–236
    self-monitoring in, 238–239
    self-reinforcement in, 234
    techniques for, 223–224
    termination of hypnosis in, 246
    treatment approach in
        basis of, 229
        buddy system in, 230
        contracts in, 230
        "edge" in, 228–229
        health benefits and, 231
        motivation level index in, 229–230
        quit cards in, 232–234
        smoking as learned habit and, 227, 228
        weight gain and, 232

withdrawal symptoms in, 230–231
triggers in, 233
Socratic questioning, 357–358, 359
Somatization. See also Camptocormia
    in Ellen phobia case, 315
Somato-attentional technique, in Ellen phobia case, 327–329
Somatoform disorders. See also Camptocormia
    challenge of, 131
    common issues in, 132
    differential diagnosis of, 131–132
Somatoform symptoms, as social communications, 147
Split-screen technique, in childhood sexual abuse therapy, 104, 105
Stabilization, through hypnosis, 9–10
Stanford Hypnotic Susceptibility Scale (SHSS), 18
Stimulant medications
    for ADD/ADHD, 271, 274
        side effects and limitations of, 274–275
Stimulus generalization, in emotional self-regulation, cue images for, 160–162
Stop technique, in multimodal therapy, 351, 359
Structure, hypnosis for, 7
Subjective units of disturbance scale (SUDS), hypnotic rating of, 359–360
Suggestibility, hyperarousal and, 100
Suggestion
    in adolescent enuresis hypnosis, 298
    in anorexia nervosa, 61–62
    assessment of client responsiveness to, 397, 398
    direct
        caution in use of, 401–402
        effects on therapy, 217–218
    in emotional self-regulation therapy, 163
    indirect, 372–373
    for mood change, 163–164, 165
    posthypnotic, 13
    recommendations for, 401–402
    in smoking cessation, 240–245
    unexpected affect following, 402–403
Suggestive therapy. See also Emotional self-regulation therapy

ABOUT THE EDITORS

Steven Jay Lynn, PhD, is a Professor of Psychology at the State University of New York–Binghamton and is an Adjunct Professor at Ohio University. He also maintains a private practice. Dr. Lynn is a former president of the American Psychological Association's Division of Psychological Hypnosis, as well as a fellow in numerous professional psychological organizations and a diplomate of the American Board of Psychological Hypnosis. He has received awards for the best book published in 1991, 1992, and 1993 from the Society for Clinical and Experimental Hypnosis. Dr. Lynn is an advisory editor to many professional journals and has published more than 125 articles and book chapters on hypnosis, memory, and child abuse.

Irving Kirsch, PhD, is a Professor of Psychology at the University of Connecticut. He is the editor of *Contemporary Hypnosis*, on the board of the *International Journal of Clinical and Experimental Hypnosis*, and a fellow of the American Psychological Association. He is also past-president of APA's Division of Psychological Hypnosis.

Judith W. Rhue, PhD, is a Professor of Family Medicine at the Ohio University College of Osteopathic Medicine in addition to maintaining a private practice. Dr. Rhue is a fellow of the American Psychological Association's Division of Psychological Hypnosis and of the Society for Clinical and Experimental Hypnosis and has received awards for excellence in research from both societies. Dr. Rhue serves on the editorial boards of the *International Journal of Clinical and Experimental Hypnosis* and *Contemporary Hypnosis* and has written numerous articles and book chapters on hypnosis, fantasy, and child abuse.